The Big Thaw

The Big Thaw

A personal exploration
of the "new" Russia
and the orbit countries

by C. L. SULZBERGER

HARPER & BROTHERS   PUBLISHERS   NEW YORK

Library of Congress catalog card number: 56-12230

For Marina

Acknowledgment

I wish to thank Professor Hans Kohn for permission to quote from his observations on imperialism and to thank Miss Ruth Chambers for aid in preparing this manuscript.

Contents

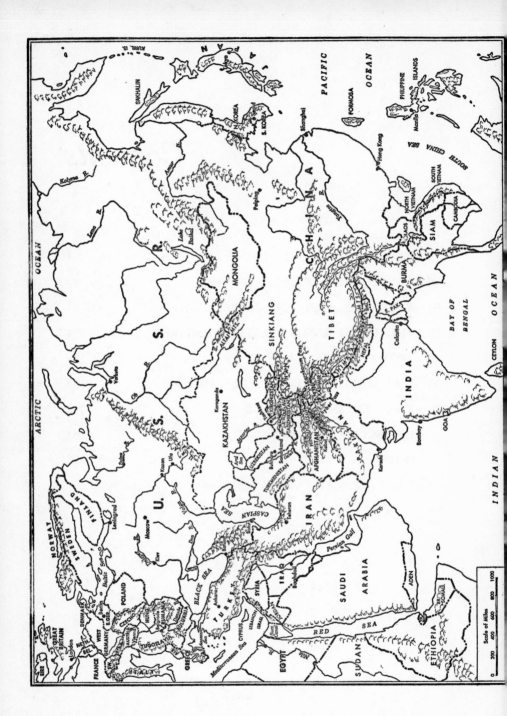

The Big Thaw

We proceed in broad daylight; they advance under cover; the game is one-sided.

MARQUIS DE CUSTINE
(*Journey for Our Time*, 1839)

I

Neither War nor Peace?

THE WESTERN world lost a battle in semantics when it accepted in common usage the Soviet term *coexistence*. Surely the good, old-fashioned word *peace* is preferable. One of its dictionary meanings is "freedom from international hostilities." During less complicated eras, peace was held merely to be absence of war. If there was no fighting, there was peace. Such is the case today.

It is fruitless to argue that the Cold Peace which has replaced Cold War is not what we were accustomed to prior to 1939. Throughout the thirties this was a tormented world— even before fighting began in China, Ethiopia and Spain. After the first great conflict, an older generation was already talking with nostalgia of that better peace it knew earlier in the century. But the practice of peace, unfortunately, is not constant. Peace, on the whole, prevailed in 1910 despite an armaments race and uneasy jockeying in Africa and the Balkans. Much of the world was at peace in the 1920's. And it is at peace now, turbulent as that peace may be. Perhaps we will never know a better peace.

1

The fact that our political system is in irrevocable conflict with that of the Soviet bloc does not obscure the fact of peace. For generations, intermittently interrupted by local outbreaks, the Catholic Austro-Hungarian empire was at peace with its neighbor, the Moslem Ottoman empire. Yet each was ideologically sworn to the other's eventual destruction. This is the kind of peace prevailing now. Coexistence, perhaps, is nearer to the phrase invented by Leon Trotsky immediately after Russia's 1917 revolution. He kept the army mobilized along the German border. But he sought to stop actual combat. "Neither war nor peace," he called this tactic.

We would do well to accustom ourselves to the restless period described today as Coexistence. That is likely to be a normal condition for our generation. The muddy description —Peaceful Coexistence—is a Bolshevik invention. Its meaning is inadequate. Lenin employed the term in 1920. Stalin developed it further when he reported to the Fourteenth Communist Party Congress on December 18, 1925. He said:

There has been established a certain temporary balance of power; a balance which has determined the current phase of Peaceful Co-existence between the land of the Soviets and the countries of capitalism. That which we once believed to be a short respite after the war has turned out to be a whole period of respite. Hence a certain balance of power and a certain period of 'Peaceful Co-existence' between the world of the bourgeoisie and the world of the proletariat. . . . We are living through a period of accumulation of strength which has great significance for future revolutionary initiatives.

This initial Peaceful Coexistence was exceedingly temporary. In 1927 Stalin told the Fifteenth Party Congress: "If two

2

years ago it was possible and necessary to speak of a period of a certain equilibrium and 'Peaceful Coexistence' between the U.S.S.R. and the capitalist countries, now we have every basis for declaring that the period of 'Peaceful Coexistence' is receding into the past."

When Stalin first employed this cumbersome term, Soviet dogma accepted the prospect of inevitable war between Communism and its ideological enemies. This was Lenin's doctrine, revised in 1956 by Khrushchev. Peaceful Coexistence was originally viewed as a tactical breathing space, a "whole period of respite" during which the new revolutionary state would accumulate strength before resuming battle. The phrase then implied a mere hiatus in war.

How, it may be asked, does revival of the term differ in implications from its usage thirty years ago? No one can be absolutely certain of the answer. It would appear the Soviet Government is frankly determined to press the global cause of Communism. This, it believes, with the fanaticism of early Islam, alone can save the world. But Moscow no longer sees war as the road to victory.

The U.S.S.R. has made its own experiments with thermonuclear weapons and realizes how devastatingly horrible they are. Furthermore, its military leaders have persuaded the Soviet Government that fissile explosions know no political boundaries.

Continuation of War by Other Means

Therefore, the term Peaceful Coexistence no longer refers merely to an interval between battles. That being the case,

3

what is its present meaning? The answer is to be found in a modified definition, Competitive Coexistence. One can detect in Soviet understanding of this phrase awareness of implicit possibilities in a new form of contest for world leadership. Coexistence is no longer a temporary interlude. It is a permanent new strategy. Peaceful policy, to reword Clausewitz, becomes the continuation of war by other means.

It would appear that sometime in 1955 the committee that rules the U.S.S.R. concluded it must compete for global paramountcy on a new basis, that Lenin's old-fashioned theory of war must be discarded as too dangerous. In early 1956 Khrushchev confirmed this. When Bulganin and Khrushchev visited Tito, they agreed that Socialism should be allowed to develop differently in different lands. This permitted Moscow to do away with the ideological isolationism of Stalin. Less official emphasis is now placed upon faithful imitation of the Soviet political model.

Hence, countries not yet considered part of the orbit can be freely aided in concord with Soviet ideology. And their support can be enlisted for Communism's global aims. If they are not in Russia's camp, they can at least be for it. In other words, Moscow has matured and broadened its diplomatic conceptions to harmonize with an economic and political contest that may exclude war as a means but doesn't forget ultimate aspirations.

The world is rapidly becoming aware of this Soviet strategy's potential force. Peaceful Coexistence appears to have been abandoned as a tactical maneuver. Instead, in a new competitive form, it has become a strategic means in itself. It might be well for us to appreciate the logic of this situation. The Competitive Coexistence of Bulganin and Khrushchev is more brilliant, more significant, more durable and more dangerous to our own position than Stalin's Peaceful Coexistence ever was.

Soviet Russia has been ahead of us in grasping the true political significance of Competitive Coexistence. In essence this adjustment may be described as follows: War on any major scale seems currently outmoded, not because it is immoral but because it is suicidal. Diplomatically, the "summit" conference in July, 1955, appeared to ratify what was already a scientific fact.

Therefore, in any contest for world influence, economic aid to uncommitted countries assumes still greater importance. Moscow is keenly aware of how the United States program for foreign assistance helped our international position. It too wishes to make political friends abroad and, in similar fashion, is attempting to do so. This is the basic "competitive" aspect of coexistence.

Yet, to enter into such forms of global rivalry, two things were necessary from the Soviet point of view. The first was to prepare its highly centralized internal economy for the added burden of expanded foreign operations. The second was to adapt the ideological outlook. Both trends have been maturing perceptibly.

If, as appears to be the case, Moscow rules out chances of a new great war, somewhat more emphasis can be placed upon developing peaceful technology and production. This provides more excess in terms both of technician manpower and fabricated output. It can be invested in underdeveloped lands of the Communist bloc, such as China, and in underdeveloped lands being courted, such as India and Egypt.

While nobody, of course, knows what Moscow can lend abroad, a program of this nature would have been less feasible under what we know as Malenkovism. Malenkov wished to sacrifice the rate of increase in capital investment for a sharp upsurge in output of consumers' goods. That would have lifted the Soviet Union's own standard of living far more rapidly than is currently foreseen. But it might have cut down foreign aid.

It is therefore no accident that such drastic revision in planning was abandoned. Malenkov's theory went out when Khrushchev and Bulganin took over in 1954. The committee that runs the U.S.S.R. apparently decided it could not risk lagging in the world production race without risking defeat in Competitive Coexistence.

Possibly some compromise between Khrushchevism—all-out emphasis on heavy industry—and Malenkovism may develop. But it is improbable Moscow will permit the rate of heavy production to falter. It acknowledges our industrial head start and dares not chance falling further behind. Malenkov's ideas, if fully applied, might have meant losing the race.

Convinced that only by economic strength can it best press Communism's cause, the Soviet presidium seems to have reappraised the world position. And the first requirement was

6

to emerge from the Stalinist era's strait isolationism. For many years Soviet doctrine held that only nations clearly within its orbit could be classed as Socialist. All others were automatically capitalist and inimical. Now the Russians, have adjusted their ideological view.

What is in effect modified acceptance of Tito's doctrine is being tacitly practiced if not formally acknowledged. This dogma, defined by Edvard Kardelj, the Jugoslav ideologist, holds that both developed and underdeveloped countries are gradually moving toward Socialism by different means. He concludes: "History has decided the quarrel between revolutionary and evolutionary Socialism, approving both."

When Bulganin and Khrushchev visited Belgrade, they accepted the principle of non-interference in other states. The idea is openly espoused in such countries as India and Egypt. It thus permits Soviet policy to become more flexible because it can now speak of Nehru's "Socialism" and Nasser's "progressivism" even though they are not members of the club.

Russia has in no sense abandoned its convictions of the truth of Communism or the need for its ultimate world triumph. But different methods are being pursued to achieve this end. We would be foolish if we did not adjust our policy and far greater economic potential to meet the competitive challenge.

This is a game we really invented ourselves with the Marshall Plan, and if we play it properly another and interesting phase could develop. Once Socialism (in the Soviet sense) has been recognized to have different paths and allowed to

7

proceed along separate ways, it may eventually be found to contain within itself inherent contradictions. Lenin saw such contradictions within the capitalist world. Yet, when Communism is no longer conceived as uniform, it might well discover cleavages and centrifugal forces of its own. That is a risk the Soviet leaders must accept in exchange for more flexible tactics.

The U.S.S.R.'s leadership clearly intends to press the struggle for ideological ascendancy. It brims with confidence that, by means short of war, Communism can gain world paramountcy in an era of all-out Competitive Coexistence.

The leaders take no pains to conceal total hostility toward the political, economic and moral systems we uphold. Nor do they attempt to disguise their deliberate intention of weakening and ultimately destroying our doctrines. This, it is said, can be accomplished by non-violent means because Soviet dogma teaches that the processes of history are on its side.

Khrushchev, in explaining such convictions, demonstrates the vigor of his Leninist beliefs. For, after all, did not Lenin say: "We can and must write in a language which sows among the masses hate, revulsion, scorn and the like toward those who disagree with us"? And we—who disagree—incur this.

While sowing scorn the Soviet bosses take pains to distinguish between the peoples of those nations we know as free and their governments. It is argued that the friendship of such peoples is desired. Yet there is apparent unwillingness to recognize a salient fact: these same worthy people elect the governments Moscow so detests.

It is no longer fashionable to speak of the Cold War. This term was discarded after the "summit" conference. Nevertheless, it cannot be said the famous "spirit of Geneva" glows with any special brightness. A frank struggle for ideological supremacy continues. The rules of the game have been altered by the horror implicit in the age of nuclear fission. But the same goals are there.

The U.S.S.R. is attempting to seize a diplomatic initiative. And it has certain advantages. The United States electoral campaign diverted attention from vital external interests. Western Europe remains uneasy. There is no sign that France has escaped from political lassitude. Britain's economy is not yet flourishing. Germany's future is unclear; rearmament lags and one cannot reckon for much longer with a stable leadership.

And Asia, from Middle East to Orient, is restless. The Arab states are quarrelsome and buying arms. Israel is frantic. The Northern Tier Alliance threatens to encounter tough sledding. Moscow has announced its intention of smashing not only that pact but also SEATO. It has enlisted support from India, Burma and Afghanistan for this purpose. Meanwhile Communist China's drive for UN membership is clearly gaining. Japan's political future has not crystallized. Our allies Syngman Rhee and Chiang Kai-shek are getting old.

Aware of these facts, Moscow seems intent on pushing a dynamic diplomacy. Khrushchev proclaimed he intends to wipe out colonialism. He referred specifically to European possessions in Africa and Asia. He saw no paradox in the fact that he addressed these remarks to a Supreme Soviet including delegates from many areas subject to Russian imperialism in the Baltic and Central Asia. For, he insisted, all peoples of the U.S.S.R. are "fraternal."

AMERICA'S ATTITUDE

It is high time the United States reminded the world of our own anti-colonialist attitudes. We gave freedom to Cuba and the Philippines. For years we urged independence for India and Ireland. We incurred the anger of our Dutch allies in supporting Indonesia. We have been helping Indo-China to its feet. And quite apart from opposition to colonialism, we might well stress and restress the simple fact that what we most support is liberty—for every people.

Facing up to the meaning of Competitive Coexistence, our Government has done well in requesting large appropriations for further foreign aid. This is not, as Khrushchev understands it, to enable "monopoly" capitalism to make profitable investments abroad. On the contrary, it is to meet the challenge outlined by the forthright Soviet leadership.

This massive political contest may easily endure a generation. And unfortunately it is necessary to convince the nations of Asia and Africa that we wish to help them disinterestedly. We must prove the sincerity of our wish to see all people free. What would happen if we suggested plebiscites in areas now being discussed? It is unlikely the population of Goa would vote as Moscow imagines. Or, for that matter, Kashmir and Formosa. What about Korea and East Germany? Truly free elections there might produce results surprising to the Kremlin. The refugee stream still flows from, not toward, Communism.

The American official attitude on coexistence derives from a skeptical background. The reasons for this, as explained to me by Secretary Dulles in October, 1954, are both idealistic and pragmatic. Dulles contended that, just as the Soviet leaders do, he approaches the problem somewhat philosophically. But, he insisted the philosophies involved are opposed in essence.

As Secretary of State during the initial years of coexistence, Dulles believed that the materialistic Soviet credo leads to a view of coexistence in a purely physical sense. The ultimate vision would be of a completely ordered world with each nation and individual functioning according to fixed patterns.

Dulles' conception is more one of permanent flux. He sees Soviet conformity as a breeder of sterility. This contrasts with the freedom bred by individual differences existing in and encouraged by democracy. We believe in a spiritual view of the world, he said, a world governed by more than material things. In such a world where people are entitled to their own beliefs and differing individualities the Secretary saw these very contrasts as a source of richness in themselves.

He didn't really think the Soviet Government could admit such a type of coexistence, so different from its own monolithic beliefs. Therefore he concluded that "when we are talking about coexistence we are actually talking about something entirely different from the Russians. They believe in coexistence only within a system of conformity. There is a

11

basic philosophical clash between their conception and our conception."

Nevertheless, he conceded, this does not mean that matters cannot be adjusted with Moscow. As he put it: "We can co-exist with the Russians under our own system in the sense that we can live together in the world at the same time—as long as we don't abandon basic principles. That kind of coexistence is possible, but always on a limited and provisional basis."

Among the principles which, according to Dulles, the United States could never forsake is the refusal to accept enslavement of other peoples or nations. For example, he said that he could never agree to coexistence based upon a deal permitting the Poles or Czechs to remain under Soviet domination—in exchange for particular benefits accorded the United States.

However, even in those earlier days he said he would never advocate war to free the Czechs and Poles. War produces more evils than the evils you are trying to eradicate, he observed. But he didn't believe in a form of coexistence acknowledging the surrender of other beings' human rights in order to procure advantages for ourselves.

Dulles did not think the Moscow Government would live up to any formal agreement for coexistence more than the Kremlin adhered to the terms of the Litvinov-Roosevelt accord under which Stalin promised to withdraw support from Communism in this country.

The Dulles theory, sometimes seemingly belied by the Secretary's own public statements, differed from a far more violent approach to policy on Soviet Russia. This was generally associated with Admiral Radford. The Secretary of State believed when he wasn't making speeches for effect, that we could coexist with the U.S.S.R. and ultimately outlast it. The first Eisenhower Chairman of the Joint Chiefs of Staff was more pessimistic. He held that when the Russians found they could no longer conquer the world by Cold War means, they would seek a "military solution." Fortunately, considering the advance of weapons science, the Admiral's concepts and the logical course of action they held out for us were disregarded.

Inside the Kremlin it is probable that a similar ambivalence prevailed if, indeed, it does not still exist. We know there is a Communist school that counts upon eventual destruction of democracy by economic collapse. We know Marxist dogma says capitalism contains the seeds of its own destruction. But we also know that, despite more peaceful professions of intention and some steps in the direction of disarmament, Soviet forces remain immensely powerful and Soviet policy clearly retains an ideologically and politically hostile intent.

If the scientists are right, it is profitable to analyze only the Dulles theory and to disregard the other as a dead-end street of logic. For the scientists, who know most about these things, say that if we don't learn how to coexist upon this earth we shall cease to exist at all.

Competitive Coexistence is a dynamic condition in which ideological, economic and political systems seek to dominate each other by means short of war. Such competition can in

13

no sense be compared to the old-fashioned rivalry for position among the powers. Now for the first time the foundation of our civilization is being menaced. A threat has been developed to the moral, spiritual and ethical values that have cemented our society for centuries. The challenge to the truth of these beliefs is perhaps even more important than the physical challenge of the Soviet bloc.

The main problem to the United States is to clarify the ideals of its heritage both to itself and to a confused world. Since the beginning of the Cold War, however, we have girded ourselves with more success physically than spiritually. Our armed strength has gained perceptibly more than our moral vigor.

We do not wish nor are we able to rival the Russians in dialectics or twisting propaganda. That they have been able to describe as "freedom" a system of slavery should not affect us. The truth cannot forever be obscured by deliberate word warping. This was implicitly admitted by Khrushchev in his famous tirade against Stalin.

A Soviet "peace offensive" has convinced millions of skeptical people who are at the same time worrying about the ultimate intentions of the United States. Leaden imperialism obscures much of Eastern Europe while the world speculates concerning America's "colonial attitudes."

One reason for confusion abroad concerning ourselves is a mirrored reflection of certain confusions at home. Dulles, himself a religious man, recognized that one of our major obligations is to demonstrate "the good fruits of freedom which

14

undermine the rule of despots by contrast."

Unfortunately these "good fruits" have been camouflaged in foreign eyes—and perhaps in our own—by strange manifestations that for long were collectively called McCarthyism— manifestations that Dulles' own State Department did not escape. Suspicion and mistrust were sown among ourselves and within our institutions sufficiently to cause a shrinkage in our own self-respect and in the respect of other nations for us. This tendency occurred at a moment in history when for the first time a chink appeared in Russia's gloomy Iron Curtain. Fortunately much of this hysteria has subsided. But we remain confused by bigotry and racism, by intolerance for other peoples or their ideas.

A continuation of these trends could bring about eventually a complete change in the true values of "America" to ourselves and others. The United States then would no more resemble the United States of the past than the Athens of today resembles the Athens of Pericles.

The present clash in ideologies, Competitive Coexistence, does not mean a static life like that of two cabbages in a field, existing if they are not planted too close together. It does mean a recapture of something vibrant in our heritage, a rebirth in ourselves and in our ideals.

For, if we are frank, our long-range aspirations are no less all-embracing than those of Moscow. Communism's ultimate objective is a Communist world. Ours is a free and democratic world. Perhaps, as the militant character of Bolshevism decreases, time will be able to moderate some of the more striking clashes between the two great systems. This, at any rate, should be our modest hope. Any alternative to co-existence is too awful to contemplate. Therefore we should examine the post-Stalin Russia and seek to ascertain if there is any basis for accommodation.

II

The Russian Glacier Moves

A NEW era in the Soviet Union's relatively short history began promptly after Stalin's death. Like so many changes in Russia's murky past this too was marked by bewilderment and violence. Long-latent forces of revolution and counter-revolution were touched off in explosion. Many of their immediate consequences are not yet known. Nor can anyone, as yet, predict with certainty the ultimate shape of these developments.

The first indication that vital things were stirring within the U.S.S.R. and its stultified orbit was the outbreak of a series of bloody strikes. These would have been utterly unimaginable during Stalin's day. On May 7, two months after the dictator's death, an uprising began in the complex of slave labor camps situated around the bleak Siberian town of Norilsk. Norilsk, at the mouth of the Yenisei River, is well within the Arctic Circle. The insurrection there lasted one hundred days—until August 11, 1953. It spread from barracks to barracks. Armed suppression quelled it temporarily in May. But the desperate workers broke out once again and

17

only subsided after a general massacre.

From Norilsk the germ of insurrection spread. Strangely enough this disorganized revolution next erupted thousands of miles away in East Berlin. There, on June 17, workers protested against onerous work norms. For a while the Soviet military authorities were nonplused. At first they behaved with oddly bewildered restraint. But the movement gathered force; rapidly it extended across the entire Communist zone of Germany. While the West, which had been talking so loudly about *"liberation,"* stood by paralyzed with indecision, Moscow sent in troops and armed militia. The revolt was stamped out.

Nevertheless, one month later, the epidemic struck again, this time in another Siberian labor camp named Vorkuta. Prisoners' committees boldly organized. They presented lists of demands and bargained with secret police authorities. The concessions they obtained undoubtedly paved the way for later reform. For the regime, rid at last both of the efficiency and terror of its all-puissant tyrant, was frightened. It was apparent to all that Stalinism had not yet been able to digest man's truculent spirit of freedom.

These uprisings are possibly linked to Beria's execution. Clearly it was satisfying to the oppressed to see justice done to the most hated symbol of a hated system. A further logically connected result was Malenkov's effort to boost Soviet living standards. He sought to achieve this swiftly by increasing the output of consumer's goods. Still another consequence perhaps was the decision to call off the Cold War.

Peace was made with Tito and new efforts were initiated to relieve tension with the West. When Khrushchev and Bulganin succeeded Malenkov, they returned to Stalinist emphasis on heavy industry. But they continued to ease police controls and international strains. The trend toward pause, a hiatus in the Bolshevik revolution, a Soviet *Thermidor* continued.

It is too soon, historically, to discern the exact relationship between all these events: Stalin's death, widely spread local revolts, Beria's execution, the new course in internal and external affairs. Nor can one yet pretend to accurate prevision of the future. Isaac Deutscher, a perceptive writer on Russia and Communism, contends: "This can only be a transitional state of affairs. In the long run the [Bolshevik] party cannot remain half-slave, half-free. Either the higher ranks will have to share gradually their newly won freedom with the lower ranks or they themselves will lose it to a new dictator to whom they are so anxious to bar the road." This theory was put to a test in Poland by the bloody Poznan strike of 1956. The struggle for freedom, begun in Norilsk, is clearly a living force in many regions of the Soviet orbit.

Stalin died at a highly convenient moment. The U.S.S.R. was faring badly in the Cold War. Yet it had established itself firmly as a super-power. It was more than strong enough to afford some relaxation of the desolate, regimented life that had become the mode. Year after year, while the Russian people suffered slavery and incredible lack of even ordinary comfort, the state had plowed back 64 per cent of all accumulated new capital into the expansion of those industries pro-

19

ducing goods to be pumped into the industrial process. With single-minded obsession and regardless of this generation's misery the Kremlin had been determined to make of Russia the world's strongest nation.

When the first five-year plan was being elaborated, one of its originators, L. Sabsovitch, estimated that within fifteen years the U.S.S.R. could overtake the American economy. Later he revised his prediction downward. He claimed it would be possible "to complete the whole period of transition by 1935-1936 and to advance by that time far beyond the present level of production in the United States and probably also the level they will have reached by then, if they continue under a capitalist system." Sabsovitch was premature in his guesses. Yet he was merely echoing traditional Russian ambitions. Even before World War I, Czarist economists and some Europeans calculated that if Russia could maintain the existing industrial pace it would overshadow the rest of Europe by 1950.

This preoccupation with manufacturing power and a resultant industrial society is bound to have incalculable repercussions within the Soviet state. Already a class of technocrats has started to develop. There are today perhaps thirty million members of the "toiling intelligentsia" (including dependents) in the U.S.S.R.; architects, engineers, teachers, doctors, etc. Some of this class are far less bound by rigid dogma than the Old Bolshevik leadership. What will be the eventual political and philosophical consequences? A decade ago Arnold Toynbee wrote:

The present rulers of Russia are working with demonic energy to ensure the triumph in Russia of the very civilization that they are denouncing in the world at large. No doubt they dream of creating a new society which will be American in equipment but Russian in soul—though this is a strange dream to be dreamed by statesmen for whom a materialistic interpretation of history is an article of faith! On Marxian principles we must expect that, if a Russian peasant is taught to live the life of an American mechanic, he will learn to think as the mechanic thinks, to feel as he desires. In this tug of war which we are witnessing in Russia between the ideas of Lenin and the methods of Ford, we may look forward to seeing the ascendancy of the Western over the Russian civilization paradoxically confirmed.

Economically and psychologically the U.S.S.R. may be approaching the threshold of curious change, the gradual introduction after years of Stalinist sacrifice of a new and "bourgeois" mode of life. Already, in Moscow, there are faint hints of this.

There are many impressively large new buildings, even if their ornate architecture is now criticized. For the first time some streets have a traffic problem. Food is more plentiful. People are warmly clothed. If prices are exceedingly steep, they cannot be measured accurately because of artificial ruble rates. Housing remains short, but efforts are being made at remedy. There are now such things as bicycles, private cars and plentiful television sets.

Politically committee rule has replaced one-man dictatorship and so far seems to work. Such arguments as take place appear to be between ideologists and pragmatic managerial experts. In a curious Soviet way this perhaps approximates our own debate among New Deal theorists and businessmen. Psychologically there is a growth in national self-confidence. The regime proved it could survive the crisis of Stalin's death. Victory in World War II, establishment of Communism in Eastern Europe and above all in China, and the new role of super-power have combined to give people faith in their system. There are probably few who even imagine an alternative. The state police have been drastically down-graded in importance. The first phase of the revolution is over. The Government is apparently solidly established and accepted— if more remote from public opinion than anything we are used to. And the Communist party has sunk roots deeply into every phase of national life.

The Russian people suffered heavily on the road to this development. The first revolutionary generation knew little personal or political security. A second generation endured terrible wartime deprivations. But now confidence and relative tranquillity are slowly replacing that zeal and fanaticism which marked the early years and that fear and suspicion which developed later. The messianic exaltation of the 1920's when Bolshevism, drunk with titanic vision, hurled itself from one abrupt experiment to another is no longer apparent.

There is on a broad front a gradual retreat from the rigid political and cultural quarantine that marked much of recent Bolshevik history. The glacial formation which seems to obscure much of Soviet life and its inner perceptions is again moving. Contact with the world abroad, with things that are foreign both to the ideology and art forms of Russia now is opening up.

Under the Lid

The Russians are an exceptionally friendly people, capable, when permitted, of deep sentiment and emotion. Various European theatrical or musical troupes have all to some degree encountered their hunger for outside friendships and foreign intellectual contacts. The fact that for years under Stalin such cravings were bottled up has, if anything, increased their eagerness. The moment isolation's lid was even slightly lifted it exposed an astonishing desire for tangible relationships with the world abroad. Once again the youth in big cities let itself go in an orgy of jazz. The record collection of Moscow's Lenin Library is played and replayed and many disks are bootlegged. The capital's small smart set has taken to foreign-cut clothes brought in by friends on Soviet diplomatic missions or copied by local tailors. Vyshinsky's daughter paid 3,000 rubles merely to be introduced to a dressmaker familiar with European styles.

The new youth is developing aberrations curious to Communism. Many youngsters are keen on boogie-woogie. Zippered *stilyagi*, or "style-seekers," dress as eccentrically as any American zoot-suit addict or English teddy-boy. The well-connected jet set is enthusiastic for dancing and unconcerned about divorce. One member inherited two apartments, three country villas, four automobiles and a large bank balance from his composer father. Under the U.S.S.R.'s odd system of huge royalties, minimal estate and income taxes, and 3 per cent interest rates on savings accounts, this youngster has managed to live like a capitalist heir.

23

City sophisticates in Moscow and Leningrad have a craving for Western things. The elite have begun to take summer holidays in Central Europe's famous spa at Carlsbad. Chic youngsters like to employ an occasional English or Latin word. Foreign theatrical companies are so popular that tickets, slipped to the black market, fetch enormous prices. Such, for an English performance of *Hamlet,* were worth as much as 500 rubles ($125 at the official rate). Now that literary censorship has eased there is more scope for foreign books. Hemingway and Dreiser are the vogue among intellectuals. And there is a gingerly move to permit some travel abroad. Intourist has started to conduct trips to France and Italy.

All this is part of a slowly maturing trend reflected in various fields. Bulganin, recently, spoke of the West in a way unfamiliar to Stalinism. He admitted capitalism had its efficient aspects. Even Kaganovitch says, "The United States is rich and has a powerful industry."

The average Russian's intense curiosity concerning the United States is all the more astonishing if one analyzes available information about us. As a true picture it is about as accurate as the reflection of a Coney Island mirror.

The regime itself, by implication, admits that its knowledge of things American is incomplete. For, shortly after this lack was called to the attention of one prominent leader, a new academy was opened for the study of "contemporary capitalism." But even if there were willingness to conduct an objective study—which is not apparent—it would require years to alter the distorted impression.

24

Our political system, as reported in the Moscow press seems tailored to suit Marxist-Leninist prejudices. According to *International Affairs*, in the United States a year or two ago "it was almost enough to send a man to the electric chair or prison to speak seriously of peace." The Eisenhower Administration's economic precept is described as the "trickle-down theory—if you help big business you help the people." Labor leaders and politicians of both parties join, says the magazine, in popular deception.

The heads of A.F.L.-C.I.O., it claims, "separated by many years of bureaucratic leadership from the workers, collaborate with the most reactionary elements of government like Attorney General Brownell and F.B.I. Director Hoover." Brownell has "served notice that he will do everything in his power to wreck any labor union that fails to follow his political beliefs."

Our foreign policy is seen as based only on a desire to make money. American big business regards "tension in the international scene as a means of acquiring the maximum possible war profits." And, as *Izvestia* explains, our foreign-aid program seeks only to wring commercial advantages. Accordingly:

At first this country or that is drawn into the arms race, which is ruinous to the national economy. As a result the military program goes beyond the scope of what the country's economy can support, i.e., bluntly speaking, an economic crisis begins. Then the very ones who caused this crisis come to "help." This time they appear as quack doctors. There is begun economic support for the military program.

25

And who are these Americans, so cynically governed? Says *New Times*:

The interests of many Americans are very limited. They hardly ever read a book and have practically no knowledge of American, let alone world, literature; their ideas of history and world affairs are vague in the extreme. . . .

The one-sided education many Americans receive and the idea that is hammered into them from early years that a man must "make good" breeds in them a certain indifference to everything outside the sphere of money-making. . . .

The average American seems to be indifferent to politics, both domestic and foreign. . . . Parents who want to determine what sort of a career their child is likely to follow place a dollar bill and a bottle of whisky before it. If the child picks up the dollar, that is a good sign—it will grow up to be a hard-working and prosperous citizen. If it reaches for the bottle, it will most likely grow up a confirmed drunkard. One baby grabbed the dollar bill and the bottle and the mother exclaimed: "Good Lord, he'll be a politician."

There is admiration in the U.S.S.R. for the power of the United States, respect for our technical ability and envy of our living standards. But the contempt and misunderstanding of our politics, economics, social system and ideology—as expressed in party literature—is beyond credence.

RUSSIAN SCHIZOPHRENIA

Russian history has often shown a marked schizophrenia, zigzagging between total isolationism and admiration for the foreign world. "Westernizers" of Czarist days sought salvation in complete and rapid assimilation of European culture. They

26

were opposed to "Slavophils," who emphasized Russia's own distinctive characteristics and separateness.

Perhaps this split derives from the geography of the vast subcontinent, neither Asian nor European and not sure where to turn. Anton Tchekov mourned last century: "The beginning of Russia was in 862 and civilized Russia, as I understand it, has not yet begun." At that same time the Marquis de Custine, a French observer, remarked on "this terrible combination of the intelligence and the science of Europe with the genius of Asia."

Argument as to whether Russia leans westward or is bound up in its solitary self persevered into Bolshevik days. Stalin's dictates locked European paintings in museum cellars and boasted that practically every clever invention had been conceived unaided by a Russian. The country was urged to spurn almost anything of foreign origin.

But deep-seated curiosity about the outer world was never stilled. It is interesting to note the passionate interest of Russians in their own artists' paintings of Mediterranean scenes or in their ballets' version of meridional dances. When it was presented in the U.S.S.R., *Porgy and Bess* appealed to this innate taste, so contrasting with the flat diurnal life and landscape.

Nevertheless, in the past, for every "Westernizer" Russia had its "Slavophil." From the times of Peter the Great contacts with Europe have alternately broadened and narrowed, advanced and retreated.

It is always difficult to assess changes within the Soviet

27

Union. But certainly the self-confidence of the Russians has now immeasurably increased. This has invigorated hopes that the scope and daring of Moscow will someday overshadow the achievements of the conventional West. And it has dispelled the brooding suspicion which for so long existed that failure's hand lay heavily over Russian undertakings. The U.S.S.R.'s future obviously contains new problems. But their character differs from those of the past. And the national mood that faces them is altering.

These changes are still perhaps superficial. How deeply they are rooted in basic phenomena cannot yet be discerned. Nevertheless, they should neither be discounted nor ignored. All too often in the past we have depicted Russia as an impenetrable mystery. Yet its political intentions, its economic philosophy and its diplomatic goals are advertised enough. The Soviet phenomenon need not necessarily perplex. It remains a single-party state. Therefore, like others of our era, it can be efficient in certain of its actions. But the mere fact that it can accomplish great deeds in industry or education means neither, as Moscow says, that humanity benefits more from Communism than from any other governmental form; nor that everything in the U.S.S.R. is bad and doesn't work.

Frequently the Western visitor praises or condemns the Soviet scene to a twisted extreme. The balletomane will translate the perfections of Galina Ulanova into political ecstasy. The intellectual isolationist is astonished to find the average Russian human, kind and generous. The blind critic sees only queues and backward transportation. This is comparable to the

Soviet traveler in the United States who fails to note in our country a living refutation of the dogma that total statism is the most productive system.

THE SOVIET SYSTEM

A foreign tourist can view the U.S.S.R. from two opposing antipodes. And these, in a sense, are brought together strikingly in the symbolic microcosm of Moscow. On the one hand are the massive buildings that stand for impressive industrial progress and ability. On the other hand, in the very shadows of these buildings, are the dilapidated log houses that so belie the boast that Moscow is the world's only capital free of slums.

It is not infrequent that those abroad analyze the entire Soviet monolith from either extreme intellectual pole. There are some who see only the skyscrapers and therefore tend to exaggerate the power of the Soviet state. And there are others who, preferring to see the log cabins, deduce that the U.S.S.R. is but papier-mâché, a false front, a gigantic Potemkin village.

Patently neither view is accurate. The country has made notable physical strides. Its productivity and industrial potential are climbing fast and will continue to climb. Some of its mechanical appliances are as good as or better than anything we have. Russia's ceramic machine tools and certain nuclear devices are in advance of ours. Its political self-confidence has matured. Those who thought Stalin's autocratic dictatorship must necessarily bequeath an uneasy succession might do well to reflect.

The Soviet Union is stronger than one group of wishful

thinkers would believe and weaker than the opposite camp assumes. Advances in some fields have been achieved by sacrifices in others. The country still has a long distance to progress. Its agriculture is backward. Despite every effort to mechanize, too much manpower is wasted. Living standards are far behind those to which we are accustomed. Railways are inefficient and highways almost nonexistent. The problem of building adequate housing for a burgeoning city population constitutes a headache. Administrative bureaucracy, except at the highest levels, is frustratingly awkward.

Yet, despite these extreme contrasts, it is necessary for us to view the U.S.S.R. through a properly focused lens. Russia by tradition is indeed secretive and reserved. Such has been true under Czar or Commissar, and this confuses us just as our own lack of inhibition and apparent contradictions often bewilder the Soviet mind. Russia is a vast, inchoate land, still in the midst of a political experiment that admittedly has not yet found final form. It is replete with juxtapositions of twentieth-century efficiency and pervasively backward inefficiency. But it is really no more mysterious than we choose to make it.

In any scrutiny of the Soviet scene Moscow plays a particularly important role. It is the magnetic lode of all that is best in the present-day U.S.S.R., a particularly favorable snapshot of the state. The city itself has always held a very special position in the Russian heart. Long before the Bolshevik revolution, proverbs boasted: "He who has not been to Moscow has not seen beauty"; "In Moscow there is never a scarcity of bread"; "One can find everything in Moscow except pigeon's milk"; and "Moscow is mother to all cities."

This deep-rooted affection both antedates and postdates the era when St. Petersburg, now Leningrad, was Russia's capital. Although Moscow is far from being the world's largest, most beautiful or most comfortable city, and is often drab and dilapidated, it is by comparison with the inhospitable steppe or forest, the isolated villages and incredibly provincial towns, the apogee of ordinary Russian aspirations.

This fact is variously mirrored. University students do their utmost to qualify for jobs in the capital. Artists and actors are heartbroken if they cannot find positions there. Officials dream of ending up in the great central Muscovite bureaucracy. And ordinary laborers try to drift into that city seeking work.

As a result, the municipal administration headed until 1956 by Mikhail Alexeivitch Yasnov has taken measures to check undue population increases. Yasnov told me in December, 1955, before he moved up to the Premiership of the Russian Soviet Republic, that the capital contained 4,300,000 people when the war with Germany began in 1941. Fifteen years later, there were only a few more inhabitants—between 4,-600,000 and 4,700,000. New industrial construction is now forbidden in order not to provide new jobs. Yasnov said: "There is no need for us to create a giant city; that would be difficult to run." This freeze on growth is in interesting contrast with the gigantesque in other sectors of Soviet life.

Yasnov is a hefty man with a tough, shrewd face. His blue

31

eyes, flat nose and heavy jaw remind one of a successful New York businessman or politician who fought his way up from a construction gang. He dresses in neat pin-striped blue suit, cardigan sweater, white shirt and conservative cravat. A painting of Stalin and Voroshilov gazing over the Kremlin wall still hung in the antechamber just before Stalin was officially denigrated and another portrait of Stalin was in his office.

Yasnov admitted his biggest problem is housing. He recognized Moscow's need to catch up with the times. A large number of existing dwellings were built a century ago. They are overcrowded. Muscovites consider themselves lucky if two people in a one-room flat share a community kitchen and bath with five other families.

Emphasis is now being placed on construction of new apartment houses between five and seven stories high. Skyscrapers are *démodé*. Yasnov pointed out Moscow is not an island or built on rock, like New York, and can expand outward rather than upward. Twenty-five thousand two-to-five-room flats will be occupied in 1956-57. Tenants are placed according to income, size of family, or what Yasnov called "social position." He explained that "an intellectual deserves a study and room for his books." Such facilities now are rare indeed.

Despite Moscow's relative luxury, its plethora of opportunity as compared with the rest of the vast state, it lags pitifully behind most major cities of the world. In this it typifies the whole U.S.S.R., where Communism, until the present, has always been conjugated in the future. The day will come, it

32

is boasted, when individual wants can be satisfied according to need, not work. It isn't stipulated who will measure this. For the Utopian stage has admittedly not been reached.

But current dogma does wish to convince people the threshold is approaching. Perhaps that is why Molotov was criticized in 1955 for saying the foundations only of Socialism, not Communism, had been built. *Pravda* proclaimed "the completion of the building up of Socialism and of the gradual transfer from Socialism to Communism." It added: "Communism is not a dream and not in the distant future; the building up of Communism is a reality of our time."

Certainly every Soviet citizen doesn't now receive all he needs. But *Pravda's* implicit promise is meant to encourage. And although, since Malenkov's demotion, their *rate* of increase in production has diminished, there are more consumer's goods in many cities. Life is becoming less uncomfortable.

Yet, the Khrushchev-Bulganin Government shows no sign of reducing the pace of industrialization. Their speeches demonstrate this is still regarded as the key to national success. It is within this context that one should interpret *Pravda's* assurances of the imminence of Communism as "a reality." There is a Russian proverb: "Do not drive the horses with a whip, but with oats." This administration uses oats, but the direction is unchanged.

Advances along the way, during thirty-eight years of Soviet history, have been formidable. Still, they are difficult to assess. Since 1929 there have been no cost-of-living statistics. Nor can one gauge the price of industrialization in terms of sweat, blood, toil and tears.

The Bolshevik system has certain purely economic advantages and disadvantages. State planning, fixing goals and constantly raising them, forces the pace. And, since the state owns everything, it can combine factories, standardize or specialize by decree. Labor unions cannot bargain as in the United States. Instead, as cheer leaders, they promote enthusiasm and productivity. Technical education has been stimulated and surpasses our own in quantity.

The U.S.S.R.'s industrial program was started on the backward foundation of old Russia without those foreign investments that helped capitalist lands expand. For years Stalinism had to employ drastic means to produce sufficient urban population to run new factories.

By dint of convulsive energy Soviet Russia is now the world's second industrial power. The rate of progress has been notable. Steel production rose from 5,000,000 tons in 1929 to 41,000,000 in 1954. Compare this to the United States where between 1896 and 1916, steel output increased from 5,300,000 tons per annum to 42,700,000. Of course, the base from which we started was as different as our social and capital structure. Russia's revolution exploded in a primarily agricultural land. An industrial mass had to be created. It was —by drastic means centrally initiated.

This social shift brought with it problems. Agriculture has not yet adjusted to the change. Neither livestock herds nor farm output per man has kept up with factory production.

Seven million field workers feed our own population and have far too much left over. Yet, more than 50,000,000 farmers are needed to supply the Soviet nation.

It is difficult to calculate how much any economy produces per head. But Soviet production is growing fast. An English economist estimates it increases at a rate 3 per cent faster than in the United States. Certainly the emphasis in planning remains on heavy industry, the muscles of power. There is not yet any sign that a large increase in consumer's goods output might be permitted to conflict with capital development.

THE HUMAN PROBLEM

By advancing to the role of super-power, the U.S.S.R. has brought upon itself many of the same basic economic problems that face America. The difference of ideology has not hidden the fact that fundamental puzzles are common to any governmental system once it achieves a certain level of civilization.

Khrushchev himself says: "Only on the basis of an uninterrupted growth of production and increase of labor productivity will public prosperity multiply, the working day shrink, and the national well-being steadily grow." Kaganovitch adds that Russia's "most important and greatest question of all is the reduction of labor in production; the reduction of production costs. The solution of this basic task can be insured only through labor productivity which is higher than capitalism."

Raymond Aron, a brilliant French student of Marxism, points out in *The Century of Total War*: "The type of ownership does not itself modify the lot of the workers; it determines neither the standard of living nor the condition of work. . . . For the working class as a whole, the standard of living depends more on productivity than on the owners of the means of production."

In Russia, the requisite increase in a non-agricultural labor force needed to boost factory output denuded the countryside. This still lacks sufficiently modern production methods or individual incentives to produce. In 1928, when Stalin began his push for industrialization, only 13 per cent of the Soviet labor force was working in non-agricultural pursuits. By ruthless state interference, it was easy to multiply the urban worker population.

Because of this reservoir taken from the farms, Stalin was able to provide human energy for his machines. In 1928 fewer than 10,000,000 people were engaged in non-agricultural jobs. By 1956 there were perhaps 45,000,000. The sixth five-year plan proposes that there shall be 55,000,000 in 1960. This, incidentally, may explain Moscow's desire to demobilize as many soldiers as deemed possible.

Khrushchev recognizes that by stressing industrial output the U.S.S.R. has sacrificed agricultural efficiency. During Stalinist times he himself experimented with various plans to overcome the lag. Khrushchev took the lead in sponsoring a grandiose scheme for farm towns to be called *agrogorodyi*. These were to combine the features of city and country society.

But the dream vanished into spacious inefficiency. Masses of humanity were moved into areas built up only in blueprints of party architects. The idea fizzled. And Khrushchev, being a tough Bolshevik politician, had the crust to blame Malenkov. Now the emphasis is upon cultivating land that hitherto lay fallow, above all in Soviet Asia.

Khrushchev remonstrates that *kolkhozes* are delivering to the state only one-tenth of the bacon pigs called for in planning. Almost a quarter of the porkers sold weighed less than seventy pounds. He asks: "Is this really a pig? It is not swine but swinishness." He talks of "undernourished cattle" and dwindling poultry which cost too much and produce too little. He says Soviet hens remind him of the old folktale: "Each egg here is not an ordinary egg but a golden one."

Clearly there are three primary reasons for the failure of Soviet agriculture to keep pace with industry. First of all the peasant population has not yet, after almost four decades of revolution, been persuaded to produce as eagerly for the state as for itself. Secondly, the state has not yet been able to re-train the conservative peasantry in mass new farming methods, dependent upon machinery and orders from political theoreticians. And thirdly, the woefully inadequate transportation system and inability to store and market food has cut down distribution.

Traditions of private initiative still persist among Soviet peasants. This is confirmed by the fact the government has not yet been able to do away totally with the little family plots each collective farming household is still allowed to cultivate. It is on these tiny holdings that the peasant spends his spare time growing garden crops for sale on the officially tolerated open markets, raises a few bees, hens, possibly keeps a cow. Something less than 3 per cent of the cultivated acreage of the U.S.S.R. remains in this last "capitalist" phase. Yet, the productivity of these holdings is relatively much higher than that of the collectivized land. Private plots are believed to account for approximately 10 per cent of the country's agricultural output when computed in terms of value.

The Soviet regime, worried by the reluctant farmers' attitude, has for long sought to instill some spirit of initiative. The trend, faltering and uncertain, is toward decentralization. Yet it is difficult to inject the habit of independent thought by fiat into a people whose tradition is marked by submission to authority.

One philosophical approach to the problem had been through Bolshevism's pseudo-science of genetics as taught by T. D. Lysenko. Lysenko, a biologist more successful in politics than in the laboratory, insists the Mendelian theory of heredity is outmoded and that acquired characteristics can be inherited. What does this mean?

Lysenko is a seed expert. But his ideas transcend the world of fruit flies and plant ovules. Were his concepts to be proven —as they were only in the domain of Stalinist science—it would imply a new kind of human being might be invented. This Communist generation could theoretically produce Communist children born with the acquired wisdom of thirty-eight years of Soviet experience. Its philosophical implication is that a new mankind, more in harmony with Communism, can be created. This new Soviet species could presumably erase

38

from its heritage the vast, beclouded turbulence of the Russian past.

As the regime tried to create a more "independent" type of Russian, Lysenko's theory was convenient. It seemed that through his ideas future Soviet generations could be expected to expunge from their subconscious complexes of failure and unoriginality that mark so much of Russian history. But Lysenko, in 1956, was abandoned.

What is it that would have been avoided by new "laws" of heredity? Is it what Pushkin called "the absurd and pitiless Russian tumult"? Is it the autocracy, state worship and dependence complained of by Dostoevski, the habit of "complete submission" in which men desire "to be led like sheep"?

Evidently, if any true spirit of independence is to be achieved, national psychology must be remolded. For many years the governmental system—both Bolshevik and pre-Bolshevik—was based upon the discipline of a military camp rather than normal civic order. Everything and anything has been sanctified by faith in the state.

More than a century ago a French observer wrote: "Ambition and fear, passions which elsewhere men exhaust in talking much about them, here engender silence. This excessive silence produces a forced calm, an apparent order. . . . Other nations have tolerated oppression; the Russian nation has loved it."

Surely the Soviet Administration desires to prove future generations can escape such a dreadful spiritual heritage. That is where Lysenko might have come in handy. His disputed theories suited a political purpose. His was the scientific

39

"proof" that the Russian is not foredoomed to mental serfdom and predestined misery.

If Russia is ever to get away from the habit of autocracy, its national mind must be cleansed of pervasive forces of pre-destiny. That was the philosophical purpose of the new genetics. What will Moscow now substitute for Lysenko? Is the answer to be found in diabolizing Stalin?

ERASING A MYTH

Ever since the first great Slavic empire was founded on Kiev's bluff above the Dnieper, the state that eventually became the Soviet Union developed along rigid, formalistic lines. This was true, with few interruptions, under successive rulers of Czardom. And it has been true of the Bolshevik experiment.

No government on the sweeping steppes escaped the eventual curse of stultification. Certain historians ascribe this to the heritage of Byzantium, which Russia absorbed together with its religion. Others see it as a legacy from Mongol authoritarianism, brought westward by successive Tartar waves.

Russia's history is marked by an odd Byzantine formalism in which the state always has been deified. In 1890 Friedrich Engels, one of the gods in the Bolshevik Valhalla, observed: "In Russia itself only the official myth is tolerated." Still earlier Custine remarked: "Political obedience has become a cult, a religion for the Russians. It is only with this people—at least I believe this is so—that one has seen martyrs in adoration before their executioners . . . men who had to be gagged to be ruled according to their liking."

In *The Brothers Karamazov*, Dostoevski views this quintessential Russian problem through the eyes of his Grand Inquisitor: "Nothing has ever been more insupportable for a man and human society than freedom. . . . Freedom and bread enough for all are inconceivable together, for never, never will they be able to share between them. . . . Didst Thou forget that man prefers peace, and even death, to freedom of choice?"

Under both Czardom and Commissardom this submission had its symbolic iconography. The Little Father ruling from St. Petersburg or the grim Stalin in his Kremlin was each state, religion and virtual godhead of a particular Russian cult. While Bolshevism substituted its own orthodoxy and its own imagery, the same paralyzing inhibitions persevered.

Day after day long queues still form in Moscow's Red Square. Shuffling silently behind military officers at an artificially slow pace, they march beneath ravens flapping from their Kremlin roosts to make obeisance at the appalling tomb of the mummified Lenin and (strangely enough, even now) Stalin.

One is struck by the similarity of that gloomy ceremony and the few permitted vestigial echoes of the past. A handful of old-fashioned Orthodox believers continues to make the pilgrimage to Lavra Monastery in the ancient city of Kiev. There they scuttle through catacombs, bowing before the shriveled remains of medieval saints, genuflecting beside their coffins and, in flickering candlelight, embracing the glass lids above gnarled corpses.

41

Bolshevism's icons are replacing holy images. On revolutionary anniversaries, in every public square, appear huge posters of the Soviet leaders. By rewriting history, Stalin to a large degree created his personal mythology. Yet this could only occur in a country with Russia's adulatory habits. And his new cult of iconography persists even though the former proto-god has been demoted: silvered statues of Lenin in every public nook; paintings of Lenin, Marx and Engels in almost every private office; posters of the current bosses in garish holiday displays.

There are signs that the present Administration is seeking to erase some of this debasing subjection to the state. Gingerly the Bulganin-Khrushchev rule tries to encourage a trend toward decentralization, toward less dependence upon the all-powerful Government. Under the current five-year plan collective farms and factories are supposed to do their own programming. That is to say, having been told what goals they are meant to achieve, enterprises are instructed to fulfill these at their own initiative. No longer is the last detail of seeding or production pace blueprinted in advance by authority above.

This encouragement of original thinking is still in its infancy. Nobody can foresee how it will work. The management of a large collective farm at Dimidiv, near Kiev, says the adjustment is not difficult. But other organizations are unabashedly shocked. They are unused to the habit of creative thought and individual responsibility. For years they have relied totally upon direction from the immense bureaucracy above. It is like ordering a swaddled, uninstructed child to walk.

42

It may take years to erase the habit of fawning before authority. The psychological heritage to be expunged is rooted far back in time. But its recent example was the most terrifying of all. The age of Stalin the Terrible did not really begin to end until the death of his most dreadful henchman. Beria's execution was announced to the startled Russian people in the early summer of 1953. The day the news was broadcast a new super-department store opened its doors in Moscow. This is called *Glavnyi Universalnyi Magazin* and popularly known as GUM. The coincidence of events did not escape notice. "Boom for Beria and GUM for the people" was one sardonic Western comment.

There is some point to this brutal quip. The U.S.S.R. has drawn a new breath since the days of Stalin's dictatorship. Beria, who refused almost hysterically to submit his police apparatus to committee control, was the last vestige of personal tyranny. Russia is now experimenting with a new system— autocracy without an autocrat. Not even the Russians know if it will work.

Stalinism, as we understand the word, is out. Beria was the last admitted euphemism for that tyranny. After all, Beria once observed confidentially: "The people are nothing but sheep; they must be told what to do." It was, of course, Stalin himself who built the hideous police state that made a Beria possible. Shortly before his death the despot received Leopoldo Bravo, then Argentine Ambassador. Bravo expressed polite pleasure at the honor. Said Stalin, like some Mongol khan: "In this country even the shepherds are well treated."

43

It is difficult to imagine the atmosphere of those last Stalinist years. On one grim night in 1948 the U.S.S.R.'s Greek minority along the Black Sea coast—some forty-five thousand people—was rounded up and scattered in Soviet Asia. Prominent citizens continued to disappear. Mikhail Borodin, the Old Bolshevik who fomented Chinese revolution, died in jail. Konstantin Zinchenko, former Assistant Secretary General of the United Nations, was imprisoned. Peter Kapitza, the famous physicist, was isolated in a country cottage.

Beria's demise punctuated this era. Zinchenko is rehabilitated. Kapitza, again at work, believes none of his friends are in prison any longer. Concentration camps are shrinking. The ordinary citizen has ceased fearing the midnight police visit. In a strange Russian way the post-Stalin era is edging "back to normalcy." And the public denigration of the fallen idol, flamboyantly begun by Mikoyan and Khrushchev in February, 1956, has yet to cease.

In seeking to erase the legend of Stalin, Khrushchev set himself a herculean task. For probably never in history has there been such an instance of a man who succeeded in inventing himself. Before his death Stalinism, promoted by its namesake, had made of the little pockmarked Georgian a scientific genius, an infallible politician, a learned theoretician, a profound writer, a triumphant general and, indeed, a demigod. Khrushchev is now altering the myth into that of a man who never was.

Stalin is to be totally expunged. But Moscow's new collective rulers don't wish to risk violent reaction. They fear acting too suddenly or too sweepingly. After all, the dictator's corpse still lies next to Lenin's in the Red Square Mausoleum. Hundreds of towns, factories, farms, schools and streets still bear his name. From eastern Asia to the heights above Prague the Soviet empire is dotted with statues of the dead dictator.

All this is doomed. Khrushchev, using almost Stalinist methods, has demanded complete retribution—although he himself once served Stalin with abject loyalty. Khrushchev has ordered that the "cult of the individual" and all its consequences must be uprooted "in Bolshevik fashion." History, he decreed, must be rewritten and revised. The "democratic Socialism" guaranteed in the U.S.S.R.'s Constitution must now be realized and past wrongs repaired.

The U.S.S.R. still being a totalitarian state, such things can be accomplished in total fashion. But Khrushchev desires first to prepare his public opinion for this soul-shattering change. Too many millions of Communists in that vast shadow world have been brought up in adulation of the superman. They must be reindoctrinated.

Khrushchev spared neither adjectives, statistics nor episodes from his saga of assassination. His was a more powerful indictment of Stalin than any eclectic compilation from the diatribes of Hitler, Trotsky or the bitterest Czarist émigré. And, in every detail, it is being disseminated by Communist agitators throughout the Soviet orbit. Why?

A basic clue is seen in one passage of the famous Khrushchev speech. The new boss said that Stalin, at the end of his life,

45

wished to eliminate veteran members of the Politburo. This means not only Mikoyan and Molotov. It implies the tyrant was also threatening Bulganin and Khrushchev. Did these worthy gentlemen, fearing for their own future, help ease the tyrant into limbo? Already, distinguished Communists are explaining that when Beria was executed "it was five minutes to midnight; he had plans to seize power through his armed police and slaughter those who opposed him."

Certainly the committee now ruling Russia is being presented to the confused citizenry that recently worshipped Stalin as a heroic band that delivered the nation from tyranny. There are dark intimations that Stalin assassinated his then favorite, Kirov, in 1934 in order to touch off the first great purges.

Khrushchev claims that in 1934, at the time of Kirov's death, there were 139 members and candidate members of the Bolshevik Central Committee. Ninety-eight of them were arrested and shot after "barbaric tortures" and under the dictation of falsifying judges. They were described as "enemies, spies, wreckers." Of 1,966 delegates to the Seventeenth Party Congress in 1934, 1,108 were later arrested.

Stalin, says Khrushchev—and this is echoed daily by party agitators—"was a very distrustful man, sickly suspicious." He was given to summoning intimates and demanding, "Why are you . . . avoiding (looking) me directly in the eyes?" He suspected everyone. "Everywhere," says Khrushchev, "and in everything he saw 'enemies,' 'two-facers' and 'spies.' " And with atrocious despotism and "unlimited power" he crushed them "morally and physically." He warned underlings: "You are blind like young kittens; what will happen without me? The country will perish. . . ." He invented the phony "doctors' plot" at the end of his life and commanded that those arrested be condemned. Khrushchev says Stalin even threatened Ignatiev, then Minister of State Security: "If you do not obtain confessions from the doctors we will shorten you by a head."

De-Stalinization proceeds with curious jerks. Immediately after Khrushchev's famous speech in February, 1956, a large number of busts and paintings of Stalin were removed from public places. Then, in April, the process of erasure seemed to halt. It resumed in May. But in some regions it goes slowly —above all in Georgia, Stalin's birthplace, where there are signs of organized pro-Stalinism.

The result is considerable confusion throughout Communism's ideological empire. Tito is now hailed as a man who stood up to Stalin and rejected his false principles. Less publicly Mao Tse-tung receives similar credit. It was the Chinese Communist Politburo that first formally accused Stalin of failing to prepare militarily for World War II. The Chinese criticized Stalinist policy on Jugoslavia before Khrushchev got around to it. Yet, curiously enough, Stalinism still prevails in China and the "cult of the individual" is outstandingly applied in the instance of Mao.

Hints of separatist tendencies are emerging from the Soviet monolith. Party leaders now confide that Stalin had Voznesensky and Kuznetsov executed in 1949 for trying to establish a separate Communist organization in the Russian Soviet Republic—by far the largest in the U.S.S.R.—with headquarters in Leningrad instead of Moscow. What other local bosses have similar ideas? Is that what worries Khrushchev in Georgia? Is that why football rioters in Armenia were so sharply dealt with? Or why Bagirov, boss of Azerbaijan, was legally eliminated?

Stalin is being castigated as a cynical violator of the nationality statute supposedly guaranteeing rights of each people within the Union. Khrushchev charges him with genocide against the Karachai, the Kalmucks, the Chechens, the Ingushes, the Balkars, the Mingrelians. These are all peoples of the Caucasus and Central Asia, Moslem or dwelling in largely Islamic areas. Is Khrushchev so concerned about their fate because of his efforts to propagandize Moslem lands? Notably absent from his list of Stalin's racial crimes are the famous mass deportations of Germans from the Volga Republic, Poles from east Poland, Balts, and Greeks from the Black Sea coast; or the harshly repressive measures against Jews.

The attack on Stalinism is not going to be allowed to interfere with practical requirements of the Soviet state. Khrushchev has so far said nothing about bringing back to their homelands the millions of displaced persons within the U.S.S.R. itself. The lack of free press or free discussion, the lack of democratic political methods which permitted the Stalinist dictatorship, are unlikely to be stressed. Russia remains an autocracy.

THE SYSTEM

Undoubtedly the two most important members of the ruling junta are Khrushchev and Bulganin. Older Russians privately call them "Bim and Bom" after two famous clowns. But there is nothing clownish about them in reality. Khrushchev, who appears to be the dominant personality, is a convincing talker. He behaves like a politician campaigning for votes—in a land where votes don't count. Yet he has a keen mind. Both he and Bulganin have impressed foreigners with their intelligence and energy during their extraordinary tours of Europe and of Asia.

There are able men around the duumvirate, including many other veterans of Stalinism. Malenkov is still a force although no longer Premier. He has a reputation for intellectual brilliance and a pragmatic rather than dogmatic approach to problems. Malenkov is one of the few Soviet leaders who speak foreign languages—some Turkish (leading to the belief he is part Tartar) and a surprising amount of Latin.

There is little tangible evidence to support constant rumors abroad of rivalries within the Soviet leadership. Memory of Stalinist purges and the habit of playing a numbers game with displays of picture posters have led to persistent speculation concerning what the outside world does not know about Russia. We would do well to concentrate our attentions and deductions on the area of known fact. Certainly today there is stability in the U.S.S.R. Equally certainly, despite the significant changes, there is no democracy as we understand the word.

Organized religion has certainly been pretty effectively squashed. Churches, mosques and synagogues still function but their number steadily diminishes. Each year there are fewer priests, mullahs and rabbis. Above all among the younger generation, fewer and fewer people have an interest in spiritual matters or believe in God.

This is no accident. Soviet policy has pursued a steady campaign to extinguish faith in anything but Communism. Karl Marx wrote: "It is not religion that creates man but man who creates religion. . . . Religion is the groan of the downtrodden creature." Lenin called it "the opiate of the people" and Stalin said: "The Party cannot be neutral toward religion. . . . The Party stands for science, whereas religious biases are opposed to science."

The present Government argues there is freedom to worship in the U.S.S.R. but likewise there is freedom not to worship. It is contended that religion was forcibly opposed only when it worked openly against the state. But this is only a partial truth. The reality is that Communism, as a totalitarian and materialistic philosophy, cannot tolerate competition for men's minds by a spiritual force.

All faiths were brutally persecuted during the first two decades of Bolshevism. The pressure eased only during World War II when it was found that the suffering Russian people required solace and that propaganda about "free" worship was useful in Moscow's foreign relations. State organizations were established to regulate a spiritual valve as desired by the Kremlin. Councils for church affairs were created. An avowed Communist and atheist, Georgi Grigorievitch Karpov, supervisor of the Orthodox hierarchy, told me in 1945 his job was to "prevent distortion in the relations of church and state." That is still his task.

Today there are only fifty openings each year in ecclesiastical schools for Orthodox priests. The clergy of Judaism and

50

Islam has been choked off. Since the revolution there has been a decrease of 75 per cent in the number of Orthodox bishops and a 90 per cent drop in priests. Church organizations, supervised and infiltrated by Communist party members, are used for propaganda purposes and summoned to endorse state political decisions.

Aware of foreign interest in religion, Soviet officialdom encourages visitors to witness services in the remaining churches. Some Christian liturgical books have been published in recent years. Significantly, the first of these were printed on presses of the former Atheist League. But there have been no new Korans allowed. Islamic religious texts were impounded during the 1930's when mullahs were rounded up by the thousands.

No Hebrew Bible has been published since 1917. The few remaining rabbis use pre-revolutionary prayer books which even include a benediction for the Czar. Hebrew type fonts have been destroyed. A new liturgy is to be published but it will be an electrolytic reproduction of the old version minus prayers for the Romanovs.

The position of Jews differs from that of other believers because of political implications. Bolshevism is anti-Zionist as well as anti-religious. Stalin's principles of nationality, enunciated in 1930, did not acknowledge the Jews as a minority. The law against religious propaganda restricts the teaching of Hebrew for prayer or secular purposes.

Although officially discouraged, anti-Semitism revived in the U.S.S.R. after 1941. German propaganda spread the disease in occupied areas. The deliberate encouragement of

51

Russian nationalism by the Government brought back some of the traditional prejudices of Czarist days. Fewer than three million Jews remain in the U.S.S.R. today, including survivors of Nazi ovens in parts of Poland, Czechoslovakia and Rumania annexed by Moscow.

Everything in the Soviet never-never land is different— even anti-Semitism. It is formally discountenanced but Jews do not feel as free as other citizens. Many of the older Yiddish-speaking generation in the Ukraine and White Russia are afraid to use that language in public. There are no Jewish schools, books or newspapers. Even in Birobidzhan, an autonomous region set aside for Jewish colonization, the Jews remain a minority group.

Abroad Israel itself is regarded with increasing hostility as Moscow promotes its cause among the Arabs. The current *Soviet Encyclopedic Dictionary* calls it a bourgeois republic governed by a dictatorship of capitalists appointed by Washington and London, an Anglo-American strategic base in the Middle East.

Vis-à-vis all faiths there has been no real let-up in the U.S.S.R.'s anti-religious bias. However, Moscow appears to think the basic campaign has been won, that vestigial remnants of worship will dwindle into nothingness. Meanwhile Soviet propaganda shrewdly employs those puppet clerical hierarchies still allowed to exist. It scatters their spiritual poppy seeds abroad for highly material purposes.

In all facets of Soviet life it is difficult to distinguish between the reality as we understand it and as Bolshevik philosophy would present it. This is true not only of such abstractions as religious faith. It is also the case with the press. This, Moscow maintains, is just as free as anywhere in the world—except it has a different function. Lewis Carroll perhaps best explained such phenomena of miscomprehension. He wrote: " 'There's nothing like eating hay when you're faint,' the White King remarked to Alice. 'I should think throwing cold water over you would be better,' Alice suggested: '—or some sal volatile.' 'I didn't say there was nothing *better*,' the King replied. 'I said there was nothing *like* it.' "

We know nothing *like* the Soviet press in the United States. Lenin concluded: "The press should be not only a collective propagandist and a collective agitator but also a collective organizer of the masses"; it should educate "the masses by lively, concrete examples and patterns from all fields of life." This differs from the theories of the American Society of Newspaper Editors.

Konstantin Gubin, editor in chief of *Izvestia*, the official Government organ, once courteously explained his conceptions of journalism to me in Moscow: "My idea," he said, "is that the press must always play a public and philosophical role. But we must not only spread the naked ideas of Marxism. That would be Talmudistic. We would bore everyone. We must write interesting articles encouraging the masses."

Gubin, a solid, solemn man, believes *Izvestia* should both echo governmental views and criticize individual ministries when they soldier on the job. He cites as an example of this critical function an *Izvestia* attack on the Minister of Meat and

53

Milk. Asked whether his editorial knife had been whetted on Beria before the latter's arrest, Gubin replied: "Not all his activities were known. Therefore, we couldn't criticize him then. He camouflaged everything."

How does *Izvestia* ascertain the Government's attitude on every question? Gubin contends the well-informed editor should know the position in advance. "But how," I asked him, "would you know off-hand the official reaction should President Eisenhower today propose a joint Soviet-American exploration of the moon?" Gubin said he could always telephone Bulganin and inquire. He didn't remember when last he had done so. The inevitable implication is *never*.

The difference between *Izvestia*, voice of the Government, and *Pravda*, voice of the party, is that the former writes more about state administration at all levels and the latter concentrates on Communist matters. Thus *Izvestia* is likely to devote more foreign news space to what other governments have to say; *Pravda* beats the drum on party developments abroad. The news content is sparse. There is an old Moscow quip about no truth (*Pravda*) in the news (*Izvestia*) and no news (*Izvestia*) in the truth (*Pravda*). The Soviet press subsists on circulation and direct aid. Nevertheless, many papers now take advertising. *Vechernaya Moskva* charges 4,000 rubles for a two and one-half column display eight inches deep. At the official rate this is $1,000.

There being no competition between rival enterprises in the U.S.S.R., as we understand competition, the advertiser's art is unsubtle. Current screeds advise: "Save time—order food personally and by telephone in the order departments of Gastronom [state food] shops." Or, "On the grounds of the All Union Agricultural Exhibition an out-of-town restaurant, The Golden Ear, opened December 1; this restaurant has a wide assortment of cold and hot meals, drinks and food at all times." Or, "Corn and wheat flakes are delicious; these aromatic light flakes are like wafers; they are good with milk, sour cream, sour milk, coffee, tea and jelly; the calorie content of these flakes is one and one-half times higher than bread and they are easily digested and useful for both adults and children."

Together with the development of newspaper advertising there has been a gradual trend toward billboards ever since Mikoyan visited the United States in the thirties and brought back breakfast food and neon lights. At Moscow intersections one can now read signs saying: "To keep your money in a savings bank is reliable, profitable and convenient"; or "Beer is beautiful and nourishing"; "Lemonade is a pleasant and delicious drink"; or "Natural tea is healthful."

Advertising is competitive between products, not firms. Each ministry wants to fulfill its "norm," but everything is made by the state. In similar vein, each newspaper stresses particular aspects of the Soviet complex. But the chorus is unanimous. This system can only be really understood by those familiar with Carroll's works. He wrote: " 'When I use a word,' Humpty Dumpty said, in a rather scornful tone, 'it means just what I choose it to mean—neither more nor less.' 'The question is,' said Alice, 'whether you *can* make words mean

55

so many different things.' 'The question is,' said Humpty
Dumpty, 'which is to be master—that's all.' "

GOLD AND GOBBLEDEGOOK

As with press and advertising, financial institutions in the
U.S.S.R. bear a curious external resemblance to our own. And
likewise this is only superficial. The State controls all banking
for its purposes, internal and external. It has the population's
total resources at its disposal for any sudden whim of policy.

One of the paradoxes of our time is that the world's biggest
single bank is in the anti-capitalist Soviet Union. Vassily
Fedorovitch Popov, president of the State bank (Gosbank),
told me his institution has an authorized capital of 4,000,000-
000 rubles, reserves of another 4,000,000,000 and has
extended credits in excess of 220,000,000,000. At official
exchange rates this equals $57,000,000,000.

Popov, a short gray-haired man with alert brown eyes, is a
professional banker. He graduated from the Leningrad
Financial Academy in 1923 and immediately went to Kazan
as Deputy Minister of Finance for the autonomous Tartar
Republic. When I talked with him in December, 1955, he
had headed Gosbank eight years. This institution is so
enormous that Popov had Cabinet rank and reported directly
to the Government. Unlike smaller Soviet banks—agricultural,
industrial, municipal and savings—Gosbank does not come
under the Finance Ministry.

Headquarters are in an attractive old-fashioned building
in neo-classical early nineteenth-century style with yellow

walls and white pilasters. This housed the State Bank in Czarist times. Since Communism with its totally planned economy took over, business has multiplied enormously.

According to Popov, Gosbank takes care of all short-term banking requirements in the U.S.S.R. Credits and loans up to one year are its special province. Gosbank specializes in extending one-year credits; Government bond issues, which it does not handle, are generally on a twenty-year basis and sold through Finance Ministry savings banks. The Government decides interest rates. Savings deposits of over six months earn 3 per cent; more active accounts 2 per cent.

Funds obtained through Government bond issues or savings accounts are used to finance state projects. The banks themselves do not make money on transactions. According to Popov they are repaid by the state only those funds they have advanced, plus interest rates, plus money to cover operating overhead.

Popov explained why rates on Soviet loans to foreign countries are cheap. Internal credits earn only 1 or 2 per cent. Therefore, the U.S.S.R. is able to maintain low charges on foreign loans and still not lose money on capital advanced.

Apart from two long-term loans from Britain and Sweden "many years ago," Popov said the U.S.S.R. does not borrow from other countries. Only Soviet citizens can purchase Government bonds. According to Popov, "We have no need of foreign assistance. This is not merely a matter of policy; there simply isn't any need."

By far the greatest part of state revenues comes from

57

Government-owned and operated economic enterprises, both industrial and agricultural. Direct taxes play a relatively minor role. Rates are low. Popov said the highest income-tax bracket pays 8½ per cent. (Actually, some maximum rates go a bit higher.) During recent times the only two years when the Government operated on a deficit budget were 1941 and 1942.

Throughout the war note circulation was greatly increased to cover operating expenditures. Since then excess money has been withdrawn from circulation by decree to curb inflation. In December, 1947, old notes had to be exchanged for new issues. Only salary payments and savings up to 3,000 rubles could be turned in at par value. The purpose of this reform was to adjust the amount of money in circulation to value of goods produced. But considerable private savings were wiped out. Note circulation is deliberately restricted.

The Soviet price structure is in no sense based upon the law of supply and demand as in the capitalist system. One of the factors influencing the cost of goods is the amount of profit the state may decide to take each year, for revenue purposes, from its various Government-owned and operated industrial and agricultural enterprises. This profit slice plus the turnover tax are the principal sources of national income.

The Presidium of the U.S.S.R. is thus free to fix the price of goods not only for internal consumption but also for export abroad. It is in a position to decide these things arbitrarily in terms of what it considers political requirements to be. It can set the price, for example, of steel, grain or any other manufactured goods or raw materials it wishes to sell in foreign markets.

58

All in all, this is an intricate and tightly controlled system. Government rather than individual needs are given total priority. The real value of money in terms of what it may buy is determined by the state. This permits Moscow—if and when it so desires—to assemble very considerable amounts for foreign credits and diplomatic loans at competitively favorable interest rates.

And, curiously enough, gold, the traditional symbol of capitalism, remains a factor in the Soviet economy. This might have seemed bizarre to early Bolshevik revolutionists. However, as practical problems of fiscal administration and foreign trade faced successive Communist leaders, they were forced to adjust their initial Utopian dreams.

Before the 1917 revolution Lenin himself predicted that when Bolshevism assumed power gold would disappear as a metallic base for finance. He forecast it would be employed only for adornment and even suggested its use for decorating lavatories. But efforts to create a purely "goods ruble" failed. By May, 1918, Spunde, then Commissar of the State Bank, accepted the idea that gold was useful in settling foreign accounts.

This has been basic policy ever since. By decree on January 3, 1950, the ruble's official gold content was fixed at .222168 grams. But there is no gold backing. Nobody can turn in paper rubles and receive metallic payment—even in theory. The present ruble-dollar rate is computed on the assumption that the dollar has precisely four times the ruble's gold content.

Gold production figures are not published. Popov argues: "Gold is not the basic backing of our money. The ruble's gold content is fixed but its real value is based on goods in circulation. Gold serves as a state reserve and is sometimes sold abroad. Gosbank has large gold reserves, but we do not publish figures. I see no need to publish them. In capitalist countries gold reserve figures are published to demonstrate the security of currency. But our money is backed by the value of goods produced, so we do not need to publish figures as with other minerals. Gold is not coal or petroleum."

To us this sounds like gobbledegook, and certainly the fiscal system is confusing. It is particularly difficult to comprehend why the U.S.S.R. is so secretive about its gold. Undoubtedly it has a large annual production. American experts estimated as long ago as 1936 that while we were mining $152,500,000 worth of gold that year the Soviet Union was producing $187,000,000 worth. Samuel Montagu & Co., London merchant bankers who compile an annual bullion review, believe the Russians now produce 10,000,000 ounces of gold each year and have accumulated reserves worth $7,000,-000,000 (200,000,000 ounces).

Gold enters into the Soviet economic picture as a standard of measurement for foreign commerce. Popov explains that when the U.S.S.R. trades abroad it calculates sales and purchase values in terms of world prices and on a gold basis whether payment is made in rubles (for orbit commerce) or in capitalist money. If the Soviet Union wishes to make a foreign loan and thus reduces its gold reserves, the currency would not be weakened, as the ruble's backing is invisible.

The ruble is a closed currency, in a sense a political currency, because it has no world open-market value. Its export and import are forbidden. Outside the Soviet bloc, trade contracts are drawn up in dollars, pounds or francs, etc. Commerce with the People's Democracies is generally carried out through clearing agreements computed in ruble values but involving barter exchange, not cash.

The foreigner, calculating on a dollar basis, finds Russian prices preposterously high. A meal in a restaurant can easily cost $25. But Popov argues such comparisons are not fair. He maintains: "To judge correctly you cannot estimate solely in terms of retail prices. You must take into consideration the fact that education is free, medical service is free, rents are very low and there are numerous social security benefits. The relation of the ruble to other currencies also reflects industrial production costs. If you calculate all these elements both here and in America you get a fairer comparative relationship of price structures."

This is highly complex, impossible to assay and economically largely phony. Furthermore, Soviet economists seem unaware of the full implications of social security, pension plans and medical insurance in such capitalist lands as the United States and Britain. No money in the U.S.S.R. can buy high living standards. They do not yet exist.

Prices in the U.S.S.R.'s totally planned economy are fixed by Government fiat. Normal economic laws are supposed to have no influence. Instead the three factors officially reckoned with are: one, cost of production in factory or state farm; two, profits taken by the Government for its revenues from

61

each enterprise; and, three, turnover expenses. But the result of all this is a persistent black market in almost everything and acute shortages of all desirable goods.

The extraordinary difference of this system with its controlled prices and restricted supplies is illustrated by the following occurrence: A group of Russian scientists recently visited Copenhagen. They observed to a foreigner: "Why are the Danish people so poor? Stores are filled with things to buy. But there are no crowds of customers. In our country people have so much money that they queue up to purchase everything in sight."

I have attempted in the above summary to portray some features of the Soviet state as it is developing after Stalin. It is worth recapitulating the principal factors. The U.S.S.R. is industrially immensely powerful and scientifically advanced despite deplorable living standards. Its principal economic weakness is an agricultural problem. Personal dictatorship is *démodé*. But it has been succeeded by autocracy without an autocrat. No one can yet say if this transitional phase will work or whither it will tend. Nevertheless, it functions in a stable atmosphere. The state continues to remain all-powerful. The new "American" managerial class is not yet in control. Nor are those eventual features of "bourgeois" civilization, foreseen by Toynbee, so far an important social factor. It will be at least a decade before one can ascertain if the old cloak of rigid, dogmatic thinking will be shed by this new generation.

The state directs every single organ of life: army, religion, education, press, industry, farming, finance, work and leisure, thought and action. Thus, when the Soviet Union turns outward to the world at large it is in a remarkable position. It can exercise a totally disciplined foreign policy, capable of switching overnight in total harmony with the imagined needs of what is still a totalitarian state.

III

Russian Policy and Soviet Power

OBVIOUSLY an immense amount of the suspicion existing between the United States and the Soviet Union derives from the irreconcilable gap in ideology between free-enterprise capitalism and state-controlled Communism. This molds social structures into strikingly dissimilar patterns. We develop such strange phenomena as the specialist in trading Coca-Cola stock or the expert in beefing up a musical comedy. The Russians produce equally curious professionals like the political commissar to a relay team.

As the two systems evolve it becomes increasingly difficult for the citizen of one super-power to comprehend the other's society. The functions of labor unions, of newspaper men or of bankers are utterly different in the U.S.A. and U.S.S.R. Common words have contrasting meanings. The Soviet statesman, discussing Peaceful Coexistence, implies a status more dynamic and less reconcilable than anything we conceive. Democracy signifies something else in Moscow's lexicon than in our own.

Quite apart from essential disagreement in political, eco-

64

nomic and social systems is a heritage of miscomprehension stemming from national rather than ideological experience. The *Russian* tradition that stamped itself indelibly upon Communism is almost as hard for an American to fathom as Leninism is for the followers of Jefferson.

This is brought home strikingly by analysis of the observations of our various diplomats in Russia. Several statesmen have published their accounts. But the following comments were reported confidentially to the Secretary of State by the United States envoy:

I heard of several Americans last summer who were unable to procure visas. . . . This arises mainly from political considerations and a fear of foreign influence upon the popular mind. . . . No nation has more need of foreigners and none is so jealous of them. These remarks have no special reference to Americans. In contrary the Americans rank as high here as any other people. . . .

No communication, at least of a public nature, is safe in the post office, but is opened and inspected as a matter of course. . . . Ministers are constantly subjected to a system of espionage. . . . Even their servants are made to disclose what passed in their households, their conversations, associations, etc.

You will find no two individuals agreeing in the strength of the Army and Navy, in the amount of the public debt, or the annual revenue. In my opinion it is not intended by the Government that these things should be known. . . . A strange superstition prevails among the Russians that they are destined to conquer the world. . . . To a feeling of this sort has been attributed that remarkable patience and endurance which distinguish the Russian soldier in the midst of the greatest privations. . . .

Expediency is the great test. And what may be expedient today under a given state of facts may be inexpedient tomorrow under the same state of facts. . . . [Russia's] influence over the rest of

65

Europe is irresistible, particularly with the German states. Its vast military power and military spirit are the secrets of this ascendancy, aided by a system of diplomacy which has perhaps no equal. . . .

This is a hard climate and an American finds many things to try his patience . . . one of the most disagreeable features he has to encounter is the secrecy with which everything is done. He can rarely obtain accurate information until events have transpired, and he may rely upon it that his own movements are closely observed by eyes that he never sees. . . .

Everything is surrounded with ceremony and nothing is attainable but after the most provoking delays. . . . I may mention that the late message of the President of the United States was not regarded in all its parts as a safe document for Russian readers and came to their hands scathed with the censor's knife . . . it is difficult in many instances to see the reason of the application of this power, and no doubt it is often capricious. . . .

This is the best school in which to Americanize our countrymen, perhaps that can be found. They are enabled to view their own Government by the law of contrast and inspect it from new points of observation, and I envy not him who can do so and return without an increased attachment to our institutions.

These observations were not made by Charles E. Bohlen, our shrewd and studious Ambassador to Moscow. They were reported more than a hundred years ago by the American envoy to St. Petersburg, Neill S. Brown. But their message is so striking that one is forced to wonder how much of the psychological rift that exists today between our countries derives from ideology and how much derives from imponderable geographical and historical legacies. How much of the difficulty stems from Marx and Lenin? And how much comes from Muscovy itself?

As a matter of fact, Marx deeply mistrusted Russia. His suspicions make that latter-day skeptic, John Foster Dulles, look like the most innocent of optimists. Marx wrote (in 1867): "The policy of Russia is changeless. . . . Its methods, its tactics, its maneuvers may change, but the polar star of its policy—world domination—is a fixed star."

Friedrich Engels had little use for Russian diplomatists.

It is this secret society [he wrote] which had raised the Russian empire to its present plenitude of power. With iron perseverance, eyes set fixedly on the goal, not shrinking from any breach of faith, any treason, any assassination, any servility, distributing bribes lavishly, never over-confident following victory, never discouraged by defeat . . . it is this gang—as talented as it is without conscience —rather than all the Russian armies put together which has extended the Russian boundaries from the Dnieper and Dvina beyond the Vistula, to the Pruth, the Danube and the Black Sea; from the Don and Volga beyond the Caucasus and to the source of the Oxus and Jaxartes rivers; it is this gang which has made Russia great, powerful and feared, and has opened up for it the way to world domination.

Analyzing the methods by which these statesmen worked, Engels concluded:

Russian diplomacy prefers to utilize, for its own ends, the conflicting interests and greediness of the other powers, to set these powers against each other and exploit these enmities to the advantage of the Russian policy of conquest. . . . This Jesuit order . . . uses the continually changing goals of the competing Great Powers for the attainment of its own single, never changing, never-lost-sight-of objective: the domination of the world by Russia.

It is indeed extraordinary how faithfully the intellectual disciples of Marx and Engels who now rule the Kremlin have sought to continue such political methods. It is today an article of Communist faith that the "conflicting interests" of the capitalist countries will in the end divide and destroy them— to the benefit of Russia.

Discussing the situation at the end of the nineteenth century Engels finally predicted—in words startlingly similar to those later used by American statesmen:

> Danger of a world war will vanish on the day when the situation in Russia permits the Russian people to draw a thick line under the traditional policy of conquest . . . and to attend to their own vital interests at home—interests which are threatened in the extreme—instead of fantasies of world conquest.

Certainly the conclusions of Marx and Engels seem remarkably prophetic of Soviet techniques. The methods of Stalinist diplomacy and power politics were every bit as brutal, ruthless, cynical and voracious as those of all his predecessors wrapped together. Now there is a New Look. The techniques have changed. The talk is of peace and friendship, of economic betterment and cultural exchanges. The entire world, including the Russian people, hopes this mood is sincere. But surely the Kremlin cannot blame us if we are cautious, if we pursue a careful Fabian policy. The New Look came in 1953 with Malenkov. But prior to its inception, since the ninth century, every form of government in Russia, with brief interruptions, had been autocratic and totally imperialistic. And every experiment with liberalism was followed by bleak reaction. Let Moscow erase suspicions of its gloomy heritage during the coming years. Meanwhile it should be cognizant of why we are so wary.

We want peace. We welcome everything the U.S.S.R. now says in favor of it. We hope that awareness of the impossible dangers of nuclear war have expunged all thought of conflict from the Kremlin's collective mind. But we cannot forget that, although he is now frowned upon, the late, great Stalin wrote:

"A diplomat's words must have no relation to his actions—otherwise what kind of diplomacy is it? Words are one thing, actions another. Good words are a concealment of bad deeds. Sincere diplomacy is no more possible than dry water or iron wood."

E. V. Tarle, leading diplomatic historian of the U.S.S.R., observes that: "From time immemorial the idea of disarmament has been one of the most favored forms of diplomatic dissimulation of the true motives and plans of those governments which have been seized by a sudden 'love of peace.' This phenomenon is very understandable. Any proposal for the reduction of armaments could invariably count upon broad popularity and support from public opinion."

THE GOSPEL OF LENIN

These blunt asseverations stem quite as much from Leninism as from Czarism (so disliked by Marx) or Stalinism (so disliked by Khrushchev). Lenin was a faithful reader of the works of that early nineteenth-century German general, Karl von Clausewitz. Clausewitz contended: "A conqueror is always a lover of peace (as Bonaparte always asserted of himself); he would like to make his entry into our state unopposed." Lenin copied this aphorism into his notebook and delightedly appended the words: "Ah! Ah! Witty!"

69

Khrushchev's savage posthumous quarrel with Stalin involves method, not philosophy. Like the dead tyrant, he also claims to be an excellent Leninist. Lenin remains untarnished. Khrushchev referred to "our party's holy Leninist principles." He concluded his tirade: "Long live the victorious banner of our party—Leninism."

This is of signal importance in trying to discern the pattern of the new regime. Khrushchev has renounced Lenin's doctrine of inevitable war. But nothing else was discarded from that prophet's ideological legacy. And Lenin said: "As soon as we are strong enough to defeat capitalism as a whole, we shall immediately take it by the scruff of the neck."

He warned: "We cannot forget, unless we have become bourgeois pacifists and opportunists, that we are living in a class society, that there is no way out, and there can be none, except by means of the class struggle and the overthrow of the power of the ruling class."

Khrushchev claims he wants peace. Lenin wrote: "A social pacifist is a Socialist in words and a bourgeois pacifist in deeds; bourgeois pacifists dream of an everlasting peace without the overthrow of the yoke and domination of capital." Later he added: "We have always declared it to be absurd for the revolutionary proletariat to renounce revolutionary wars that may prove necessary in the interests of Socialism." And again: "Every 'peace program' is a deception of the people and a piece of hypocrisy unless its principle object is to explain to the masses the need for a revolution."

Lenin acknowledged no neutralism in the ideological

struggle. He said: "Either perish or overtake the advanced countries and surpass them also economically . . . either full steam ahead or perish. That is how history has put the question." But how, if war is not the means, would Leninists achieve such victory? Lenin laid down an operating code: Divide America from Europe and encourage schism between the lands of Africa and Asia and the West. He said:

America cannot come to terms with Europe—that is a fact proved by history. . . . Everything goes to show that America cannot come to terms with other countries because they are separated by a profound economic rift, because America is richer than the others.

While reckoning upon such division, Lenin advocated splitting off all underdeveloped lands. He wrote:

In regard to more backward states and nations in which feudal or patriarchal, or patriarchal-peasant relations predominate, it is particularly important to bear in mind: first, that all the Communist parties must assist the bourgeois-democratic liberation movement in these countries. . . . Second, that it is necessary to fight against the clergy and other influential reactionary and medieval elements in backward countries. . . . Third, that it is necessary to combat pan-Islamism and similar trends. . . . Fourth, that it is necessary . . . to strive to give the peasant movement the most revolutionary character and to establish the closest possible alliance between the West European Communist proletariat and the revolutionary peasant movement.

Lenin saw no compromise. He said:

Either the Soviet Government triumphs in every advanced country in the world, or the most reactionary imperialism triumphs, the most savage imperialism, which is throttling the small and

71

feeble nationalities and reinstating reaction all over the world—Anglo-American imperialism which has perfectly mastered the art of using the form of a democratic republic. One or the other, there is no middle course.

Later he added:

In the end, one or the other will triumph—a funeral dirge will be sung over the Soviet Republic or over world capitalism.

And how prepare for such a victory? Lenin wrote:

It is possible to conquer the more powerful enemy only by exerting the utmost effort, and by necessarily, thoroughly, carefully, attentively and skillfully taking advantage of every, even the smallest "fissure" among the enemies, of every antagonism of interest among the bourgeoisie of the various countries, among the various groups or types of bourgeoisie in the various countries; by taking advantage of every, even the smallest opportunity of gaining a mass ally, even though this ally be temporary, vacillating, unstable, unreliable and conditional. Those who do not understand this fail to understand even a grain of Marxism.

George Orwell, a man of particular genius, predicted in 1946: "In five years it may be as dangerous to praise Stalin as it was to attack him two years ago. But I should not regard this as an advance. Nothing is gained by teaching the parrot a new word."

The "new word" pronounced throughout the Soviet orbit today is "Leninism" and there is nothing new about it. Stalin used it all the time. Khrushchev doesn't like Stalin's accent or interpretation. But Leninism remains the gospel.

Leninism does not frown upon autocracy. Lenin said: "Soviet socialist democracy is not contradictory to individual management and dictatorship in any way. . . . The will of a class may sometimes be carried out by a dictator, who at times may do more alone and who is frequently more necessary."

The philosophical basis for such concepts derives from Lenin's contempt for morality. He wrote:

> When people talk to us about morality we say: For the Communist, morality consists entirely of compact united discipline and conscious mass struggle against the exploiters. We do not believe in eternal morality. . . . We repudiate all morality that is taken outside of human, class concepts. We say that this is deception, a fraud, which clogs the brains of the workers and peasants. . . . We say that our morality is entirely subordinated to the interests of the class struggle.

This attitude, which Khrushchev evidently admires, is an interesting background to Moscow's new advocacy of parliamentary means to assert Communist superiority abroad. On such tactics, Lenin said:

> There can be a question only of utilizing bourgeois state institutions with the object of destroying them. . . . The Communist party enters such institutions [parliaments] not in order to do constructive work, but in order to direct the masses to destroy from within the whole bourgeois state machine and parliament itself.

Lenin foresaw the possibility that popular fronts might sometimes be desirable. He wrote:

> Only those who have no self-reliance can fear to enter into temporary alliances even with unreliable people; not a single political party could exist without entering such alliances.

To succeed in such maneuvers, he warned:

The strictest loyalty to the ideas of communism must be combined with the ability to make all the necessary practical compromises, to tack, to make agreements, zigzags, retreats and so on, in order to accelerate the coming into power. . . . If you are not able to adapt yourself, if you are not inclined to crawl in the mud on your belly, you are not a revolutionary but a chatterbox.

Lenin, who was immensely brilliant, foresaw the need for tactical shifts. He said:

Picture to yourself a man ascending a very high, steep and hitherto unexplored mountain. Let us assume that after overcoming unprecedented difficulties and dangers, he has succeeded in rising higher than any of his predecessors, but that he has not yet reached the summit. He is in a position where it is not only difficult and dangerous to proceed in the direction and along the path he selected, but positively impossible; he has to turn back, descend, seek another path, longer perhaps but one which will enable him to reach the summit.

Is that what Khrushchev is now attempting? Has he decided that Stalin's path was "positively impossible"? Has he resolved to "seek another path" to world supremacy? What would Khrushchev have us believe? There are Leninist teachings other than that of war's inevitability that Khrushchev must also specifically abandon if he wishes to convince us of his good intentions.

And there are certain Leninist preachments we would indeed like to see practiced. For example, Lenin boasted: "Soviet power is a new type of state in which there is no bureaucracy, no police, no standing army." He said no nation should be unwillingly kept in thralldom but should have the right to secede.

He added: "Can a nation be free if it oppresses other nations? It cannot."

The Soviet leadership, astute, experienced men, must understand why with this background the West is chary of accepting at face value sudden new professions of friendship. But what of Leninism? That is still the gospel. And we know what Lenin taught. Even if his credo of "inevitable" war has now been scrapped, his global quest for communization remains accepted doctrine. The Russians are by nature and political conception patient. They should not blame us if we wait to test the duration of their latest tactical turn. It was Lenin, after all, who advised: "When dealing with world history one counts in decades. Ten or twenty years sooner or later makes no difference."

MOSCOW'S DUAL AIM

The ambition of Czarist Russia, as described by Marx, was world paramountcy. The ambition of Bolshevism is ideological hegemony. Stalin's great genius was to unite these two aspirations. Russian conquest and revolutionary domination became one and the same. Has Khrushchev abandoned either aim? Has he even separated one from the other?

There is not yet any convincing evidence that the ultimate objective of Soviet foreign policy does not remain global ascendancy. Moscow seemingly wishes to avoid war. There are indications that Marshal Zhukov has stressed how suicidal a modern conflict would be. But, as the most recent Soviet encyclopedia says in its article on *pacifism:* "To eliminate the inevitability of wars, it is necessary to destroy capitalism."

The U.S.S.R. makes no secret of such intentions. Co-existence to us implies acceptance of differing political systems. To the Russians it means only temporary pause in the process of ideological subjugation. Communism appears convinced it can triumph without war. Marx taught and the Soviet leaders believe in eventual total victory. Molotov explained to me in 1956: "We should like the change-over to Communism (by the rest of the world) to be as painless as possible." That is small comfort.

Within this framework one must analyze current Kremlin diplomacy. It seeks to overrun the world through peace, not war, but nevertheless overrun it. And it does not intend to relinquish what it has already gained. Zhukov recently observed quite frankly: "We will never give up any areas we have conquered." This means not only new Soviet territory. It also seemingly refers to political satrapies including East Germany. One way or another, the implication is, they *must* be kept within the imperial orbit.

Europe is not at present the principal arena of Moscow's diplomatic dynamism. Policy in the West is concentrated on digesting what has been gained already. The new emphasis is aimed eastward and southward. And precisely because China is being built up, Russia doesn't wish to be edged out in the Orient. This is one reason for the intensity of Soviet affability toward India. Peiping, wherever possible, is being subordinated to Moscow. The Kremlin seeks to establish an ascendancy vis-à-vis China while that country is still weak, as France might have sought ascendancy over Western Germany through the ill-fated E.D.C.

The Russians are pressing their diplomacy in Asia and the Middle East. This was rendered possible only after they agreed in Belgrade that Socialism could have other forms than rigid Bolshevism. Since then Moscow found itself free to regard such men as Nehru and Nasser as Socialists and friends—something their political inhibitions had previously precluded.

Khrushchev nowadays stresses the aid the U.S.S.R. can send abroad. It was no joke when he told the Indians: "We shall see who has more engineers, the United States or the Soviet Union."

The countries where there is greatest specific concern are Afghanistan, India and Egypt. The Russians can exploit the feudalism of Afghanistan. Isolated from the West by Pakistan's blockade, the Afghan economy was subject to Soviet tutelage even before Bulganin proffered a $100,000,000 loan. Now it is difficult to see how the tottering kingdom can evade the eventual fate of its former independent neighbor, the Bukhara emirate—absorption in the U.S.S.R.

The approach to India is more delicate. Expressions of ideological interest are taboo. Khrushchev pretended no knowledge of the Indian Communist party when he talked to Nehru. "Why, I have never even met an Indian Communist," he said. The Indians maneuvered skillfully to avoid too close an embrace. C. D. Deshmukh, then Finance Minister, dodged Soviet aid as distinct from trade. Russian capital investment was restricted. The Indians tried without much luck to barter their own products at satisfactory prices. When his effusive Soviet guests had left the Mayor of Madras remarked: "I am glad to see their backs." But the forthright Moscow line paid

77

dividends. Both Nehru (the only important political factor) and public opinion were impressed by Soviet support for India in Goa and Kashmir. Commerce is growing.

Another Soviet diplomatic effort is developing in the Middle East. Most Arab envoys in Moscow are already starry-eyed. The Northern Tier—which we sponsored but didn't join— brought inherent Levantine differences to a breaking point, encouraging Russia to move in. She has. A few words and a little gold from the Soviet's immense reserve go a long way in that chaotic area. The Kremlin is deliberately strengthening Egypt to exploit the differences among capitalist powers which for so long have inhibited Western policy in the Levant.

The Kremlin realizes what an enormous role non-Communist Asia can play in helping the U.S.S.R.'s international position. There is an effort to emphasize Russian and Asian interests that coincide. And the Oriental countries are delighted by this attention.

They counsel the West to "understand" these Russian friends. "You must be patient," advises the naïve little Burmese Ambassador in Moscow. "The Russians are only timid. They are like lizards in Burma that are so shy we have to cajole them from their holes." "And what do you do with the lizards when you get them out?" a colleague inquired. "Kill them," whispered the Burmese.

The Soviet leaders have often demonstrated brilliant if cynical perspicacity. They must comprehend why we still tend to analyze their present foreign policy with an eye cocked to a consistently dangerous past. We would tend to be more sympathetic if the Kremlin gave better proof today of what Engels wished—attending to its population's "own vital interests at home." Malenkov began such a policy in 1953 and 1954. But, as pointed out earlier, this would have reduced foreign-aid potentialities during this era of competitive coexistence. Therefore the regime once again sacrificed immediate interests of the Russian people for the sake of foreign aspirations.

Those who succeeded Malenkov abandoned his new economic outlook. They obviously believed that preservation of the Soviet imperial system and success of Communist policies both at home and abroad called for still further strengthening of the U.S.S.R.'s heavy industrial plant. Such, economically speaking, is of course pure Stalinism.

On the other hand the ruling committee has continued many aspects of Malenkov's New Course foreign policy. This permits more time for consolidation of post-Stalinist controls at home. It facilitates the wooing of allies and lulling of opponents in other countries. The Kremlin recognizes its own need for time and international relaxation. Industrialization of China and final integration of satellite-bloc economies—necessary to tighten an economic hold before political grips can be really relaxed—require several more years. And, although many apparent concessions to "liberalism" have been made since 1953, there is no indication that Communism's basic line has been discarded. Communist doctrine and faith in its ultimate world triumph did not die with the old Georgian dictator.

79

The new Soviet diplomacy is practiced most flamboyantly by Khrushchev and Bulganin and others of the rapidly developing team of traveling salesmen. The U.S.S.R. has been quick to discover and exploit techniques of the flying visit. And the very contrast of this jet-age affability with Stalin's gloomy isolationism gives it a special value difficult for others to equal. But, as in other foreign offices, the day-to-day spadework of drafting and implementing policy decisions is done by professional statesmen.

THE DIPLOMATISTS

At various time I have talked with the more recent Soviet Foreign Ministers. Shepilov, the huge, handsome successor to Molotov, is a man of energy and charm. After he visited Egypt, Colonel Nasser confided to me: "I always used to think all Communists were thieves. Now I know differently. Shepilov is nice." Certainly, Shepilov is a hard-working ideologist, learned in the devolutions of Marxism, and an expert propagandist schooled both in *Pravda,* which he edited, and party agitation bureaus.

Nevertheless, by all odds the most attractive and humanly appealing of the Kremlin's diplomatic agents was Maxim Litvinov, Commissar until 1939 when Stalin decided to treat with Hitler. In April, 1945, I visited him for the last time in the old Narkomindel (foreign affairs commissariat) where he was doing duty as vice-commissar. White, flabby, nervous, he was dressed in the then new (since discarded) uniform of government officials, looking like some ridiculous operetta general; rumpled and unpressed, with food stains on the pompous lapels. He strode up and down ceaselessly, complaining about a deteriorating situation both at home and abroad, excoriating the restrictive press bureau and censorship which kept him from seeing anyone or saying anything to the world, concluding: "Things were different when I was in Washington" (as wartime Ambassador).

Litvinov was already in disgrace. He was consulted on virtually nothing. He did not know that Marshal Tito was at that very moment arriving at Moscow airport. He did not know that two hours hence the Soviet pact with Japan would be denounced. Yet he knew enough to see how badly the postwar world was going to shape up. "Nobody," he said, "listens to my advice or pays any attention to what I say. But things look gloomy for future world security. The San Francisco conference [where UN was born] has been called too soon. It will suffer. There are still too many problems. The situation is developing badly. First the West makes a mistake and rubs us the wrong way. Then we make a mistake and rub you the wrong way." I concluded in my notes, on leaving him that afternoon: "He was a regular Jeremiah, full of gloom. He didn't say so outright, but he seemed to think worse trouble was coming. A bitter, cynical, old revolutionary, isolated and alone; he knows he's had it." A few weeks later, I saw him at the May Day victory parade. He refused to take his seat in the Red Square grandstand erected for dignitaries not prominent enough to stand with Stalin atop Lenin's tomb. "I belong with the people," he explained to me. In 1952 he died.

Andrei Vyshinsky, another Foreign Minister, was a contemptible being, vain, arrogant, presumptuous, treacherous.

81

Somehow he acquired a reputation in the West for wit and charm. Vyshinsky, a Polish Menshevik, proved the excellence of his assimilated Russian Bolshevik qualities by bullying Eastern Europeans and seeing to it that Stalin's political opponents were shot or hanged while he was public prosecutor. Once when Vyshinsky (in 1947) was boasting to me that he was, in addition to other duties, charged with controlling censorship and that this was a crutch for journalists, guiding them only to the truth, I replied: "I prefer Pushkin's definition: *'Tsensura dura*—censorship is foolish.'" He snapped back: "You should consider yourself lucky that I am only your censor and not your prosecutor." I did. His record for convictions was almost perfect.

But of all the Soviet Foreign Ministers the most typical, most efficient and technically most successful has been Vyacheslav M. Molotov. A true Old Bolshevik, he even looked the part of the complete Stalinist man. For Communist Russia, like ancient Thrace, has tended to seek gods in its own image. Molotov, unlike Shepilov, came from this divine mold. The casts are about five feet five in height, brachycephalic, thick-necked, thick-waisted, thick-legged, and generally of undistinguished but benign countenance. Add spectacles, a small mustache and a face like an inverted soup plate and you have Molotov, effigy of Bolshevik diplomacy. He is still regarded by many members of the Soviet intelligentsia as the Talleyrand of our time.

Curiously enough, this exponent of Stalin's brutal foreign policy survived well into the post-Stalin era. A study of his methods is revealing not only in terms of past performance but perhaps in terms of future dealings with other Soviet leaders. For Molotov must go down in history as a shrewd, cynical practitioner of statecraft. Few diplomats have made such a virtue of patient obstinacy. His earlier revolutionary colleagues seemed to underestimate his intellect although acknowledging his capacity for work. Lenin supposedly called him "the best filing clerk in Russia."

But foreigners who had to deal with him developed a begrudging if often infuriated respect. Dulles wrote: "I have seen in action all the great international statesmen of this century. . . . I have never seen such personal diplomatic skill at so high a degree of perfection as Mr. Molotov's." Churchill remembers him as "a man of outstanding ability and cold-blooded ruthlessness. . . . His cannon-ball head, black mustache and comprehending eyes, his slab face, his verbal adroitness and imperturbable demeanor were appropriate manifestations of his qualities and skill."

Bedell Smith called him "coldly self-possessed." Byrnes thought him "devious." But that former Secretary of State added: "He will win your reluctant admiration by the resourcefulness he exhibits in his delaying tactics. . . . If we are correctly informed about the patience exercised by Job, I am certain Mr. Molotov is one of his lineal descendants. He has unlimited patience as well as a fine mind and tremendous energy."

A French diplomat who attended the Foreign Ministers' Conference in Berlin in 1954 concluded afterward: "Molo-

83

tov's awkward-appearing diplomacy actually secured a brilliant success. I am now convinced his main objective was to bring about a conference between the Western powers and Communist China. He not only obtained this (the 1954 Geneva meeting on Vietnam); he even managed to have the West propose it."

When I talked with him last in January, 1956, Molotov himself pretended to modest estimates of his own ability. I reminded him of Dulles' opinion on his abilities. He replied: "That statement about me is an obvious exaggeration." I asked him which of the Western statesmen he knew had proved most able.

He observed: "In every country there are experienced diplomats. In the United States Cordell Hull was certainly such an experienced diplomat. I had occasion to meet Mr. Hull here in Moscow in 1943 and during the previous year in Washington. Also, there is no doubt that in Great Britain Eden is a very experienced diplomat."

It may strike one as interesting that Molotov should single out these two men—the dead Democrat and an English Prime Minister, withdrawn from daily diplomacy—as the ablest of his occidental colleagues. For such must be the inference of the Soviet Minister's remark—oblique, as usual. However, this assumes logic if one remembers that Hull and Eden were Foreign Secretaries together with Molotov during World War II when Big Three relationships were based upon alliance.

Molotov was an Old Bolshevik and this is the key both to his character and his techniques. He could look back upon a long career of revolution. Born in March, 1890, as Vyacheslav Mikhailovich Scriabin, during his conspiratorial youth—and he was already active in the 1905 uprising as a boy—he assumed various aliases: Ryabin, Zvonov, Prostota and Mikhailov. Finally he chose Molotov. "Molot," in Russian, means "hammer."

He studied economics in Kazan and St. Petersburg but never received a university degree. He published five books, apart from compiled articles and speeches. All of these were on conventional Communist subjects. The 1943 Soviet encyclopedia described him as Stalin's closest companion in arms. When I last saw him in his offices on the seventh floor of Moscow's new skyscraper Foreign Ministry there were still only two sets of portraits there: large paintings of Lenin and Stalin in the antechamber, smaller etchings of the same men in his private sanctum.

That Molotov should have continued his career successfully through so many upheavals, purges and counter-purges is no accident. Under his stolid exterior, like the system he represented, he was always a flexible opportunist. As Foreign Minister, he was chief diplomatic agent in four distinct phases of Soviet policy: the pact with Nazi Germany, now played down by Muscovite historians; the victorious Allied coalition of 1941-45; the Cold War; and the current period of Competitive Coexistence. These zigzag shifts with which his name is linked did not in any apparent sense disturb him.

Indeed, the Molotov of 1956, sitting at the green baize council table of his paneled, heavily furnished office, politely

85

lighting long Russian cigarettes for the visitor, removing his glasses and fiddling with them as he blandly replied to questions, seemed quite as confident of Communism's world triumph as during any past era of his long career as revolutionist.

To him there was no contradiction between Moscow's expressed desire to coexist peacefully with capitalist countries and its proclaimed conviction that, in the end, it would victoriously squash them by ideological power. Such an outcome, he maintained, was merely scientific logic.

"After all," he insisted, "this was first said over one hundred years ago by Marx and Engels in the Communist Manifesto, published in 1847. Have you read the Communist Manifesto? Yes? Well, Communism thinks that it is scientifically true that history is moving ahead from one social system to another, to a more perfect social system. We think that Communism is a better system, a more progressive system, and that it will historically triumph. This is our conviction. But we do not wish to impose our conviction. We merely consider it a well-founded conviction. It reflects historic processes.

"According to the doctrine of Communism, one of two systems must be victorious and must prove it is more progressive and in accordance with modern requirements. We believe Communism is that system which can bring to peoples of the world more favorable material and spiritual conditions of life.

"This does not mean that no important changes are taking place within the capitalist system. These changes are taking place. Our men of science should carefully follow how the capitalist states are developing. Changes are also taking place within the Socialist countries engaged in building Communism. Those changes too should be studied. But the essential part in this historical process, as we see it, is that Communism is called upon to take the place of capitalism eventually as a more progressive system."

Although admitting that changes are occurring, Molotov did not envision any perceptible narrowing of the ideological gap. And here is a probable clue to essential differences between the rigid traditions of Soviet Communism and new heresies arising in Eastern Europe. He argued:

"Basically the two systems are contradictory. Capitalism is founded upon a system of exploitation of one people by another people, one class by another class, and one person by another person. Communism rejects the theory of such exploitation of one man by another man. In that sense the two systems are incompatible.

"But the change-over [and by this Molotov meant the "inevitable" triumph of Communism] depends upon historic conditions. We should like the change-over to Communism to be as painless as possible. We think that only when the people of a particular country desire a change, the change-over to Communism is desirable. This is a matter to be decided by the people of each particular country."

Molotov maintained that during an "interim period" the existing irreconcilable political systems can and should coexist and even co-operate. He added: "States now exist with different ideological systems. They should live at peace and should co-operate for their own good and the peace of peoples." When asked if he considered such an interim truce period could endure indefinitely, he answered: "I agree with that."

From Molotov's courteous if ponderous verbiage the following may be deduced: Although both capitalism and Communism are experiencing some change in this modern era, Moscow continues to view the two systems as incompatible, as implacably hostile. There is no third or middle way despite the tactical maneuverings of the new collective leadership. This is where Moscow, the great Communist matrix, disagrees with the pragmatic ideology developed by Titoism during its heretical prime.

Shepilov, like Molotov, appears to feel that opposing ideologies should not only coexist but also co-operate for an indefinite period of time. That period would be used by Moscow to consolidate its own position. And it would, in the end, be punctuated by Communism's global triumph.

Marx taught, and Molotov believed this is inevitable. Never given, like Vyshinsky, to flamboyance or dramatics, Molotov was always a meticulous and careful person. He was dressed soberly in dark blue suit, blue cravat and light blue shirt; the accumulation of papers on his massive desk was tidily arranged; the bric-a-brac with which Russian officialdom adorns its office marshaled in serried rows: marble inkwells, lamp, penholders, blotters; the little wooden desk clock synchronized to the second with the grandfather clock in the corner.

Order, hard work and precision have been the keys to Molotov's character; occasional chess his principal relaxation.

He used to play the violin. "I gave that up before going into political activity," he recalled to me with a controlled smile. Ever since he has been taking pains to make revolution. Carlyle, rather foolishly, said genius was an infinite capacity for taking pains. Molotov's talents have been of this non-luminous sort.

Karl Radek, the witty *Pravda* editor whose brilliance earned him death in the great purges, referred to Molotov as "Stone Bottom" for his ability to sit things out. This characteristic earned him particular renown during the last decade. He was always the man *par excellence* for conferences, seemingly never in a hurry.

It is difficult to summarize the abilities of this Soviet Minister. He has never displayed remarkable brilliance or originality. But he proved the stubborn, unembarrassed agent of an implacable apparatus. As is so often the case, Churchill perhaps best measured him: "Certainly in Molotov the Soviet machine had found a capable and in many ways a characteristic representative—always the faithful party man and Communist disciple. How glad I am at the end of my life not to have had to endure the stresses which he has suffered; better never be born. In the conduct of foreign affairs Mazarin, Talleyrand, Metternich would welcome him to their company if there be another world to which Bolsheviks allow themselves to go."

TSENSURA DURA

The guile, deception and ability of men like Molotov and Shepilov are abetted by the powerful Soviet propaganda

89

apparatus and a censorship of varying rigidity which seeks
to obscure from the world the realities of Russia. Engels
wrote. "Everyone knows in what chains the Russian press lies
bound." Yet, despite worship of Engels, censorship remains
a blot in the Soviet Union today.

Undoubtedly there is a tendency away from the blind and
utterly ridiculous restrictions that marked the Stalin era.
Along with the all-pervasive secret police and more blatant
trappings of autocracy, the total, arbitrary censorship of the
past is gone. I have visited the U.S.S.R. on five occasions during the last fifteen years. Now for the first time it is possible
to write with some degree of freedom.

Some years ago Vyshinsky boasted to me: "It is my responsibility to see that you write the truth." What Vyshinsky
meant was that only what he saw fit would be permitted to
leave the U.S.S.R. in dispatches by foreign correspondents.
Such is no longer strictly the case. A good deal of serious
comment can be made—comment that would have caused
Vyshinsky to shudder. Censorship is easing. Russian editors,
confiding their own dislike of the institution, predict it will
someday disappear.

That day had not yet come in 1956 when I was last in the
Soviet Union. Newspapermen, filing dispatches in Moscow,
submitted them to the cable office with the significant words
"corrections at my risk" typed out above their signatures. And
such "corrections," often made after many hours' wait, remain
all too frequent. In almost every column I sent from the
U.S.S.R. at least a few words were eliminated. One, analyzing

implications of Bulganin's and Khrushchev's speeches to the Supreme Soviet, was killed. That is to say it was submitted to censorship on December 30, 1955. It is still there.

One can deduce the present purposes of censorship from what is deleted. An effort is apparent to make the Soviet scene seem less restrictive and more appealing than is actually the case. Violent shifts and obvious inconsistencies in foreign policy are deliberately disguised. But particular emphasis is laid on brightening the internal picture. For example, I wrote in 1956:

1. That it was impossible to gauge the price of the U.S.S.R.'s impressive industrialization "in terms of sweat, blood, toil and tears." The words "blood, toil and tears" were stricken. Why? Presumably they reminded the outside world of forced labor, forced collectivization, the misery and death rolls of dictatorship.

2. That, in the process of squashing the Mohammedan faith in Soviet Central Asia, "religious texts were impounded." This was taken out. It would be embarrassing to any regime masquerading as "free"; above all when such propaganda is aimed at the Islamic world.

3. That Khrushchev, in addressing the Supreme Soviet, "saw no paradox in the fact" that his attacks on colonialism were addressed to delegates from "formerly independent areas" in the Baltic and Central Asia. I referred to deputies from Latvia, Lithuania and Estonia and the emirates of Kokand and Bukhara, all of which had their own Governments until

91

gobbled up by Moscow. This was presumably a disconcerting reminder.

4. That "trying to compute the exact value of dollars versus rubles in terms of real worth is like comparing caviar and goose eggs." I quoted Popov, head of the state bank, as telling me (which he did): "If you measure consumers' goods prices they may seem very steep compared with yours." I wrote: "Prices here bear little direct relationship to the quantity of goods manufactured." All this was cut.

5. That the 1947 currency reform had "wiped out considerable savings and hoarded profits." This is an understatement. But it was deleted. I quoted Popov as saying (which he did): "When we grant credits abroad we are not looking for profits." And I commented: "This philosophy of course allows Moscow to venture capital abroad for political and diplomatic purposes on a favorable competitive basis." This was cut.

The censor is still peering over one's shoulder in Moscow. But he no longer breathes down one's neck. He seems to consider his function more or less that of propagandist, touching up the picture so the world will think better of the Soviet system, its accomplishments and its intentions. He is particularly sensitive about the standard of living.

Restrictions are loosening. Nevertheless, it is difficult for a Russia accustomed to censorship since Czarist days to discard the habit. In *Otchko,* a card game widely played in the U.S.S.R., it is illegal to deal off the top of the deck. Statesmen seeking to comprehend the ins and outs of Soviet policy might be advised to master this pastime. For the practice of state-craft by the Kremlin often resembles these methods of dealing.

The cynical competence of Czarist diplomacy has been surpassed by the Soviets' Commissarist diplomacy. Uninhibited by any logic other than continued pursuit of the main goal, it veers sharply left and right, backward and forward, paying no heed to its own past deviations and unresponsive to a muted public opinion.

One function of Moscow censorship today is to facilitate this process. It covers up the illogic of sudden diplomatic shifts, and tries, whenever possible, to obscure the zigzag tactics of the Kremlin. For example, I wrote that the Russians had adjusted their ideological view in order to embrace countries outside the Soviet orbit although until recently "Tito was called a Fascist and Nehru imperialism's tool." These words were stricken. The censor's job is to rewrite facts of history and to forget distortions of the recent past.

Any reference to ultimate Soviet aspirations is eliminated. For example, I wrote: "The policy enunciated by Khrushchev and Bulganin is profoundly simple. The Communist bloc would coexist and compete peacefully with capitalism. But the goal is still world paramountcy." This was cut.

The following observation was deleted: "Double standards are, to say the least, confusing. To what degree is this [Russia's] Government deceived by its own slogans and blinded by its own propaganda? Until such delusions are erased it will be difficult to place much faith in professions of intended coexistence."

93

Censorship obliterates such comments. It is perhaps comprehensible that the Soviet Government does not like them. But Russia's regime is now presenting itself to the world as enlightened and a champion of freedom. There is little validity in this claim as long as there is a censor dealing from the bottom of the deck.

The censor has helped devise in reality an image similar to Plato's famous cave.

Behold [wrote the philosopher] human beings living in an underground den, which has a mouth open towards the light and reaching all along the den; here they have been from their childhood, and have their legs and necks chained so that they cannot move, and can only see before them, being prevented by the chains from turning round their heads. Above and behind them a fire is blazing at a distance, and between the fire and the prisoners there is a raised way; and you will see, if you look, a low wall built along the way like the screen which marionette players have in front of them over which they show the puppets. . . . And do you see men passing along the wall carrying all sorts of vessels, and statues and figures of animals made of wood and stone and various materials which appear above the wall? Some of them are talking, others silent.

You have shown me a strange image, and they are strange prisoners.

Like ourselves, I replied; and they see only their own shadows, or the shadows of one another, which the fire throws on the opposite wall of the cave.

This is the chain of censorship and the fire of propaganda. And it is no accident that these two branches are carefully co-ordinated by the Foreign Ministry. To encompass its aims abroad the state must advertise its virtues. But, since these have never attained in reality that beneficial level long proclaimed, the censor must gild the correspondent's moldering lily.

The body of Bolshevik man is improving. But what becomes of his soul? Oscar Wilde, who had not heard of Lenin, observed: "It is to be regretted that a portion of our community should be practically in slavery, but to propose to solve the problem by enslaving the entire community is childish." This is the paradox the censor would obscure.

POWER POLITICS

Regardless of the vigorous world tours of Khrushchev and Bulganin, those Columbuses of Soviet advertising, Moscow's patient, guileful diplomacy is bound to persist, ever probing for weaknesses in the ideological and political defenses of the outer world. And, whether the Kremlin talks peace or truculence, this policy is always implicitly backed by a massive military establishment.

A certain Capitaine Michel Garder, writing in the highly respectable French military journal *Revue de Défense Nationale,* advanced an interesting theory on the role of the army in Soviet diplomacy. He wrote that Bulganin (a political marshal) had prepared a thesis for the degree of Doctor of Military Science in which he developed the idea:

Modern war is a psychological war, the armed forces merely serving to stop an armed attack or, eventually, to occupy territory conquered psychologically. It must be waged by every possible means, capable in the first place of forming the Eastern nations

95

into a monolithic bloc; then in the second place, these means must be capable of breaking up the political structure of the adversaries by opening a breach in the principles of capitalism and rallying to the Marxist truth the greatest possible number of Western peoples. . . .

Garder added:

It is therefore a question of a purely psychological war in which armed conflict will only be contemplated as a last resort. This has now been the thesis of the directors of Soviet policy for almost ten years. [The army] by the fear it inspires, completes the effect of psycho-political action on other countries. It also represents the eventual punishment which will fall upon those who have refused to choose the pathway of salvation—that is to say, the Marxist-Leninist truth.

This is a very interesting idea. It may well be a sound interpretation of Soviet policy—certainly until recently. However, the Bulganin "thesis" upon which the observations are founded is non-existent. The document is a forgery. Furthermore, current Soviet tactics seem aimed at minimizing implicit threats of military power. Rather than menace the outer world, the Kremlin leadership now strives to follow the Aesopian precept of cajoling us all with friendly warmth in hopes that the uneasy West will strip its protective coat. To a considerable degree this method is succeeding.

Nevertheless, although the U.S.S.R. is releasing hundreds of thousands of conscripts and trying to appear a unilateral leader in world disarmament, it remains the greatest single military power. Specialists estimate Moscow could still mobilize four hundred divisions within thirty days of the outbreak of a war. It maintains a minimal air-force level of twenty thousand modern planes. It has stockpiled, in its arsenal of conventional weapons, enough tanks, mortars and anti-tank guns for three hundred divisions. It has artillery enough for eight hundred divisions. It has the largest submarine fleet in the world and the second largest surface fleet in commission. Above all, it is perfectly evident that the Russians have made astonishing advances in the discovery, manufacture and use of nuclear weapons.

The Soviet air force is technically advanced. Ever since Professor Hugo Junkers supervised secret construction of a plane factory near Moscow in 1922, it has been closely in touch with German aerial developments. This is still the case. Russian designers are competent and inventive: such engineers as Ilyushin, Gurevitch, Mikoyan (brother of the politician), Lavotchkin, Gudkov, Gorbunov and Yakovlev, who brought out the famous IL, MIG, LAGG and YAK series. Since 1918 the U.S.S.R.'s top scientists have followed developments in the highly regarded TSAGI (Central Aerodynamics and Hydro-dynamics Research Institute) and the Zhukovsky Air Academy (named for Nikolai Y. Zhukovsky who, together with Andrei Nikolaievitch Tupolev, fathered Soviet air power).

The army, which is by far the dominant service in the Soviet Union, has gained considerable prestige since Stalin's death. It has a much higher specific gravity than before but cannot be said to be a coherent political force as such. However, its influence, through Zhukov, the great hero, is creeping back.

97

And the military has a direct impact upon the conception of the U.S.S.R.'s foreign policy although it is impossible for the outsider to measure this. Somewhere in the vicinity of Moscow, Marshal Ivan S. Konev is supposed to have an international headquarters which is the Communist world's equivalent of SHAPE. There he presumably has facilities for the joint staff of the Warsaw pact, or, as it is often known in the West, Anti-NATO.

The location of Konev's command post is not public knowledge. No signposts point along the exterior boulevards like those that guide the way to the Allied planning center outside Paris. Nor does the seat of the Communist alliance display flags of member nations—the U.S.S.R., Albania, Bulgaria, Hungary, East Germany, Poland, Rumania and Czechoslovakia.

Since May 14, 1955, these countries have been linked in formal coalition. Their Ministers of Defense serve Konev as deputy comanders. The Chinese People's Republic is represented by an observer.

The Western term, Anti-NATO, is accurate. Moscow frankly admits this is a counterpart. For, it is argued, the U.S.S.R. proved NATO was hostile when it applied for admission and was refused. On March 31, 1954, Russia sent a note to the United States, Great Britain and France suggesting they join an all-European security group. Simultaneously the Soviet Union offered to discuss its own entry into NATO. The Western answer was negative.

Eight months later, representatives of Moscow and the

satellite governments met with a Chinese envoy. They declared that if the Paris agreements to rearm West Germany in NATO were ratified, the Communist countries would sign a military pact to safeguard "against possible aggression." The May, 1955, Warsaw meeting implemented this threat. And the authoritative Soviet publication *International Affairs* says the pact proves the peaceful policy of the U.S.S.R. and its allies, "who do not threaten anyone, who do not covet alien territory and who have no desire to impose their will on anyone."

It is always interesting if not always profitable to examine the other side of any question. Alice, when she wandered through the looking glass, discovered as much. For one familiar with the philosophy of NATO and the functions of SHAPE it is fascinating to scrutinize the Warsaw pact.

"Its application," says *International Affairs,* "is not bound up with any theoretical or abstract criteria. . . . In modern conditions the right of self-defense should not be limited to the individual action of any one country subjected to attack. It is impermissible that a victim of aggression should be isolated and forced to defend herself utterly unaided and usually in unfavorable conditions. . . . From this follows the need for a joint defense system."

Any man from Mars visiting this uneasy planet would find noticeable similarity between such sentiments and those expressed in Paris, NATO's seat. And in Moscow, as in the West, there is supposed to be a "political consultive committee" and a "joint command" to establish "combined armed forces." Where is the gimmick?

NATO is possibly not familiar enough with Anti-NATO to realize, as *International Affairs* contends, that if any signatory of the Warsaw agreement, such as Russia, were to "impose its will on any of the others, this would be regarded as a high-handed, arbitrary act." The "identity of the basic principles and political aims" of all members is proclaimed. Nevertheless, it is said, any nation regardless of ideology can apply and join.

Such is held to be untrue of NATO. Our alliance, of course, includes various governmental systems. Anti-NATO does not. But we would not admit Russia. Therefore, Moscow sophistry reasons: "The essence of military blocs lies in their exclusive character. The exclusive bloc [NATO] is directed inevitably against those who are not allowed to take part in it."

The Warsaw treaty is held to be a reply to the West's "positions of strength" policy. NATO was formed in 1949; Anti-NATO in 1955. But the U.S.S.R. already had bilateral military pacts with every other member except Albania, starting with the Soviet-Polish alliance of April, 1945.

It requires expert comprehension of semantics to know when a bloc is not a bloc. The Warsaw coalition is a non-bloc. NATO is a bloc. Its professions of peaceful intention are held suspect. The Soviet Government regards Anti-NATO as a political necessity until there is agreement on a European security plan. Then it would be willing to scrap the Warsaw coalition—in exchange for the scrapping of NATO. Stalin once wrote: "I think that a well-organized counter-offensive is one of the most interesting forms of offensive." That, presumably, goes for politics as well as war.

Because of the Soviet orbit's immense military power, the United States has been suspicious of the true value of Russian disarmament formulas. We want some valid form of mutual check-up. But our diplomacy has had no success in budging Moscow opposition to Eisenhower's "open skies" inspection plan. The Russians consider this merely a formula to permit espionage. Yet we believe that until some such agreement is reached, there can never be real disarmament.

Nevertheless, as the U.S.S.R. is acutely aware, scientists are preparing to achieve the President's objective despite Russian objections. Probably in 1957 our first earth satellite will be launched. Depending upon its success, other larger and more complicated installations will be rocketed later into space.

From such devices, rotating on fixed gravitational paths, it will be possible to photograph wide areas and transmit back the results. Within the predictable future it will be technically feasible to send cameras far above the U.S.S.R. to achieve what the "open skies" plan seeks but Moscow refuses to grant.

In international law there is no precedent for this kind of aerial survey. It is implicitly accepted that the lower skies above a country are national territory. Aircraft must receive permission to fly over foreign soil. But how high does this legal territoriality apply? At what point above the earth's surface can an object be held to be vertically above one country and not another? When does the moon quit Russian skies for those of Poland?

101

Because of difficulty in resolving this international question, our first earth satellite will probably be launched on a course that avoids the U.S.S.R. This in itself is fairly perplexing because the Soviet Union covers almost a sixth of the world's land. Nevertheless, it is certain that eventually our own and other nations' devices will be violating each other's air space.

Within a decade such satellites may be sufficiently perfected to provide intelligence experts with much of the information the Eisenhower plan would seek. Already it is possible for cameras projected in rockets high above the earth to photograph through cloud masses with accuracy capable of detailed magnification.

The idea of accords between nations to inspect each other's territory would prevent surreptitious military buildups for surprise attacks. Even when the age of push-button war arrives it is believed preparations for such sudden assaults could not be totally hidden. Intercontinental ballistics missiles will require large installations and fuel tanks difficult to camouflage.

The necessity for mutual inspection has dominated our disarmament thinking for a decade. Without such safeguards, no nation can accurately check on another's intentions. Moscow's opposition may be merely a delaying tactic. Surely the U.S.S.R. is also experimenting with devices which, in addition to meteorological exploration, could be used to spy out the land. Would the Kremlin not be in a better bargaining position to discuss regulation of international space and an "open skies" inspection plan when it too has workable earth satellites?

In co-operation with the Soviet military, Moscow's diplomacy generally tends to stall while developing important new physical capabilities. For example, it is already hinted that Russia would be happy to see some kind of super-power agreement forbidding countries other than the U.S.S.R., the United States and Britain from manufacturing nuclear weapons. Other nations would be restricted to the peaceful application of atomic energy.

The Kremlin seems quite prepared to keep China out in the cold of this new military age if the English-speaking lands will do the same with France. But, even if this is the U.S.S.R.'s diplomatic wish, it cannot long succeed. Industrially advanced countries like Sweden will not remain in the nuclear-weapons dark for long no matter what the great capitals decide.

Does Moscow also hope to ignore the "open skies" plan until it too has an earth-girdling satellite capable of photography? And does it then desire to negotiate directly with the United States on a basis of parity? Does it calculate that then the heavens may be legally carved up; that then it will no longer be possible to prevent the nations of the world from celestial espionnage?

Soviet foreign policy, like our own, is moving into outer space. But Moscow's ideological orbit on this earth remains the major political problem of our generation.

IV

The Third Rome—Western Empire

An old Russian proverb says that "Moscow is the head of the entire world." Czarist Russia sometimes proclaimed itself "the third and last Rome of Christianity; there will be no fourth." It inherited not only the religion and ceremonials of Byzantium but an overweaning aspiration to much of that empire's territory.

Until their disappearance, the Czars persisted in a traditional drive for Constantinople, for Greece, for absorption of the South Slav tribes in the Balkans, for the Mediterranean littoral of the Aegean and Adriatic seas. Russian intellectuals invented pan-Slavist theories as an excuse for devouring their kinsfolk in Eastern Europe: Poles, Czechs, Slovaks, Bulgars, Serbs, Croats, Slovenes, Macedonians and Montenegrins. The Moscow patriarchate sought to establish a religious hold over the Orthodox peoples of what are now Rumania, Bulgaria, Greece and much of Jugoslavia. As Poland was partitioned and repartitioned and the strength of Prussian, Austro-Hungarian and Ottoman empire ebbed and flowed, Russian domain insistently sought to obtrude westward into Europe's heart.

This appetite for the Danube Valley and the seacoasts of the

Aegean and the Baltic was reasserted by Bolshevik policy. As the Soviet state gained power it revived an interest in Central Europe and the Balkans. To the old forces of pan-Slavism and politically controlled Orthodoxy was added the immense dynamic power of Communist ideology. From 1919, when an abortive Marxist coup seized and held power briefly in truncated Hungary, underground conspiratorial parties schemed to upset the established order; to gain for the Revolution and for its bastion, Moscow, domination of the Continent's heart.

All this at last became a feasible reality during the latter months of World War II. The Western allies showed remarkable lack of understanding of Soviet political strategy. Disinterested in the evident logic that, by breaking the Axis backbone of Europe, a vacuum would be created that must suck in Russian power, the United States and Britain instructed their armies to concentrate on defeating Wehrmacht remnants west of the line that later became known as the Iron Curtain.

There was never an Allied effort to break into Belgrade, Vienna, Prague or Berlin ahead of the Red Army. General Patton's troops were leashed in western Czechoslovakia. Churchill tried to salvage the situation when American planners overruled his strategic alarms by making a private deal with Stalin to carve up Balkan spheres of influence. On a slip of paper he scribbled a cynical arrangement declaring Rumania totally within the Russian orbit, Greece within the British orbit, and leaving half of Jugoslavia and most of Bulgaria and Hungary to Moscow. Not even this deal could be

105

validated. Churchill saved Greece. But the rest of the Balkans fell to Soviet power politics. Only the tenaciously independent Jugoslavs' revolt prevented complete domination by Moscow of all the area north of the Olympus massif, west of the Trieste-Stettin line, and up to the sandy Baltic shores.

Allied strategy concentrated upon swiftly winning the war without thought of the consequent peace. Therefore, Moscow was able to create in Eastern Europe an imperial domain exceeding dreams of the most voracious Czars. Imperial Russia had at various times added to the Great Russian orbit the Caucasus tribes, the Ukrainians, Moldavians, Byelorussians, Ruthenians, Poles, Latvians, Lithuanians, Estonians and Finns. Of these, it has become generally accepted that, despite traditions of prior independence, the peoples of the Caucasus, the Ukraine, Byelorussia and the Baltic states are no more likely to be pried loose from Muscovite control than New Mexico and Texas are likely to be severed from the United States.

The outlines of Soviet policy in Europe were plain long before V-E Day. It was equally clear that once the U.S.S.R. had staked out its claims to the west, it would shift the dynamics of foreign expansion eastward into Asia. These observations are not based on hindsight. George Kennan, at that time United States Minister-Counsellor in our Moscow Embassy, reported to the State Department in September, 1944: "Two hundred million people united under the strong, purposeful leadership of Moscow and inhabiting one of the major industrial countries of the world, constitute a single force far greater than any other that will be left on the European continent when this war is over; and it would be folly to underestimate their potential—for good or for evil."

The author of this book in a series of dispatches to *The New York Times,* wrote during the spring of 1945:

There are many who think that basically Soviet foreign policy regards Europe as a back door, if an exceedingly important one, and Asia as a front door. It would seem from the facts that this back door would be slammed, in a security sense, along a line roughly from Trieste to Stettin. . . . The current diplomatic crises of Europe that directly affect the interests of the Soviet Union on the one hand and Britain and the United States on the other, focus along a rough and shifting boundary area extending from Trieste in the South to Stettin in the North.

This, it is becoming increasingly clear, represents a line that security-conscious Moscow would like to see established as a minimal western frontier to the security zone, or *cordon sanitaire* in reverse, that Soviety policy makers think necessary. . . . This line . . . represents a westward shift of what before the war was considered the western border of the area commonly known as East Europe. In 1939 the line ran from Fiume to Danzig. . . . The moving of the East-West boundary so much further into Europe is an important development.

Russia, which has signed bilateral military pacts with the three westernmost Slavic countries—Jugoslavia, Czechoslovakia and Poland—wishes to bulwark these lands and, by so doing, also bulwark itself against a potential Germanic *Drang Nach Osten* by a *Drang Nach Westen* of its own. . . . On both sides of this vague Trieste-Stettin line which zigzags across the heart of Europe there have been tremendous political changes. . . . To the East, Russian influence, politically and diplomatically, is stronger than it ever was in the past, even during those Czarist days when much of Poland belonged to St. Petersburg and Uncle Ivan was regarded as the liberator of the Slavs from the Ottoman Sultan. . . .

As World War II ended, the U.S.S.R. rapidly pushed its military and political control up to the Trieste-Stettin boundary. Only when this area in the West had been sealed off did emphasis shift dramatically toward Asia. Russia's European empire is now in a process of consolidation. Austria has been removed as a neutral segment. East Germany is not to be regarded as a permanent satellite but more as a potential Trojan horse for the neutralization of an eventually reunited Reich. Jugoslavia has escaped from total Kremlin domination as a result of Stalin's foolish miscalculations. But it remains ideologically sympathetic, economically co-operative and politically friendly. Trieste was chipped off the southern anchor of the line which now commences in the suburbs of that harbor. And it is possible that Stettin, the northern outpost, will some day be re-ceded to the Germans in exchange for agreement to accept the rest of the Oder-Neisse frontier with modern Poland.

What has happened in the new imperial domain carved out of Eastern Europe by the third (and Communist) Rome? It is evident the post-Stalin regime has rewritten Bolshevik doctrine to embody a considerable number of the heretical ideas propounded by Marshal Tito. This allows Moscow to pursue a more flexible policy in Asia and in the non-Communist lands of Europe where Communism seeks to ally itself with Socialist and Leftist parties in a new popular-front strategy. But in the Soviet satellite empire between the Baltic and the Black Sea, it will be difficult to discard all vestiges of strict Stalinist methods of control no matter what new ideological slogans are advertised by more "liberal" Bolshevik statesmen.

This apparent dichotomy can be explained in terms of Russia's national interests. Stalin had condemned all those who did not strictly imitate the patterns of Bolshevism. U.S.S.R. policy-makers now reconcile themselves to divergent trends of Communism in China and Jugoslavia. Yet they retain an authoritarian grip in their satrap empire through many of the same Stalinist puppets installed after World War II and sanctified by the Cominform.

Clearly Khrushchev seeks to adjust official Communist credo to conflicting Soviet requirements. On the one hand he wants to retain an iron hold on Eastern Europe. No other way than Stalin's seems to have been discovered in Albania or Rumania, for example. But to keep the diplomatic initiative Moscow has seized in other and less static areas, he has had to admit the validity of many of Tito's claims.

When Jugoslavia broke with Russia, the dispute originated in pure nationalism. Belgrade wanted real independence and Stalin refused to accord it. Soon the debate widened into theory. It came to resemble those theological arguments of the Reformation period between Protestantism and the Catholic mother church. Now, unlike Rome, the Kremlin has seemed to reconcile itself with heresy. That is because its interests are material.

Khrushchev discarded outright Stalinism when he agreed with Tito that the world is no longer divided only into two blocs of capitalist and Socialist states. Now he recognizes

109

gray areas in between. He accepts Tito's theory that more than one road leads to Socialism. He admits this ideology can gain power by other than revolutionary means. And he discards Lenin's dictum that war is inevitable while capitalism exists.

Tito came to maintain that not he but Stalin was the heretic of Communism because the Soviet dictator ignored the principle of equality among all Socialists and insisted upon central organization of the Communist orbit. He resented the Cominform as an instrument of Soviet control. He argued that the Russian experiment was no valid model for revolution elsewhere. The world proletariat, he claimed, had other duties than merely promoting Russian power and prosperity.

Only a month after Khrushchev's pilgrimage to Belgrade in the spring of 1955, one of Tito's main theorists, Veljko Vlahovic, criticized Bolshevism for failing to take into account a changing world. Vlahovic pointed out that former colonies were now free lands, that progressive forms of capitalism had emerged, that the advance toward Socialism was no longer limited to revolutionary means.

Khrushchev has gone a long way toward meeting these objections. He has written into Moscow's official credo many of the amendments he had already been forced by fact to recognize. Stalin's concept of the Soviets' "leading role" in world revolution is soft-pedaled.

Clearly the Communist catechism has been modified. Can the reformist trend be checked? The dilemma between Soviet world ideology and Russian national interest continues to exist. Stalin had solved this with ruthless simplicity by amalgamating the two currents, by proclaiming they were actually the same. He contended the only test of a Communist's sincerity was blind support for Moscow, no matter how its tactics shifted.

Khrushchev modifies this conception—but only where it suits him. For, at least in parts of Eastern Europe, Stalinist methods are likely to prevail. Can the Kremlin put into practice there what it has begun to preach in other areas? Is it afraid that when its fist relaxes, national currents will arise too powerfully and run athwart the interests of Moscow?

POLAND

Surely the most interesting and potentially the most important of the newly communized countries now tied into the Soviet orbit is Poland. Situated in the great plains and forests between Byelorussia and the Ukraine to the east and the German flatlands to the west, the Poles have never had a natural frontier. Their fluctuating history is a permanent testimonial to this geographical embarrassment. Since World War II the entire country has been, as it were, picked up bodily and moved westward. What was once eastern Poland is now Russified and bodily incorporated into the U.S.S.R. Its surviving refugees have been pushed deliberately into former German areas seized, with Moscow's approval and encouragement, by the Communist Government of Warsaw.

Almost any Polish Communist will argue in confidence that as a matter of simple geography his country must get on with Russia, no matter what regime rules Moscow. For Poland is the filler in a sandwich. Throughout history the Poles have

111

been squeezed between their German and Russian neighbors, caring little for either of them.

There is little doubt that at this juncture, despite a traditional westward orientation of Polish psychology, fear and dislike of Germany remain uppermost. The dreadful Nazi slaughterhouses of Majdanek and Oswiecim have been turned into museums commemorating terror. A former SS adjutant in Warsaw for an international festival was beaten up when recognized. A Polish diplomat contends: "You Americans have your West German allies; we have our East Germans. But rest assured that we intend to keep our Germans just like this." He slowly clenched his fingers.

Soviet Russia plays the role of Orwell's Big Brother to Communist Poland now, and most Poles, who detest their Slavic cousins, don't like it. Many seem to have the same blithe confidence in their talents for national survival, however, that they had when their cavalry trotted out against Hitler's tanks.

As long ago as 1947 Jakub Berman, then a member of Poland's Politburo, was dreaming of international relaxation and coexistence that would permit Communist Poland to develop as an independent force. Berman was purged in 1956. But nine years earlier he told me: "I am convinced that Western capitalism and Communism can exist side by side together without war. It is difficult to prophesy what kind of political synthesis might develop from the two. In Poland we hope a new and separate evolution will result, differing from both those systems typified best by the Soviet Union and the United States."

112

Warsaw has yet to develop such a dream. When Jugoslavia broke with Moscow, Poland was ordered to hop on Stalin's anti-Tito bandwagon, and did. Pale imitations of the Belgrade heresy were squashed. Even if such leaders as Gomulka were not executed for their Titoism, they were purged. But now they are slowly edging back.

Will Khrushchev's new Russia permit Polish nationalism to seek really different social forms? There has been some remarkable discussion on this within the Warsaw Politburo. There are signs of new and vital stimuli. And sharp criticism of the regime itself has been published. In late 1955, Adam Wazyk, editor and poet, wrote a "Poem for Adults" saying:

> There are Polish apples unobtainable by Polish children, there are children scorned by criminal doctors, there are boys taught to lie, there are girls taught to lie. . . . There are people who are robbed in the streets by thugs for whom legal definitions are sought, there are people waiting for papers, there are people waiting for justice, there are people who have been waiting for a long time. On this earth we appeal on behalf of people who are exhausted from work. . . . We appeal daily, we appeal through our party.

This complaint could never have been printed during the Stalinist era. The issue of the magazine that carried it was banned but the author remained free. And other writers joined the attack. The theater is at last coming alive and dealing frankly with political problems.

Polish nationalism is a powerful force that survived cruel tortures in the past. And the country is now more ethnically Polish than ever as a result of postwar surgery. It is 96 per cent Polish by blood and 95 per cent Roman Catholic by

113

religion. Despite the arrest of Cardinal Wyszynski, the primate, and of other clerical leaders, and despite creation of a somewhat phony Catholic "front" movement, the population retains dogged allegiance to Rome.

The self-confidence and conceit of this vital people vis-à-vis their powerful Slavic neighbor is almost touching. They admire Soviet power and techniques. But they look down on the Russians as awkward country bumpkins with no taste in art, no sense of humor, no style. Somehow, now that it is the fashion even in Moscow to denigrate Stalin, there is hope of better things to come. The Polish Communist party—officially condemned by Stalinism in 1938—was rehabilitated in 1956. Its crime had been "nationalism." Does this mean, people ask, that nationalism will now be the mode?

The answer to this question cannot yet be given. Surely the Kremlin doesn't intend to give complete free reign to such an individualistic nation. Already tough Soviet negotiators have forced the Poles to integrate their newest five-year plan into U.S.S.R. requirements. Moscow is never going to forget that Poland, the biggest satellite, borders right on Germany. And many of the same men who rule Poland were there during the Stalinist era they now condemn. But a new current of independence is beginning to stir. And when misery prompted the Poznan riots in the spring of 1956, Warsaw ignored Russian counsel on how to crush the perpetrators.

In the Silesian region taken over from the Germans there is a colony of Polish miners who used to live in France. There they always voted Communist. Now they want to go back—

114

and can't. Recently a group of them was asked: "What do you miss most? The countryside? French wine? The people? "Liberty," they replied. This yearning, combined with economic hardship, is what lay behind the Poznan incident and, indeed, most of Poland's present internal stirrings.

In a physical sense, there is much to be admired in the Polish effort to reconstruct a devastated country. From our point of view, perhaps, the Poles often go about their task the hard way. There is a good deal of overlap planning and misplanning directed by a highly centralized bureaucracy. Despite the permitted safety valve of Communist "self-criticism," once the regime makes a decision it must be carried out. Nevertheless, the rebuilding job is being done.

From the very start the local Politburo took the line that Poland's national traditions must be preserved as the country was physically restored. Hitler sought to destroy the *national* character of the Polish people. He ordered Warsaw razed methodically to the ground. He sought to impress wherever possible a Teutonic stamp upon this vital nation. He failed.

When the so-called Lublin Government (concocted in Moscow) came back to Warsaw behind a Soviet army on January 17, 1945, it resolved to reconstruct the capital upon its former site even though that was but a heap of rubble. It resolved to re-erect famous old houses and monuments exactly as they had been in the past. And finally—an unusual feature in a Communist state—it resolved to rebuild churches demolished by the Nazis.

In Gdansk there is special significance to this program.

115

Gdansk is the famous old Hanseatic Danzig, a largely German free city in 1939 when Hitler decided to make it a *casus belli* for the war he wished. All through that August he sent in his squadrons of rough "tourists." Toward the end of the month his cruiser *Schleswig-Holstein* paid a "courtesy" call. Early September 1 her guns opened fire on the near-by Polish naval base, Westerplatte. World War II was on.

Before the conflict ended Danzig was in ruins. Today there is hardly a German left in town. Gdansk has risen again as Polish. High-gabled narrow Hanseatic houses have been safely reconstructed from broken heaps of bricks, their narrow fronts decorated with medieval patterns, their gay windows staring over a frozen Baltic shoreline that is purely Polish for the first time in seven centuries. The only signs of Germany's tenancy are grim old tombstones on the paving of that enormous Gothic warehouse, the barnlike Cathedral of the Virgin Mary.

While Danzig died beneath Nazi and Soviet artillery exchanges, the SS was completing Hitler's order to obliterate Warsaw. Captured Wehrmacht pictures show demolition squads methodically planting charges, squirting gasoline about and igniting it with flame throwers. This was to be Poland's punishment for the Warsaw insurrection led by General Komorowsky-Bor's anti-Communist but anti-German underground.

The present regime is somewhat embarrassed by this heroic uprising. It still depicts it as a criminally useless gesture, doomed to failure, that caused the unnecessary death of thousands. But it cannot satisfactorily explain why Marshal Rokossowsky's Soviet army (for he was then a Russian officer) didn't cross the Vistula to help.

Be that as it may, Hitler's wish was disappointed. He succeeded in destroying 87 per cent of the capital. Nevertheless, Warsaw is again a busy city of 1,000,000. Its old town has been scrupulously reconstructed with its tall, eaved houses and squares. Churches and monuments are back from a dusty grave. When Jerzy Albrecht, a rising young Communist, was president of the City Council, he used to say: "Every Pole feels a deep emotional attachment for Warsaw. We could not rebuild elsewhere as Hitler hoped. We are Poles. Already we have done 70 per cent of the job. When we have our prewar population of 1,300,000 we will consider the task accomplished." Josef Sigalin, chief city architect, adds: "Our people felt they had no birth certificates until Warsaw lived again."

The extraordinary emphasis on rebuilding symbols of the past, upon "Polishness" and upon the nation's history has no equal in that part of Eastern Europe under Soviet political suzerainty. It is an interesting phenomenon to observe old monuments and churches rising again beside the new industrial trappings of a Communist society.

This raises an interesting question. Poland is undoubtedly becoming potentially a greater power than it ever was before. It has received sinews through emphasis on heavy industrial development, even at the cost of great sacrifice in comfort imposed on the present generation, and by acquiring Silesia from Germany as the result of Soviet dictate. But, together with that strength, it retains an astonishing amount of purely na-

117

tionalistic vigor. This, Communism cannot quench—nor has it really sought to. If Moscow ever truly eases the grip which hitherto has been so firm, what will develop? Poland is by tradition an intensely nationalistic country. Where will this nationalism lead two decades hence? Can the new wine of Soviet-brand Socialism be retained unaltered in old Polish bottles?

In Wroclaw, once the principal city of German Silesia, every one of modern Poland's tortuous problems is reflected in microcosm. It symbolizes the agonizing demographic war between Slav and Teuton. It is now populated almost entirely by Poles expelled from eastern territories awarded Soviet Russia. Therefore it contains the psychological difficulties of a displaced persons' center. It is being simultaneously rebuilt from ruins and heavily industrialized. Strains and stresses of this process are mirrored in a crime wave and disturbing alcoholism.

Finally, Wroclaw, called Breslau by the Germans, is a famous Catholic seat and diocese. This brings to the fore that vitally important conflict between church and state which, while for the moment dormant, is bound inevitably to be renewed. Wroclaw's churches are well attended. People are more religious than before the war. The reasons why are evident.

In 1939 some 630,000 people lived in Breslau—mostly Germans. Today the population is 370,000. Only 2,500 of them are German, according to the Communist governor of Lower Silesia. Of the Poles now living there less than 7,000 resided in prewar Breslau.

The westward Slavic push has flooded to the Oder and the Neisse rivers. Most of the Germans who once dwelled there fled to their partitioned country. The Warsaw Government insists the frontier question has been permanently settled. But nothing is ever permanent in Eastern Europe. The mere fact that the Poles emphasize in their monuments that Wroclaw was technically theirs from the tenth to the fourteenth century shows how long these issues simmer.

Marian Naszkowski, acting Foreign Minister and member of the Communist Central Committee, told me in 1956: "We consider the Oder-Neisse border has been definitely regulated. Peace with a unified Germany can only confirm this fact. We signed a treaty at Zgorzelec in 1951 with the German Democratic Republic delimiting our boundary." Nevertheless, many Poles still worry now that two German states are getting arms. What will be the situation a couple of decades hence?

The population that moved into Wroclaw from what is now the U.S.S.R. originated mostly in a strip of territory from Vilna to Lvov. They like to regard their new home, humming with reconstruction, as a Polish "Wild West." In a sense they are right. Germans were the Indians.

What with rebuilding and emphasis on industry, Wroclaw is a tough workers' town. To discourage drinking the Government forbids home distillation, limits hours when schnapps is sold and continually boosts liquor prices. Drunks are photographed and their pictures displayed above sarcastic slogans.

A psychological uneasiness implied in this craving for drink is being met in two ways. The Government is building

119

schools and playgrounds, encourages entertainment and theaters. Circuses are stressed as much as bread. Wroclaw has a remarkable stage for a provincial town.

The other outlet is religion. Since the first sharp drive against Catholicism, when Cardinal Wyszynski was arrested, Communism has changed its methods. For the moment worship is surprisingly free. But the state is aware that throughout Poland's troubled history the church has often represented popular protests against oppression. Someday it would obviously like to squash or alter it.

A fellow-traveling religious layman's organization known as P.A.X. now seeks to win mass sympathies. So far it has failed. The Poles go faithfully to services. But they commune in silence with priests they know oppose the Government.

The Vatican has not helped its case. It failed to name a Polish bishop when the Wroclaw see fell vacant. Instead it sent in a vicar general. To many a Pole Rome appears to take sides in the Slav-Teuton quarrel, regarding Silesia as still German. This pleases few people east of the Oder-Neisse line.

Presumably, like Poles and like Germans, the Vatican feels it can afford to hold the long historical view. Yet for our time the Polish-German border now seems a fact, apart from relatively minor modifications. Too many families have been displaced to move again—except by war. And everyone says war is out.

In Wroclaw as elsewhere in Poland the regime is certainly unpopular. The social experiment forced upon them is repugnant to the population—though some are economically

120

better off, especially in backward rural areas. But even those who hate the Communists have little interest in the London *émigré* Government. "The *émigrés*," they say, "are finished. They have lost touch. We cannot turn the clock back. We want change; but something new, not old. And we want to stay in Wroclaw. This is Polish soil. We'll keep it."

Poland's economy is experiencing the distortion of two revolutions—both imposed by Moscow. The first is geographical, the second political. But they are simultaneous in impact. The resulting strain is immense as Poznan showed.

Before the war it was primarily an agricultural country. Despite a social system criticized as "feudal" by the present Communist regime, there was ample food. Now Poland is essentially industrial. More than half its prewar territory was absorbed into the Soviet Union. In exchange the western frontier was moved up to the Oder-Neisse line, incorporating the coal and manufacturing provinces of Eastern Germany —Silesia and Pomerania.

As a result of this drastic surgery present-day Poland has a smaller farming area than prewar Poland. Even without accompanying social revolution this geographical transformation, which moved an entire country westward, would have seriously altered its economy.

Suddenly a peasant nation took over the great Silesian factory complex, second only to the Ruhr in European industrial importance. The per capita economic output was perforce boosted. But what did the Poles themselves get out of it?

It is extremely difficult to analyze combined effects of war, occupation, geographical and social revolution upon living standards. Statistics now published are limited and disguised. Nor can they be compared with those of the prewar regime. For the two Polands are as different demographically as in ideology.

Nevertheless, it is apparent that emphasis on heavy industry rather than consumer goods has been of more benefit to the power of Poland's huge ally, Russia, than to the comfort of the Polish people. Under successive three-year and six-year plans the Silesian basin was harnessed to requirements of Soviet empire. Under a new five-year plan it will be co-ordinated directly with concurrent programs in the U.S.S.R. and other East European satellites.

Meanwhile the cupboard is bare of consumers' goods. This cannot be attributed only to war hangovers, because such is not the case in Italy or Western Germany. Yet Warsaw openly complains of inadequate supplies of simple items like electric bulbs, clothing, shoes and crockery. The situation is even worse in terms of food. Poland, once among Europe's richest larders, cannot now feed itself. It has to spend hard currency to import grain. The central statistical bureau complains of "continued shortages of certain food articles such as meat and processed meat as well as animal fats."

This lack cannot be explained by map-making. The eastern lands lost to the U.S.S.R. were agricultural but not rich. The hunger that now grips Poland stems directly from social revolution. For the Polish peasant is reluctant to produce. He is on a slow-down strike.

Despite a decade of strenuous effort to enforce collectivization, the program has bogged down. Seventy-six per cent of what the Government calls "peasant land" remained in private hands in 1956. Peasants balk at pooling property or handing it over to the state. On the collectives themselves—the largest proportion of which are in former German territory where refugees from the east have been resettled—there is inadequate incentive for production. And individual farmers, forced to deliver crops at artificial prices, just aren't doing so.

The peasants seem to have won a first round in their stolid battle. The Government has for the nonce abandoned enforced collectivization. Instead a new propaganda campaign of inducement is beginning. A gradual approach was ordered, with encouragement to start co-operatives of a Scandinavian variety. The administration reluctantly concludes "an excessive disproportion between agriculture and the speedily developing industry is being *acutely* felt."

The state wants to rectify this situation with a seemingly curious dual policy. On the one hand it openly hopes to increase the output of independent farmers by encouragement. Yet, simultaneously, it intends to press for collectivization "on a principle of voluntariness." Just how such dichotomy can be resolved is difficult to see. The individual "peasant's initiative" is to be protected. Even the prosperous so-called *kulak* can reckon with a few years' toleration. But the heat remains on. There is no real Titoism yet in Poland. Belgrade abandoned the struggle to collectivize the land. Warsaw merely appears to be giving the peasant a breathing spell—in order to feed the worker.

The party berates its agents for "inadequate ability to win over the poor people, lack of militancy in striving for the political isolation of the *kulaks,* ideological weakness in rural areas, inadequate effort to improve the existing collective farms." The Politburo is reorganizing its forces and altering its tactics. But a new atmosphere of criticism, questioning, debate has begun. Traditional Polish vigor is stirring in the post-Stalinist atmosphere of Warsaw. Can this, in the end, impress itself upon national policy decisions? Would Moscow tolerate this?

CZECHOSLOVAKIA

Apart from Poland, the only other satellite wedged between gigantic Russia and potentially resurgent Germany is Czechoslovakia. There the problems of control are different. The Czechs have great resilience but little of the vital energy or anarchistic poetry of their Polish cousins to the North. Of the relatively more advanced nations within the Soviet orbit, they are invariably the last to seize initiative or opportunity.

The most impressive new landmark in lovely baroque Prague is a monstrous huge statue of Joseph Stalin dominating the bluff above the River Vltava. Mournfully regarding this atrocity, Czechs observe: "We needed schools. And our Government spent millions on this—this thing." Below the monument the ice jam on the Vltava breaks each spring. Great cakes flow downstream. And the people of Prague regularly wonder if seasonal change will symbolize political change as well. Will the forbidding spirit of Stalinism really melt?

124

Czechs are by nature a very patient nation and less prepared than certain other Slavs for the bolder sort of action. They sit back sullenly, comforted in the promise of their old hero, Jan Hus, that the truth will prevail—"*Pravda vitez.*" But they are unready to combat for that truth which both they and we know as freedom.

One intelligent citizen of Prague observed to me: "We are not a fighting race. We have never really fought since the fifteenth-century Hussite wars. After the Habsburgs took over, Czech mothers brought up their children in a tradition of passive resistance. They have told them: 'Don't say what you really think. There is no need for others to know.' The result is Schweikism—that bumbling obstinacy expressed in our classic novel *The Good Soldier Schweik.* Schweikism is a method. But it is not an adequate national philosophy."

The Czechs pray for peace and hope for gradually increasing liberty. They have no interest in anyone starting a war to free them or to change the ideology they did not have the courage to try to change themselves. They say: "Unlike Jugoslavia, we did not fight against the Germans and we were never ready to fight against the Russians. We have no Marshal Tito. And we don't want to be blown up—whether by a highly polished American H-bomb or a cruder Russian model."

The Czechs understand the meaning of freedom as well as anyone in Europe but aren't prepared to die for it. They take refuge in mild sarcasm. Satire keeps the flickering independent spirit alive. "You Americans," they say, "don't know what satire means. You have no need for veiled reference or in-

125

direct allusion. Your press, your stage, your radio can speak out bluntly. For centuries under occupation satire has been our solace."

This produces a spate of mild jokes tolerated by the gradually maturing Communist regime. For example, in a recent play: "Always recognize the secret police. They are unobtrusive and travel in pairs." Or, says one reincarnated character to another: "I never managed to be born to rich parents." Reply: "You're lucky—now." Or again: "An impressionist artist paints what he sees. An expressionist paints what he feels. A Socialist realist paints what he reads in the papers."

The Czechs, who spent many years under Austrian and German domination before their present tutelage, take curious comfort in quips. They try sincerely to keep alive self-respect through the national sense of humor. They wish that the West would manage to expand its contacts, for theirs is inherently a Western nation. But they are not going to rise in arms for the sake of political change. And they scoff at our propaganda urging a tougher course.

In this respect both the Communist Administration and the vast majority of those who dislike it are in implicit accord. Vaclav David, Foreign Minister and a member of the party's Central Committee, told me: "We want to improve our cultural relations with the Occident. We crave expanded visits, exchanges of music, plays, ideas." Of course he hastened to add, Prague demands that America terminate its radio and balloon campaigns and restrictions on strategic trade.

Both Government and people—which is to say those who

oppose the regime—think improvement in Czechoslovakia's situation can be decided only by the East, not West. A Communist observes: "There is a new wind blowing from Moscow. We welcome it." An anti-Communist adds. "What is, is. You can't help us. We are passive by nature. Hitler destroyed our morale—or what was left of it after the West betrayed us at Munich. Some of us became Communists. And most of us became Schweiks."

This passivity produces a fundamental split between rulers and ruled. The people hope devoutly a new liberalism breathed from Russia will provide that elbow room in which the Good Soldier Schweik knows how to operate. But the Government, cautious and careful, moves gingerly in any new direction. It budged little during the switch from Stalin to Malenkov. And it will wait watchfully before it follows Khrushchevism to its logical conclusion and scraps the monument upon the bluff— and what it stands for.

As East Europe's Communist countries mirror Moscow's changed ideology, such reflections are likely to come last in Czechoslovakia. For in one respect its rulers are certainly an adequate image of the people they claim to represent: wary, patient and not inclined to stick their necks out.

Czechoslovakia went overboard on Stalinism. Prague is the only orbit capital aside from Moscow and Sofia to boast a garish necropolis where Communism's hierarchy is preserved in Egyptian style. A great stone hall of the dead is flanked by Czech and Soviet flags. The antechamber is filled with empty tombs awaiting clients. Klement Gottwald, first Communist

President, lies mummified, Soviet fashion, chest covered with medals and body encased in glass.

The regime is reluctant to discard even the symbols of what brought it to power. This was indicated to me by Antonin Zapotocky, co-founder of the Czechoslovakian Communist party, first Secretary General, member of the present Politburo, President of the Republic and, as much as any Czech can be, boss.

Zapotocky is an affable individual whose appearance is much younger than his age, over seventy-two. He has a ruminative long nose, exceptionally long ears, blue eyes, a pleasant smile marred by one steel tooth, and an air of extreme caution. In his spare time he writes novels. Sitting in his office within the ancient Hradcany Palace of Bohemia's kings, he interpreted the new Bolshevik line, one March day in 1956.

Only three weeks before the dissolution of the Cominform, I pointed out to the President that not once in the torrent of words pronounced in Moscow when Khrushchev met Soviet Deputies was that body mentioned. What did this signify? Said he cautiously: "It is not usual at such congresses to discuss the Cominform. But there has been *no* change in this status. It may be altered in the future. But nothing has altered it yet." And yet the next month the ax fell. How about Czechoslovakian ideology? Zapotocky's reply: "I don't think there will be any changes. The necessity for collective leadership and the cult of the individual had already been discussed in Moscow at the Nineteenth Congress in 1952. This influenced a number of parties including ours. One cannot speak of different ideology. Only of adaptations resulting from the changed world situation. I think there is no reason for any particular policy switch."

When Malenkov succeeded Stalin and emphasized light industry, Czechoslovakia shifted only slightly. Therefore it had but a short hop back to the Khrushchev line. This experience seems to be kept in mind today. For, said Zapotocky, any trend toward relaxation isn't going to slow up his country's drive for more collectivization of agriculture.

"We wish to achieve a higher level of production," the President contended. "In order to do this we must farm on larger plots of ground. From this principle stems the policy of collectivization and the need to unify all smaller plots. In 1955 a number of co-operatives which the farmers had been forced to join fell apart. But we have changed our practices. During the first two months of 1956 the number of new collectives increased."

Not only does Czechoslovakia intend to stick to its present road; for long it continued to regard Stalin as a great man. Zapotocky said that despite the Moscow reappraisal: "Stalin deserves great merit for his fight against Trotskyism after Lenin's death. He also deserves great praise for industrializing the Soviet Union. Collective leadership reduces chances of mistakes. Individual authority has been criticized and remedied. But the process neither denies the merit nor reduces the role of Stalin. He will always remain a great personage in the Communist movement and in the history of Czechoslovakia's liberation. Our monument to him in Prague recalls this alle-

129

gorically. Recent developments do not affect the value of this. We have no intention of altering it."

At that point Zapotocky made a truly strange comparison. He said: "In Czechoslovakia you may see a number of memorials to our first President, T. G. Masaryk. None have been removed—except by zealots who were punished. Masaryk will remain a historical figure although his political ideas were different. Likewise, Stalin's memory is honored."

This was an odd observation. Masaryk's name was widely honored once in monuments, streets and schools. But, since 1948, it has been deliberately and totally erased. Is this what Zapotocky meant by linking Stalin's reputation with that of Czechoslovakia's George Washington? Does he imply that Communism's symbol will follow democracy's into limbo?

The Communist regime in Prague isn't interested in building a bridge between East and West. Said Zapotocky: "If by 'bridge' you mean a policy of fence-sitting, we oppose it. We wish to build Socialism here and to base ourselves on Socialist countries." Evidently the only bridge he is concerned with links Communism's immediate Stalinist past and its still uncertain Khrushchevist future. The President doesn't want to step off precipitously in any false direction.

Along the German border in Western Czechoslovakia are great industrial centers and famous mountain resorts where the wine-bibbing Europeans used traditionally to cure their ailing livers. Among such spas none was more famous in the pre-war world than Carlsbad or, as Czechs call it, Karlovy Vary. Now it is famous in the East—and shows it.

In 1938, when I first visited Carlsbad, it was a curious symbol of an era about to end. Luxury hotels still entertained sickly millionaires and vacationers. Horse-drawn carriages rolled along quiet streets that exuded nineteenth-century tranquillity. But the atmosphere was tense. A restless Sudeten German minority, prompted by Hitler, was daring to build a state within a state. This was the center of those Nazi activities that destroyed Czechoslovakia. Only the amiable drozhky drivers, masseurs at thermal stations and their overfed clientele seemed unaware of the horrible future shaping up.

There are few Germans in Karlovy Vary today, no more carriages,. no more millionaires, scarcely anyone from the West. Great hotels gape vacantly. Stores, mostly owned by the Communist state, are filled with unimpressive goods. In the long colonnade where water gushes from the Sudetenland's famous radium deposits, solemn, chunky Russians in bellbottom trousers, fur hats or the visored caps that seem to be Socialism's fashion walk embarrassedly up and down, guzzling the medicaments once so coveted by sickly rich.

The old villas with pretentious fronts have been taken over by the state and are placed at the disposition of such visitors as China's Marshal Chu Teh or the impassive but apparently liverish Mr. Molotov. East European tourists march in phalanx past the Soviet bookshop and into dreary restaurants.

Karlovy Vary is now a jewel of the brave new world of Marx and Orwell. There the bright young Moscow "jet set" craves to take its holidays. It symbolizes strange traditions and unknown cultures. These are still envied by the influential in that immense Communist orbit stretching from China to this town so near the German border and the mysterious West.

Serving a greasy lunch, a waiter will remark: "Ach, yes, times are different. This is the best hotel today. Once it was fourth class." It is dirty, drab and miserable. Its plumbing shows an Asian impact. Yet, for the current clientele, from the U.S.S.R.'s ideological empire, Karlovy Vary represents the very height of undreamed luxury. The costly shoes badly mass-produced in state-run factories are still cheaper and better than anywhere else within the Soviet sphere. Somewhat tawdry consumers' goods displayed in Government shops are the joy of Communist housewives loaded with ruble-bloc currency. Carlsbad's standard of living has sunk. But it remains above the norm that Moscow sets.

Karlovy Vary is symptomatic of the change in all Sudetenland, that industrious, tortuous area where German has contested Slav since medieval times. The famous draught Pilsener beer is now undrinkable in Pilsen. All good brew is exported—eastward to a thirsty Russian orbit or westward in quest of the hard money Czechoslovakia needs so much.

In Cheb, the citadel of Emperor Frederick Barbarossa, where romantic Wallenstein was slain, gray death has settled. To be sure there are new buildings. But the Gothic Church of Saint Nicholas is almost empty even on a Sunday. And fine old houses, wrecked eleven years ago by war, remain to be repaired, paint peeling from their battered fronts, wind shrieking through broken windows.

This part of Czechoslovakia was freed by United States

132

troops. Our First Division got as far as Pilsen before it was halted to allow the Red Army to liberate Prague. But even this American endeavor is now being deliberately erased from Czechoslovakia's carefully molded memories. Outside Cheb a simple gray pillar commemorates those of the First Division who died for Czechoslovakia. Three enormous road signs have been erected to block it from view. Paint listing the roll of honor has washed off in the rain. Ultimately, inevitably, the monument itself must go. In June, 1955, the authorities quietly removed from Pilsen a plaque in memory of Americans who died there.

It is a dreary picture that one has in Sudetenland today. Government charts show how fine life is, how much, much better off the workers are. Even when valid, it is hard for statistics to measure happiness. In Karlovy Vary the earnest Russians take their medical concoctions. In Pilsen the workers in whose name all this is built contemplate tasteless beer. Freedom and gaiety are not computed on graphs.

HUNGARY

Unlike the other Communist states bordering upon the Western world, Hungary is not Slavic. In fact, ever since the Austro-Hungarian empire dissolved in 1918, Hungarian policy was worried by its demographic isolation in a sea of Slavs. As long ago as 1940 Count Csaky, then Foreign Minister of the right-wing Horthy regime, showed me a map of Central Europe with the warning: "If necessary, we will fight with anyone to prevent these peoples from joining across our state."

133

He pointed to the Slovaks of southern Czechoslovakia, and to the Croats and Slovenes of northern Jugoslavia. He added: "Then we would be racially devoured." Csaky miscalculated. Hungary joined the German hordes. It paid for this mistake by submitting to Russian political hegemony. But it has managed to retain a national vitality. The island of Magyars, descended from ancient Tartar horsemen, is still a solid entity.

Matyas Rakosi was the most famous boss of Communist postwar Hungary and, until his ouster during the summer of 1956, proved an extraordinarily durable man. By his own account he survived nineteen years in prison, seven in solitary confinement. He survived underground intrigues on behalf of the Comintern. He led Cominform attacks on Tito's Jugoslavia and long survived Moscow's drastic change of line. He survived the death of Stalin, the shift to Malenkov's "new course" and the switch back under Khrushchev. When the U.S.S.R., fount of his political inspiration, emphasized collective leadership and the end of one-man rule, Rakosi sought stubbornly, but in the end without success, to keep the seat of local power.

Steeped in the traditions of conspiracy, he seemed to have formed the habit of obscuring facts. When I asked him if Rakosi was his real family name he answered yes. Yet his own Foreign Office would admit that when he was born sixty-four years ago in a village now in Jugoslavia his surname was Roth. He Magyarized it while studying in Budapest.

As a Comintern agent in Europe Rakosi used many passports and thirty different aliases. A prisoner of the prewar

Horthy regime in 1940, he was released to the Soviet Union in exchange for battle flags of 1848, then captured by the Russians. He recalled to me with pride: "It is an irony of history that the same standards were taken again in Austria by a Russian army—the Red Army. And they were again returned to us. At national parades they head our columns. I find it a highly agreeable sensation to see them there."

Rakosi speaks fluent English, Russian, German, French and Italian plus more than a smattering of Turkish. He explains this talent accordingly: "Forty-six years ago I studied to be a diplomat. I wanted to enter the consular service and attended the Oriental Academy, our only diplomatic school."

He is extraordinary looking: barely five feet tall but with an enormous, powerful chest that has slipped a bit with age; large head, shaven and bald, shaping up to a point; heavy jaw, shrewd brown eyes, friendly smile, several gold teeth and a hoarse, resonant voice. "In my youth," he confides, "I was a sportsman. I still row and swim." He used to read the American and English press assiduously. But, says he: "I found they kept repeating the same rubbish. In January, 1956, I canceled my subscriptions—all but the London *Economist* and *New Statesman*."

Always he followed Moscow's shifting party line with slavish enthusiasm. When asked for his views on Stalin or the 1956 Bolshevik Congress, he answered with a smile: "I agree with Comrade Khrushchev and Comrade Mikoyan." In the hall outside his office was a Stalin portrait. In the antechamber hung a snapshot of Stalin lighting a pipe. And again behind

135

his desk was Stalin. Hungary made formal obeisance to the new "collective leadership." But Rakosi retained his private pictures.

Despite the zigzags of Communism's erratic course, Rakosi was until his fall brimful of confidence. He paid lip service to Stalin's faults, Tito's virtues and the good qualities of his hitherto-disgraced Hungarian colleague Bela Kun when Moscow changed its tune. But how deep did this run?

Said he: "I am an optimist by nature. My parents bequeathed me health. I survived difficult years. A Hungarian prison was no high school. Often I lived in darkness. But I kept fit by using my cell table as a weight for exercises. When I emerged, full of energy, the keeper was most dissatisfied." Rakosi is exuberantly devoted to the Soviet Union. His wife, a ceramic artist, is Russian. For him all winds blow from the east. "To be a successful power nowadays," he observed, "you must have a population of at least one hundred million." These are not the words of a Tito.

Hungary, he used to claim, is on the crest of a wave, a Soviet wave. He would add: "Every day the papers are full of news agreeable to us—even if disagreeable to America. China has joined our camp. There have been changes in Vietnam, North Africa, Egypt. Adenauer's regime is disintegrating. A man must be blind if he doesn't see the direction in which history moves." And, he boasted, "This is a free wave. Look around. You will see free people."

One looked. One discovered that Hungary's current literary genius, Gyula Illyes, had recently written: "The earth, our earth, is always heavier, heavier with one more corpse. . . .

The fallen always increase in number and anguish always increases."

Rakosi has an interesting way of changing his mind. In 1952 he called Tito "a long-standing agent of the capitalists and fascists" and "a traitor." In 1953 he talked of Stalin as "the beloved," "the great," "the dearest friend of the Hungarian people." He added: "Joseph Vissarionovich Stalin was the wisest leader and teacher of our age." And in 1954 he lectured on Bela Kun, his old comrade and head of the short-lived 1919 Communist Government in Budapest, criticizing him as an ally of the Social Democrats who "did not understand" the peasants.

Times, as Rakosi himself happily admits with quotations from the Latin, change. This is especially true for those who set their watches by the Kremlin clock. What does Rakosi say today of the man he almost deified and the man he castigated?

Of Stalin: "We hold exactly the same opinion as Khrushchev and Mikoyan. Everybody makes mistakes—especially when they get old. This was the case with Stalin. To measure a man's historical value you must be able to look backward over a certain span of time. Your people thought Coolidge wise and strong simply because he didn't speak. Now he is no longer considered so smart." To this writer it was astonishing enough when Antonin Zapotocky mentioned Stalin in connection with T. G. Masaryk. But Stalin and Coolidge—*mirabile dictu.*

As for Rakosi's old friend and enemy, Bela Kun: "I had been in prison twelve years when he disappeared in 1937.

137

Therefore, I couldn't judge his later actions. But during our revolution of 1919 and the preparation for this revolt he did excellent work. He made blunders, too, of course. But it was not by pure chance that he was the leading figure of our revolution. He is one of our great figures: the outstanding figure of our revolution."

And Tito? "We were misled on Titoism. That was one of the works of Beria's gang. He sought to create a situation that would weaken the bonds of Socialism. Now we are trying to forget this disagreeable episode and to improve our relations with Jugoslavia. After all, Lenin thought there was no doubt that every nation is moving toward Socialism. Excuse me, but I even include the United States. Each country takes its own special steps. Tito was absolutely right. Our relations with Jugoslavia are not healed but are healing. When they are healed I would be glad to ask him back into the Cominform." A few weeks after this extraordinary statement the Comiform was dissolved.

Rakosi came to admit it was a mistake to try to execute his former colleagues, headed by Laszlo Rajk, on charges of Titoism. "That was a mixed grill," he observed. "Beria and his agents always worked to mix up truth and untruth. But we wouldn't have such a process today. That is a phase that has been ended."

Rakosi was never embarrassed to rewrite history. For him the end always justifies the means. He recalls that enemies have accused him of "salami tactics"—cutting away all opposition slice by slice. With a smile of satisfaction he observes: "That is the job of any good political party—including the Communists. I won't patent the process."

That being the case, how do "salami tactics" apply? Take the instance of the church. He says: "With the development of our schools, slowly and without any big conflict the influence of the church will steadily diminish. Without acknowledging it the Catholics are accommodating themselves to the situation. The church is well known for its ability to make separate peace."

Despite acceptance of Moscow's brand-new iconography, he adhered until his fall from power to his old course inside Hungary. For, said Rakosi in March, 1956: "We remain strongly for collectivization and for the superiority of the collective system on the land. In industry, likewise, we are sticking to our line."

And the police? "A stronger state is in no need of a strong hand administratively. And there is no doubt that every country within the Socialist camp feels stronger. But the question of the police was not raised at the Twentieth Congress in Moscow. Certainly, as long as capitalism is strong, we need a strong state. And part of a strong state is a strong and loyal police. There will be no change in this."

Rakosi was a dutiful Communist leader who regarded the Soviet Union as the source of all truth. And when the masters of the Kremlin changed, Rakosi went along with them. But his sentiments and habits had been molded by too many decades of patterns only lately discarded in Moscow for him to drop them lightly. He learned to speak with the accents of collec-

139

tive leadership. But the words were Stalinist. Therefore he had to go.

Curiously enough, the most renowned and popular man in Communist Hungary is not a political boss but a youthful army captain with a name surprisingly like that of Ikaros, the first man to fly. This is suitable. For Sandor Iharos, a lanky individual with long, pointed features and a shock of brown hair, holds six world's running titles.

Hungary, with a population of less than ten million people, is a nation of remarkable athletic ability. Apart from Iharos it has international champions in soccer, water polo, swimming, fencing, gymnastics, wrestling and boxing. But the captain, with records at fifteen hundred meters, three thousand meters, two miles, three miles and the six thousand-meters relay, is the best—a national hero.

Iharos is a mechanic, at present doing service in the army. He works as a clerk in the sports section of the military, which allows him two hours free each day for practice. But his training methods might amaze many a Western coach. Although he doesn't smoke, Iharos eats and drinks anything, including the national dish of goulash, not a feature of the average athlete's menu, and beer. He is not a member of the Communist party, which is unusual since, in Eastern countries, that organization generally seeks to co-opt the famous. He says that all he knows about Marxism is what he learned in those routine courses now required in school.

When he talks, rather earnestly, softly and almost with **embarrassment**, Iharos reflects little of the strident theory of

140

"Socialist emulation" so common nowadays in other fields of Hungarian life. "I train hard," he says. "I have trained for seven years. I like to run. I like competition. I like to win."

Nevertheless, conversation with him reveals perfectly plainly why members of the Communist bloc are rising to prominence so rapidly upon the field of sport. The U.S.S.R. itself is at the top. And Hungary—astonishing for its size—comes just behind its Big Brother and the United States in Olympic rankings. The answer is simple, for, as the captain explains: "We have no professionals here. There are only amateurs. All athletes are workers."

What this means, of course, is that within the Soviet orbit nobody can be banned from competition for professionalism, for the simple reason that such a category is not recognized. As Iharos says: "The state analyzes sporting events and chooses and encourages the best athletes. They are helped more in Socialist lands than under capitalism. If a runner makes a good time he gets more state aid and more help from his nationalized enterprise. He is invited to join sports clubs and gets better and better equipment. His conditions are improved. And, in a sense, he tries to beat his target the way a worker might exceed his norm.

"It is possible," adds Iharos skeptically, "that ideology helps in a psychological way. Maybe our athletes are inspired by the new national life and the urge to produce better results. But on the whole I doubt this. After all, world's records are being constantly improved in capitalist as well as Communist lands. The real answer is in training, constant training, anywhere."

141

This is a sensible observation in terms of individual efforts in the realm of sport. But it does not cover the subject as far as national, or what the Communists would term collective, endeavors are concerned. For, as things stand now, the capitalist world competes internationally against the Communist world hampered by the self-imposed handicap in almost every field of eliminating its best athletes as "professional." Since the category does not even exist within the Soviet orbit, there is no difficulty here.

It is an odd aspect of Competitive Coexistence in athletics, where surely the idea is practiced in its simplest and most satisfying way, that the West deliberately ties one hand behind its back before entering the arena by disqualifying many of its ablest sportsmen. Neither Hungary nor the Soviet Union has famous professional basketball teams or tennis players barred from international competition. Everyone works for the state, which deems itself a monolithic amateur.

Surely this is no answer to the interesting question of what makes Sandor run. But it is at least a partial answer to why the Soviet bloc *en masse* is rising so rapidly in the field of sport. Possibly, these complicated days, we might do well to analyze the semantics of the athlete on both sides of the ideological curtain as we already have begun to discern differences in the comprehended meaning of such common words as "democracy" and "peace." At least in competing against muscular opponents representing another social system we could consider revising restrictive standards they have already made outmoded.

142

RUMANIA

If one sets aside the obscure little mountain republic of Albania, isolated like some small Communist leper colony upon the Adriatic, there is no doubt that the most bewildered and groveling European satellites of Russia are Rumania and Bulgaria. The Rumanians symbolized their beaten-down servility by harboring the now-defunct Cominform after that organization withdrew from Belgrade following the Titoist rebellion. From 1948 until its dissolution in the spring of 1956, this famous international propaganda agency had its seat in Bucharest.

For reasons comprehensible only to conspiratorial Marxism, however, the location of Cominform headquarters was supposed to be a mystery. The Rumanian Foreign Office pretended it didn't know where it was and refused to solicit appointments with its officials on the grounds—"this is an international committee and we are not responsible." Foreign diplomats were equally ill informed. A Jugoslav diplomat explained: "When we had the Cominform in Belgrade its exact whereabouts was one of our most closely guarded secrets."

Why all this cloak-and-dagger nonsense? Were the leaders of Communism embarrassed about something? What did they wish to disguise, the rumblings of their new iconoclasm as they commenced to tear down old idols?

In March, 1956, I visited the Cominform headquarters situated within an entire square block in a somewhat sordid section of Bucharest at the intersection of Valeriu Braniste

143

and Turturelelor streets. With the exception of a house across the way at No. 24 Turturelelor, supposedly the information office, the entire establishment was located inside a fenced-in compound. Its publications—primarily the weekly journal called *For a Lasting Peace, for a People's Democracy*—were, however, printed a few miles away in the immense new building of *Scanteia*, daily paper of the Rumanian Communist party.

The fence around the Cominform compound was solid and high enough to bar an outsider's vision. The two main gates— on Valeriu Braniste and on Turturelelor—were metal. At each of them, when one pushed inside, was a sentry box containing plain-clothes Rumanian guards in peasant fur hats and long, brown homespun coats. They spoke both Russian and Rumanian. The first thing they demanded was the visitor's *propusk*, which is Russian, not Rumanian, for permit. This intruder's *propusk* happened to be a *New York Times* calling card, which stimulated some perplexed telephone conversation between sentries and unknown party bureaucrats.

The Cominform enclosure was occupied by several seedy-looking apartment houses of five or six stories each, all painted an unfortunate shade of yellow. It included a playground where dozens of rotund little children, dressed to the ears against the cold spring winds, jabbered happily in Russian.

A continual procession of people carrying such publications as *Pravda* and *Kommunist* under their arms passed in and out, always flashing *propusks* in the form of a little red book containing a photograph and Russian inscriptions. Occasionally

144

an important functionary would drive in the Turturelelor gate, swung open slowly by the guard, and leave his Soviet Zis or Pobieda automobile in the slushy car park.

Turturelelor 24 was the only Cominform building protected visibly by a uniformed Rumanian official, in this instance a gendarme in boots and bedraggled blue coat. Inside was a filthy antechamber containing one scratched-up table, torn and stained rugs, some chairs, large pictures of Lenin and, even then, believe it or not, Stalin. Two steel doors led to offices inside. One of these had a speakeasy-type peep window cut into it. This in turn was covered over with brown paint except for a narrow slit through which inquisitive dark eyes occasionally peered out.

The last executive director of the Cominform was M. B. Mitin, editor of its journal and a member of the Soviet Academy of Science. Needless to say, he was Russian. When one applied to see him one was told to wait while *The New York Times propusk* disappeared within the first steel door, held gingerly by an individual wearing a black billed cap. Another gentleman, in leather hat, coat and boots, chatted happily about the weather while smoking, ecstatically, the proffered American cigarette. Finally word came out, brought by two characters in caps and boots. The word was this: "To see Tovarisch Mitin you must apply at the Rumanian Foreign Office."

The bureaucrat assigned by the Rumanian Foreign Office to disdain the press seemed somewhat bewildered when informed of this. "Who told you to apply again to us? The

145

Cominform itself? Do you know where it is? Well, there must be some mistake. I suggest you go back there again and tell them you wish to see Tovarisch Mitin. Come to think of it, this may not be worth while. I have heard he is out of town."

The Cominform, which since its invention in 1947 held only three formal meetings, was doomed to disappear once the U.S.S.R. made amends to Tito. But the fact that its openly Russian imperialistic seat was latterly located in Bucharest symbolizes the way in which Moscow regards that Danubian capital. Before the war and revolution, Bucharest had the lovable cheek to call itself the Paris of the East. It was proud of its finely dressed women, its comfortable, well-furnished houses, its pretentious restaurants, night clubs and sophistication. Everyone with claims to education spoke French. A Latinity of Rumania, its traditions and aspirations, was proclaimed. More than some Continental capitals, Bucharest had its seamy side: astonishing corruption, beggars as well as barflies, hovels as well as mansions. But it was colorful and full of life. Above all, it was gay.

Today Bucharest might call itself the Moscow of the West. The city's face has not been lifted. Instead, by miraculous new methods of psychological town planning, its face has been dropped. Some strange glandular injection has altered its composite personality. Maybe, as Communist propaganda claims, the people are happier. Such things can never be statistically computed. But the people don't *look* happier. And the gaiety has vanished.

It is now a drab and earnest capital, bedecked with Red placards exhorting Marxist man to fill his norm. The women, once more intent upon frivolity, have been given equal rights, including the Muscovite privilege of shoveling snow. The same big houses are there, with ornate façades staring out on avenues and parks. But, inside, tenants are stacked up like sardines, and hallways are redolent of cabbage. The old restaurants, taken over by the state, cater more to mass production than the palate. A queer red substance called "Manchurian caviar" has ousted the Danubian sturgeon's egg. Although the country boasts automotive assembly plants, their products must go elsewhere. Few cars skid through the empty streets.

The old and somewhat ostentatious hotels fulfill their functional duty as shelters. But the Ambassador smells like a Turkish bath. The Athenee Palace, a cynosure of prewar pleasure, entertains serious gentlemen in Russian-tailored suits; earnest women wearing woolen stockings; and anonymous characters standing about in leather coats and those visored caps once fashionable on golf links and now the Communist mode.

The hotel bar, once cluttered up with British intelligence agents and later by arrogant Nazi officers, is now about as lively as a crematorium. Piled behind the counter are costly bottles of weird gins and brandies manufactured in the popular democracies and drinkable only by their citizens. The bored individual who presides complains: "Nobody leaves a tip. They say 'What for? You get a salary from the state.' Yes. Three hundred thirty-five lei [fifty-six dollars] a month. And I have two children."

The former self of Bucharest is poignantly recognizable.

147

Tall, dark peasants with saturnine faces, sheepskin coats and conical fur hats still stride into the indifferent eastern wind blowing along the Calea Victoriei. But the city has been transmogrified. Its character has changed.

Essentially this was produced by deliberate extinction of the bourgeoisie. Bucharest, beneath the tinsel, was primarily a middle-class city with both the virtues and the faults that this implies. It derived its life blood from the lawyers, doctors, bankers, businessmen who lived in the comfortable homes that have now become shabby boardinghouses. This class has been wiped out.

It furnished much of the death roster of the revolution's most violent phase, of the unhappy press gangs who labored to dig the now abandoned and utterly useless Black Sea canal, of the cellmates in gloomy prisons. Its survivors, disorganized, disillusioned and distressed, are on the whole second-class citizens unable and unpermitted to adjust to the brashly confident new world about them. Their pitiful last belongings are sold for a song in commission shops. Their families are breaking up.

An extremely intelligent play which—beneath an unnecessary coating of propaganda—discusses this social change was recently the talk of Bucharest. This described the disintegration of a happy bourgeois household during the revolutionary decade. Three members are arrested; three make the political adjustment of becoming fellow travelers; one commits suicide and one goes mad. A bewildered character asks the Communist schoolteacher who lives in a requisitioned room: "How can you be so categorical, violently loving some people, violently hating others?" Says she: "When you believe in something, then you are categorical." And the matriarch, a scientist, advises: "Don't lose hope. Parents are bringing up their children. Don't waste time on illusions."

There is a brutal reality about the new drab Bucharest that is difficult to compare with the carefree glitter of the days before the war. The people, beneath their unstylish clothes, look much the same. Physically the bourgeoisie is not entirely dead. Its ghosts plod in and out of familiar doorways on unaccustomed schedules of unfamiliar tasks. Their eyes mirror no heaven.

Yet, with the cruel destruction of Rumania's decadent aristocracy and cultivated middle class, the revolution has accomplished positive achievements that cannot be ignored. This was stressed to the author during a visit to the museum that used to be a Hohenzollern palace. Among the departed dynasty's few good points was a taste for the paintings of El Greco and ability to acquire them. In 1940, when the late King Carol scuttled out of his country while a Hungarian army was occupying Transylvania, he took with him much of this collection. But he left three Grecos, including a Marriage of the Virgin that is one of the world's loveliest possessions.

While admiring this in the new national gallery, I was interested in the reactions of two young Rumanians who kept shifting about until the light shone properly. "Ah," said one of them, "he painted from his heart. He was seeking truth

149

and freedom. That is not Socialist realism."

This led to conversation, in German, on the padded bench beneath a Velázquez portrait. One participant was a student, perhaps twenty-five years old, who hoped to be a writer. The other, stocky, redheaded, with heavily callused hands, operated a lathe in a machine plant. Neither was a party member but both, with reservations, supported the Communist regime.

Redhead, who was thirty-three and married, earned 800 lei a month and complained this was inadequate. Said he: "Two months' salary to buy just one new suit. How many hours for an American worker? Perhaps twenty? Well, there you see how much better off you are. You are rich and we are poor. You are lucky and we are not. You won your freedom when all of Europe was still autocratic. Yet we want the same things you do. All around the world everyone has the same aspirations—freedom, happiness, shelter, food, work and the right to education.

"I know I do not earn enough. Everything costs too much. But I have liver trouble. Last autumn I was sent to a sanatorium and cured. What did it cost me? Hardly anything. I am a worker. You know what things were like here before the war?"

The student interrupted: "The upper classes were intelligent, but you cannot imagine how corrupt they were. When we sought leadership we had none. But you read about the famine and the peasant uprising? We needed revolution. We know *this* revolution was imported from outside. But the majority of people—the workers and the peasants—needed it."

Said Redhead: "Of course the Government is too abject. It always echoed Russia. We were astonished to read the truth on Stalin. At last the truth—the truth we already knew. Our Government is an experiment. And it makes terrible mistakes. People are dead. People are in prison. People have lost their freedom because of these mistakes. But even a government can learn. We want freedom as much as anyone. And freedom comes when the people insist upon it from their hearts. We will insist.

"We know as well as you do what is wrong. But don't be misled by your own propaganda. We know propaganda—yours, ours and Russia's. We know what we want. It isn't what you seem to think. It isn't what we had before the war. Time will go on. Things will evolve. People are only free when their inner spirit demands it. Ours does. This Government came in with terror. I have no use for bloodshed and class war. We have seen pitiful things. But we are on the path of progress. This is a reality. You Americans should not ignore it."

A colloquy in a museum is difficult to measure on the scale of values. But it is of some interest in a country where a highly suspicious regime seeks desperately to isolate the foreigner; where the average citizen, remembering those still in jail, avoids the simplest conversation. What can one conclude?

A diplomat who knew Rumania before observed: "This is a ruthless, determined Government which faithfully follows

151

every Soviet whim and revolutionary pattern. It has brutally stamped out middle classes, prosperous farmers and the mere thought of liberalism. But Rumania was a horribly backward land. I wonder how many foreigners really knew it. Today at least the soldiery is paid and fed. The officers don't sell off all the rations. Even though they hate collectives, peasants are better off. You see them buying in the shops. That was once a rare occurrence. As for the workers, I simply do not know. I suspect they are not very happy."

Truth, at best an abstraction, is almost impossible to discover. The remnants of the bourgeoisie shiver with dread at their own real thoughts. The press is befuddled with propaganda. Even the literary classics are censored for unfavorable mention of Russia. The first and physical phase of the revolution is bewilderingly complete. But the second, the spiritual phase, is brewing. As the machinist says: "People are only free when their inner spirit demands it. Ours does."

BULGARIA

South of the Danube and now linked to Rumania by Europe's longest bridge, common ideology and a somewhat unenthusiastic alliance imposed from Moscow, is the Orthodox, Slavic country of Bulgaria, southernmost Continental outpost of the modern Russian empire. The Bulgarians are tough, hard-working, frugal peasant folk with a sense of color and natural talent for music. But they are unlucky. Except for tiny Albania, their country was the last Balkan region liberated from the Ottoman Turks. They lost three of their last four wars. Being pro-Russian by tradition, they have always consoled themselves in time of trouble by murmuring: "Grandfather Ivan from Moscow soon will come and help us." Grandfather Ivan arrived in September, 1944. Like the man who came to dinner, he is still there.

The regime now ruling Sofia resents it when we term Bulgaria a satellite. Why? A law on the statute books stipulates: "All Soviet citizens living in the People's Republic of Bulgaria, irrespective of when and how they obtained Soviet citizenship, have the right to apply for work in the due order in all state, co-operative, public and private enterprises and institutions and to practice any other profession *without the special permission required for foreigners*." Communists pretend this is only to ease the position of former White Russian refugees. If so, the country needs lessons in legal drafting.

The only career open to Bulgarians in the U.S.S.R. is spreading revolution. Their postwar leaders were graduates in that profession. Georgi Dimitrov, first boss of this People's Republic, who now lies preserved Soviet-style off Sofia's main street, was secretary of the Moscow Comintern. So was former Premier Vasil Kolarov. Vulko Chervenkov, Premier until 1956, taught at Moscow's Lenin Institute. Anton Jugov, his successor, was a Soviet agent in Jugoslavia.

But Russians in Bulgaria can operate in many less specialized fields. Apart from advising the highest military and civilian echelons, they hold important posts in banks, industries, factories and hospitals. They are better paid than

153

their Bulgarian colleagues and cause resentment by buying out the shops. Their private relationships with local citizens are disdainful. In Sofia they have their own restaurant where no Bulgarian is admitted—like a British club in prewar India.

Bulgarians, accustomed for centuries to foreign domination, express their present discontent in sullen jokes. They attribute shortages of goods to Russian greed. In their language *tovar* means "to load." "*Tovarisch*" say the peasants, "only loads his train here. He never unloads anything." A feeling exists that work goals fixed serve primarily to benefit only Soviet well-being. Not long ago a hen was found hanged before the Plovdiv City Hall. Beneath it fluttered a placard reading: "I committed suicide. I could not fill my norm."

The Sofia Government seeks to advertise not only the benefits of Communism but the perfection of all that is Russian. While it has removed the "Czar Liberator" label from the old statue of Alexander II in front of Parliament, the monument itself still stands. The most popular musical comedy, dealing with revolt against the Turks, plays up the benevolence of Russia.

Two Bulgarians recently stopped to admire one of the few American automobiles in Sofia's streets. "Is that Russian?" asked one. Said the other: "I know what kind of a car it is. But can I trust you?" The Bulgarian tends by nature to be egalitarian and what he terms "progressive." Yet many members of the Communist party today complain: "We are political prisoners. We believe in Marxism. But we want to decide ourselves how to apply it here."

154

Chervenkov, Premier at the time of Moscow's famous twentieth Bolshevik Congress when, in early 1956, the anti-Stalin line was charted, was the last satellite boss to hop on the bandwagon. Even by his own definition he didn't do well. Once he criticized the man who "sways whither as the strongest wind blows him" as "a weather vane, not a leader." He added: "The leader must be able to grasp new tendencies while still in embryo, he must be able to foresee events and not trail in their wake to wait for them to hit him on the nose."

That was before Khrushchev trampled on Stalin's grave. When the change came, Chervenkov was hit upon the nose. Sofia's museum was filled with Stalin's portraits. Posters of the unlamented leader were still among the few inexpensive articles on sale. And Nikola Vaptsarov, most popular Communist poet in Bulgaria, was hailed in Stalinist terms as proof that "Socialist realism secures to art a creative freedom without precedent."

Undoubtedly the emphasis will shift now that Weathervane Chervenkov was sacrificed to new winds from the east and replaced by Jugov. But most Bulgarians are skeptical. Sitting in grimy cafés, they mutter across their *slivovica*: "We hope for better things. But we have lost our faith. What is the difference so long as the word still comes from Moscow? Our peasants have a proverb—'The wolf can shed his coat but not his habits.'"

Communism seeks to attract small powers by promising them industrialization and a balanced economy. Therefore, after the revolution had firmly clamped itself upon Bulgaria,

155

it set out to follow this customary pattern. But that country is difficult to industrialize. The same monolithic goals that might, for example, suit Czechoslovakia are hardly applicable there.

Probably 90 per cent of the Bulgarians are peasants. They are accustomed to till the soil, dance their merry *horos* and design magnificent embroideries. They are attached to their folk customs. Girls still take love potions and wear bat wings in their girdles to attract lovers. In the mountain fastnesses of Pirin old wives talk about their friendly dragons, human bodies covered with lizard scales, skimming four feet above the ground.

When this rural population was pressed into a Marxist mold the outcome was almost chaos. The major result, when farmers were brought into the cities as an artificial proletariat, was creation of a major housing crisis. Today, by law, two people must sleep in every room in Sofia.

To provide additional manpower for factories, land was collectivized more swiftly than in any other satellite. This inspired deep resentment among the peasants and in 1951 they revolted, quitting the *kolkhozes* in droves. The pace was slowed down. Although about 60 per cent of the land had been socialized already—more than anywhere else in Eastern Europe—the regime forbore further effort.

During the same period of abatement Chervenkov, brother-in-law and successor of Dimitrov as Bulgaria's Communist boss, sought to establish his ascendancy as strong man. Temporarily, as long as pathological Stalinism remained the

156

orbit mode, he succeeded. He eliminated his chief rival, Traicho Kostov, as a Titoist. But another leader, Jugov, remained a potential opponent.

After Khrushchev and Bulganin made their peace with Jugoslavia there were rumors that Chervenkov's political head was part of the payment Soviet Russia made to Marshal Tito. Chervenkov more or less disappeared from public view in Sofia in the latter part of 1955.

However, in January, 1956, Chervenkov went to Moscow and remained several weeks. He had apparently mollified the Kremlin and seemed firmly in the saddle. The pace of revolution was again stepped up. And the direction of this effort was changed. Bulgaria is now to stress agriculture heavily and to become primarily a provider of food and raw materials for the Soviet orbit.

Chervenkov brought back with him a large Russian loan— 370,000,000 rubles. At 2 per cent interest rate this will be repaid in ores, such as uranium, and in crops. Industrialization was de-emphasized. The new budget greatly raised the proportion of agricultural expenditures.

At the same time the rate of collectivization has once more been accelerated. In 1956 so many more thousands of hectares were brought into what is called the "Socialist sector" that the proportion of arable land collectivized begins to approach totality.

Many forms of pressure were applied against the private farmers who had still held on to their property. Some of them, hoping to outwit the Government, had taken out Communist party cards. Now all Communists, by fiat, must join *kolkhozes*. Forced deliveries to the state have been stepped up for individual peasants. And the debts of those who join collectives are being annulled.

Bulgaria, already well ahead of other satellites in the degree of agricultural socialization, is on the way to becoming one big *kolkhoz*. And the peasants, while sullen, are slowly ceding. There does not seem to be any open opposition. All this represented a victory for Chervenkov. Yet, as a symbol of Stalinism and an enemy of Tito, Moscow ordered his ouster.

The revolution in Bulgaria seems to have entered a new phase, one that, in the sense it stresses farming, is more suitable than the earlier type of planning. But, because of its emphasis upon forced collectivization, it makes the regime no more popular than in the past. So the Bulgarians are at best reluctant Communists. They have often tended toward agrarian Socialism but they like to hang on to their little plots of ground.

The people are grudgingly appreciative of some of the accomplishments of their new regime: its excellent medical services, good school facilities, care for children and free vacations—a new thing in that country. But they do not welcome the price they pay for this—their freedom.

Not long ago two foreigners were traveling in the countryside and stopped at a small tavern. A group of peasants came along and, after eying them suspiciously, joined them in a glass of wine. One of them lifted his glass, looked about and said: "I drink to liberty."

BALKAN FEDERATION?

As Soviet foreign-policy tactics shifted, hitherto truculent Bulgaria was ordered to improve relationships with its traditional enemies, Greece and Jugoslavia. The Soviet Union would be pleased to destroy what remains of the Balkan pact, an alliance of Jugoslavs, Greeks and Turks. And Bulgaria, a particularly dutiful satellite, is playing an assigned role.

Sofia commenced making generally affable gestures toward the West. It initiated negotiations to restore diplomatic relations with the United States. But particular emphasis was devoted to the Balkan neighbors. Relationship with Greece was renewed. Bulgaria agreed in principle to pay Athens reparations fixed by the 1947 peace treaty.

Bulgarians and Greeks have been enemies for a long time and fought three recent wars against each other. When both were occupied by the Ottoman Turks many Greeks held ascendant positions in Bulgaria. Orthodox services were conducted in the Greek language until, thanks to Czarist Russian pressure in Constantinople, the Church was Bulgarized less than a century ago. Together with the Jugoslavs, the Greeks and Bulgarians share the ancient province of Macedonia. This has been a source of friction among the three neighbors.

Macedonia manages to intrude into almost any Balkan discussion. The Bulgars have tended to insist that the Slavic Macedonians are really Bulgars, not a separate people. In

159

December, 1944, when Sofia and Belgrade were both subservient to Moscow, Edvard Kardelj, one of Marshal Tito's top
lieutenants, sought to negotiate an agreement with the Bulgars
for union of all South Slavs.

Sofia accepted in principle. But it insisted on unification to
take place on a basis of condominium. That is to say, Bulgaria
as one entity would have as much power in the suggested
federation as all Jugoslavia. Belgrade wanted Bulgaria to be
a single republic in the South Slav grouping with no more
authority than any of the individual Jugoslav provincial republics—Serbia, Croatia, Slovenia, Montenegro, Macedonia
or Bosnia and Herzegovina.

In 1947 Tito and Dimitrov, then boss of Communist Bulgaria, signed an agreement at Bled. This approved federation aimed eventually at also absorbing Greek Macedonia
and Salonika. But Jugoslavia broke with the Cominform.
Dimitrov died. General Markos, the Greek Communist rebel,
was purged by Moscow and eventually his insurrection
collapsed.

Now that the Bulgars are dutifully making peace with Tito,
their thoughts turn naturally to Macedonia and the moribund
Bled agreement. The Jugoslavs, who have learned many lessons during the last nine years, argue that friendly relations
are a fine thing—but on a brand-new basis, not embarrassing
forgotten accords.

Nevertheless, Sofia's Foreign Ministry contends the Tito-
Dimitrov pact should not be considered dead. What Moscow
thinks is impossible to say. Skeptics suggest the Kremlin is using

the Macedonian cards as a potential trump in the game with Tito—to counter Belgrade's pretended neutrality between big-power blocs. Chervenkov was certainly sacrificed to win Jugoslavia's favor.

There is a nationalist section in Bulgaria's Communist party which admires Tito for what he has been able to get away with in the Marxist world. And the large if silent popular opposition might be ready to buy Titoism and a Jugoslav passport to escape from the status of Soviet satellite that still is Bulgaria's role.

There are thoughtful people in Southeast Europe who believe that ancient Macedonia may figure in Moscow's new Balkan strategy. The curiously intricate argument proceeds accordingly:

Now that they have been given official permission to think, some Communists evolve an original explanation of the Soviet drive against the "cult of the individual." They conjecture it is aimed less at dead Stalin than at living Mao Tsetung and Tito. And they speculate that no single Russian today has the personal renown of either the Chinese or Jugoslav leader. The U.S.S.R. must perforce be guided collectively because there is no outstanding man. But Mao, as an individual, is a massive figure in all Asia. And Tito, as an individual, is a symbol of independence throughout communized East Europe.

It would be convenient to the Russians if these demigods could be cut down to size. Mao's China rivals Soviet prestige in the Orient. Likewise, the greatest force working against

161

Russian control of the European satellites is Titoism. Is the Kremlin seeking to oppose these currents by deflating their personalized symbols? There is similarity is phraseology between some of today's Soviet attacks on Stalin and yesterday's diatribes against Tito.

This is fascinating conjecture. Nevertheless it seems unlikely that Moscow's new policy could be inspired by so risky or diabolical a gamble. There is, indeed, ample evidence the Kremlin is continuing to placate Tito, not undermine him.

The question is therefore posed: Does the Kremlin again contemplate offering him Bulgaria; to try and lure him from his independent fortress with promises of South Slavic empire? Is Moscow afraid that if it fails to restore its former influence in Jugoslavia, Titoism might eventually dissolve the Soviet bloc now that the appearances of strict Stalinist controls are slowly vanishing and independent thought is uneasily encouraged?

This may sound like a startling idea but it is certainly not new. Czarist policy promoted union of the Balkan Slavs under Russian hegemony although without success. Stalin toyed with the project. Tito himself was highly interested until his relations with the U.S.S.R. cooled off.

In fact, during 1947, the scheme was almost realized. General Markos, who favored it, was leading the Greek Communist rebellion. Part of the price he was believed ready to pay Jugoslavia for aid was, in the event of victory, cession of Greek Macedonia and Salonika. There is a Slavophone minority in northern Greece.

At the same time Dimitrov supported the plan. In August, 1947, he journeyed to Bled, Jugoslavia, accompanied by Jugov, who succeeded Chervenkov as Bulgarian Prime Minister.

As related earlier, Tito and Dimitrov secretly agreed to federate their countries and eventually to incorporate Greek Macedonia. Bulgaria was to come into Jugoslavia as a seventh People's Republic on a parity with the other six states. This was reported back to Stalin. He vetoed it by withholding approval unless there was equal condominium between Belgrade and Sofia. Stalin knew Tito would not accept.

There the matter rested until the end of the year, when it was clear Tito was becoming too independent minded to suit Moscow. Suddenly, after the Russians had already withdrawn their technical missions from Jugoslavia as a warning, Stalin invited Tito and Dimitrov to visit him. Tito, suspicious, sent a mission headed by Kardelj.

Stalin was irked by Tito's failure to come. Nevertheless he told Kardelj and Dimitrov he had changed his mind; Bulgaria and Jugoslavia could go ahead and federate on any basis; he accepted the Tito plan. Furthermore he demanded federation immediately. Meanwhile, Kardelj discovered from indiscreet Bulgarians that Dimitrov had actually brought along a tentative list of cabinet members for the proposed unified state. Among posts claimed for Bulgarians were the Ministries of Interior and Economics.

This was a tip-off. Tito, an expert in the business, knew the Interior Ministry, with its secret police, was the Trojan horse

163

in any Stalinist program to absorb a country. His relations with Moscow were already on the verge of a total break. He had no desire to be devoured from within. The project lapsed and soon his war with the Cominform began.

Dimitrov died. He was succeeded by Chervenkov, who detested federation. Markos disappeared and is probably dead. Tito is now allied with Greece. While again friendly with the Soviet bloc, he insists this friendship must be founded on new bases. But do the Russians think the same?

When I asked Jugoslav and Bulgarian leaders whether the Bled accord was buried, the Jugoslavs said yes, the Bulgarians said no. They indicated a desire to revive it. Furthermore, Chervenkov, the opponent, was ousted and replaced by Jugov, the proponent. Finally, a new agricultural drive began in Bulgaria to totally collectivize the land. About four-fifths of this was swiftly brought into the "socialized sector" as compared with only 17 per cent in Jugoslavia.

What does all this add up to? Does Moscow think it can bribe Tito back into its bloc by giving him suzerainty over Bulgaria? It is unlikely Jugoslavia would relinquish its freedom of action to realize this territorial dream. But is the Kremlin clever enough to revive the scheme without any visible conditions?

Were this to occur it would kill the faltering Balkan alliance of Jugoslavia, Greece and Turkey. Military clauses of that pact are aimed only at Bulgaria. Athens would suspect a new Slavic revisionist drive. Italy would be nervous. Tito's relations with the West would cool. He would be forced by

164

isolation to rely increasingly on the U.S.S.R.

Secondly, the highly collectivized Bulgarians would come into Jugoslavia as a Stalinized bloc of over seven million operating under a substantially different economic and political system from Titoism. They would be in position to assume control as a co-ordinated fifth column much as Stalin had once planned to grab power through a Bulgarian-managed secret police. The goal would be the same.

Russian-sponsored South Slav unity is an old idea, but nobody can prove this is the policy now planned by Moscow. The only circumstantial evidence is Jugov's rise and Bulgarian willingness to revivify the Bled accord. If the Russians attempt such a devious maneuver, one may hope Belgrade will not fall into the trap. Tito saw the catch as long ago as 1947. He should see it as clearly now.

165

V

Tito and the Hajduks

JUGOSLAVIA is the one piece of Russia's postwar European empire which fought itself clear of Soviet domination. It is not likely that this curiously vital if chaotic country will ever again willingly submit itself to foreign controls. This is true despite ideological similarities and racial kinship. Tito reestablished his independence the hardest way. He defied military threats, expert subversion and economic blockade. Eventually he succeeded in extorting from Moscow the most sweeping political apology in modern history.

The Kremlin is again seeking to seduce him with offers of Balkan domination and a place in the Marxist Valhalla. But while Tito lives, certainly, and afterward, probably, it won't regain ascendancy. He wishes friendship, even ideological kinship with Moscow; but not subservience. Tito is no fool. He should know his South Slav history. When the Ottoman Turks captured Stjepan Tomasevic, last King of Bosnia, for a second time and executed him in 1463 at Jajce (Tito's first Partisan capital) they grimly announced: "Only an idiot gets bitten twice by a snake from the same hole."

166

Jugoslavia is a strange racial and religious conglomeration, yet it is dominated by the Serbs, a fearless, poetic, lazy, audacious people. Throughout four centuries of Turkish rule their brigand leaders, the *hajduks*, never relinquished their forest domains. The last *hajduk*, a romantic Robin Hood named Pavle Dokic, died only in 1938. When I first visited the country, five hundred royal gendarmes, commanded by a general, were tracking him down in wooded mountains near the Bulgarian border. He composed a valedictory letter, saying: "Dear Sirs. I have to shoot to the last shot at the militia bands and leave three bullets for myself. For I see that their eyes are bloodshot against me." A few days later he raped a young shepherdess who mutilated him with his own knife. Dokic committed suicide. Beside his body was found a carefully composed diary boasting :

In Heaven there is one God and one Pavle Dokic on earth. Only these two remain powerful. The world will remember the last *hajduk*. I will have a step like a youth. And I will travel like a hero. And will feed like a wolf. I will be like God in Heaven; for now we remain, only us two, He in Heaven and I on earth. As we *hajduks* say, so must it be; and there will always be us *hajduks*. For the forest without *hajduks* cannot be as Heaven without God. Here I have arrived this lovely summer to freedom in the open spaces, to hear what I have most loved on earth, that players play for me a parade march and the Turkish *rastanak* and the *Gjurdjevski kolo* and *Tamo Daleko*. Sadness for others I have lived through. I have lived that the whole people know me. On all sides is my portrait.

The entire bloody and fiercely independent Southern Slav tradition is dominated by ferocious anarchism. Even today a

167

hero of the Serbs is the folk-song prince, Kraljevic Marko, who fought fifteenth-century sultans, Hungarian feudal lords and anyone else at hand, sharing his adventures with a bibulous piebald stallion named Sharac with whom he carefully divided his red wine.

The insouciant durability of the Serbs and their brothers, the highland Montenegrins, has always transcended their executive talent or political logic. Yet it served to keep alive a spirit of unyielding independence despite frequently overpowering odds. Before World War I, an Austrian soldier in Bosnia, then a province of the Hapsburgs, asked the Montenegrin sentry facing him:

"How dare you fight us, such a tiny insignificant people as you are?" The calm reply: "Oh, we are not so small. We and the Russians number over 150,000,000." This mixture of impossible conceit and confidence in Slavdom remains a vital force today; but the pan-Slavism is a theoretical concept, an emotional mystic force. At no time has it obscured the astonishing regional nationalism of the South Slavs.

Their contempt for suffering and death has nothing to do with individual political leanings. In 1932 a Communist underground leader named Petka Militic was arrested and daily tortured by the King's police. He used to tease his tormentors, yelling: "Come on, torture me. I'll know how to torture you when we come to power." When Drazha Mihajlovic, redoubtable leader of the *Cetniks* and Tito's main opponent, was captured, he accepted his death sentence calmly, head held high, remarking only: "The whirlwind, the

168

world whirlwind, carried me away."

In November, 1950, I visited Archbishop (now Cardinal) Stepinac in the oppressive Lepoglava concentration camp where Tito himself had been imprisoned by the monarchy. In his little cell, coolly regarding the jack-booted guards beside me, he observed. "Whether I go to a monastery, or whether I remain here, or whatever should happen to me, I am utterly indifferent. Such things do not depend upon Marshal Tito. They depend only upon the Holy Father, the Pope, and upon no one else. I am content to suffer for the Catholic Church." Afterward a Communist guard, who hated the priest, begrudgingly confided: "That is a brave man, a Jugoslav."

When Tito's Communist party seized power after World War II it was not foisted upon the country by a conquering Soviet army as in other countries of East Europe. It had its own military record, based on considerable popular support and efficiently led by a small, hard-bitten group of leaders. Seventy-nine per cent of the delegates to the Fifth (1949) Party Congress had served in prison under the old regime. When the Jugoslav party had only four thousand members, it managed to send twelve hundred as volunteers in the Spanish Loyalists' international brigades. Only six hundred survived. Tito, incidentally, organized their transportation from hideouts inside France.

Jugoslav Communism's contacts with Moscow were always minimal. When the organization was declared illegal and driven underground in 1920 its center of activities did not shift back to Moscow but to Vienna, Paris, Zurich, Dresden.

169

Unlike other Eastern European parties, few of its leaders were trained in the U.S.S.R. Only 17 of the 2,344 delegates to the Fifth Congress ever belonged to the Soviet Communist apparatus.

PRAGMATIC COMMUNISM

Tito, a Croat peasant who was drafted into the Austro-Hungarian army during the First War, took charge of Jugoslavia's Marxist conspiracy in 1937 after Stalin had purged its leadership. His real name is Josip Broz and he comes from a small village near Zagreb. He was wounded and captured by Czarist troops, learned the rudiments of Marxism in a Russian prisoner-of-war camp, married a Russian woman (his first wife, by whom he had one braggadocio son) and spent a certain amount of time fighting against counter-revolutionary troops in what is now Soviet Asia. For a time he held a minor job in Moscow with the old Comintern.

From 1939 until, as a Partisan chief he visited the Kremlin in 1944, he remained in Jugoslavia. After using many conspiratorial aliases he settled upon his present cognomen, a frequent Croatian nickname. Tito also had a habit of telling comrades: "You, do this; and you, this [in Serbo-Croatian, *ti, to; ti, to*]." When the Jugoslavs precipitated themselves into the war by their spectacular Serbian nationalist uprising in March, 1941 (which British intelligence helped to sponsor), Tito lay low until Hitler attacked Stalin. Later, during that summer he began his resistance movement, which developed into the outstanding guerrilla campaign of European history.

170

The origins of Titoism are different both in traditions and organization from other Continental Communist parties. It never depended totally on Moscow for subsistence. It was able to benefit from geography—Adriatic contact with the West—and the highly martial spirit of the Jugoslavs. It is by no means as intellectual an organization as are some of Europe's other Marxist movements. As a result, it is by heritage less dogmatic, less stilted, more pragmatic and original. These factors influenced its political development.

I have conversed with Tito many times since the latter part of the war. Traces of heresy were evident quite early. In 1946, before the Cominform row, he told me: "We will never collectivize; our farmers have a co-operative system." Later he abandoned this original conception; but only temporarily. In 1949, in the middle of the Cold War when Jugoslavia itself was threatened by Soviet troop maneuvers, Tito refused to believe in the possibility of violence. He confidently predicted: "I do not for a moment suppose that any nation would desire the recurrence of such an international conflict as that which ended recently or for that matter one which would be even worse. I make this statement despite the various differences which prevail in the world and despite the war-mongering which goes on in certain countries. Despite these facts I maintain there will be no war. I do not talk like this because we fear a war. These are the realities of the situation. I base my statements upon reality to which one must never close one's eyes." In 1950 Tito admitted the Marshall Plan (a capitalist venture) had been of "great help" to many European countries. He claimed he was not seeking to invent a new ideology but: "We merely stand firm upon the precepts of Marx and Lenin and against a revision of them. Ours is a struggle for the correct implementation of these theories applied to the conditions prevailing in this country." (This, in 1955 and 1956, became the official line of post-Stalin Russia and the entire satellite bloc).

Tito insisted that Jugoslavia would never allow ideological differences to interfere with national defense requirements and "If it is a question of our own security, we'll buy materials wherever we can." In 1952 he already observed (four years in advance) that the Cominform was "gradually being liquidated." He was confident there would "be no changes in American foreign policy" as a result of the Republican electoral victory and "I know Eisenhower will work for peace." In 1954, after two party stalwarts, Milovan Djilas and Vladimir Dedijer, were disciplined by the Communist organization, Tito boasted to me: "In other Eastern countries Djilas and Dedijer wouldn't have lived twenty-four hours. We have an entirely different attitude from other Eastern lands."

In 1955 Tito assured King Paul of Greece (after Khrushchev and Bulganin had made their famous visit of apology): "We will never go back to the Soviet bloc; once was enough. We will never associate with any bloc that does not include *both* the United States and the Soviet Union. I will not support any security organization in Europe that seeks to eliminate or ostracize the United States." The king told me Tito confided to him that he had "always" detested Stalin; that he regarded Molotov as an unregenerate Stalinist; but that

Khrushchev was not; that Khrushchev had almost been purged by Stalin as a Ukrainian separatist; that Mikoyan was also "highly intelligent and not, like Molotov, a mere Stalinist puppet." Although a Communist and now on excellent terms with Moscow, Tito undertook on behalf of Secretary Dulles to explore chances of Middle Eastern peace with Colonel Nasser—although he refused to accept the position of mediator.

From this brief recapitulation it is indicated that Jugoslavia's President has at no time since the war been dogmatically rigid. Realism and opportunism rather than doctrinal formulas have guided his Marxism. During his most pro-Russian and his most anti-Russian days a strain of commonsense pragmatism runs through his conversations. Tito calmly assumed his political and ideological course was sensible; therefore it was up to the rest of the Communist world to change. When it changed he made up—but without renouncing any freedom of action. In 1949, Jean Payart, at that time French Ambassador in Belgrade, shrewdly reported to the Quai d'Orsay that the Jugoslavs "believe they have enriched Communist doctrine" and intended to evangelize the U.S.S.R. and convert it from *its* heresy, an astonishingly cocky view if one remembers the Cominform war.

Tito is himself not a Serb. In appearance he resembles the typical Croatian Middle European, speaks German and is both more practical and less imaginative that the dominant Jugoslav race. But he seems by osmosis to have absorbed some of the audacious, egomaniac qualities of the extraordinary

173

Serbs. And, although the predominantly anti-Communistic people of Jugoslavia have affection for *no* central Belgrade government, which inhibits their anarchic individualism, and particularly for no ideological experiment based upon state controls and discipline, they shared with Tito a vast pride when Khrushchev and Bulganin came to Belgrade in the spring of 1955 to apologize for Stalin's wrongs.

On May 29 of that year Tito gave the Russians a reception in Beli Dvor, the White Palace of the Karageorgevic kings. On the whole this was a remarkable performance. It was a rainy evening and the pink blossoms of chestnut trees lining the long entrance driveway were pelted onto the road. Cars were stacked up in a traffic jam such as Belgrade never sees, while guards checked the invitations of their occupants.

Beli Dvor is a rather simple palace, square, not very large, and filled with comfortable modern imitation French and Italian furniture, undistinguished carpets and quite a few paintings (the worst ones) left over from the tenancy of the last royal regent, Prince Paul. Assembled diplomats, political leaders, generals and admirals of Jugoslavia massed in a couple of fairly small reception rooms and then the stars of the occasion arrived, walked in and stood at attention while an unnecessarily loud band boomed out the Jugoslav and Soviet anthems. In front came Khrushchev and Mrs. Broz. Khrushchev, in an incredibly badly cut Soviet sack suit that looked as if it hadn't even been pressed, stood like a little gypsy dancing bear, staring dully ahead with his jaw hanging slack and his belly falling down beneath the four buttons of his jacket. A

174

single decoration dangled incongruously from his lapel. Tito's second wife, in a white evening gown, towered over him, a handsome large woman with gleaming black eyes and short black hair, regular features and white teeth. Behind them stood Bulganin, in gray uniform, with somewhat bleary but kind blue eyes, smiling behind his beard and looking for all the world like the bandmaster in a small German spa. Beside him was Tito, sunburned, stocky, in a dandy's uniform, with a faint grin upon his face.

After the anthems, the party pushed through to an inner room, once a library for Prince Paul, where they dined in privacy. The rest of the guests ate a buffet from heavily laden tables in two salons. There was shrimp salad, lobster, turkey, pork, roast beef, chicken, strawberries, cakes, salads, salami, all spread about helter-skelter. Waiters tried with little success to pass glasses of slivovica, (believe it or not) white lady cocktails, vermouth, beer, white wine, red wine. The Jugoslavs looked, on the whole, infinitely more impressive than their visitors. One would have thought that the great military power was represented by the handsome marshal and his tall, well-groomed generals and admirals rather than the stubby little dictator and his guardians.

Vladimir Popovic, a former Partisan general, former student at Moscow's Frunze military academy, former Ambassador to Moscow and Washington and newly named envoy to Peiping, a towering, handsome man, remarked with ill-concealed arrogance: "I suppose this is the first time Khrushchev has ever been about among the people." Certainly, he

175

observed, it was the first time he had ever been submitted to the badgering of photographers as was permitted here; or that he had ridden through the streets in an open car. (The latter habit has since been enthusiastically adopted by the Soviet bosses.)

This long and dreary evening, during which the newly made-up friends ate heavily and drank still more among the leather-bound volumes of the last Karageorgevic bibliophiles, was the great fete of the twentieth century's Canossa. While embarrassed Soviet secret policemen in ridiculous suits watched the door that locked their masters in, the dolled-up spectators shifted from one flat foot to the other, perspiringly absorbed gallons of vodka, whisky and slivovica, and stared at a remote corner where, at two little tables, sat a coterie of bearded Orthodox priests in rimless stove-pipe hats and be-fezzed Moslem hodjas. When, after midnight, the performance ended, the dignitaries of this great reconciliation tottered out behind a hefty Soviet general and an immense Jugoslav: Khrushchev, clearly boiled in slivovica, the potent Serbian plum brandy; Bulganin, red-eyed and red-faced; and Tito, seemingly peering through a slight mist. When Khrushchev's gallant instincts got the better of him and he sought to embrace the ladies in clumsy Russian fashion, two of his plain-clothes agents hefted him up by the elbows, pushed him into a large, armored limousine, slammed the door and sent him home.

Such was the occasion that honored Tito's victory. It celebrated the triumph of his heresy over the Mother Church. After their extraordinary Belgrade talks, Khrushchev and

176

Bulganin began increasingly to acknowledge that Jugoslavia, after all, had chosen the True Course and that the entire, massive Soviet bloc had erred. But what is Titoism?

The Jugoslavs in a sense are the Anglicans of the Communist world. They split from Soviet Marxism for essentially practical reasons. They still maintain the orthodoxy of their tenets. But, like the Church of England, they have modified doctrine to suit their own needs. There is, of course, in this parallel one transcendently important difference: Rome never apologized to Canterbury the way Moscow did to Belgrade.

While for years Soviet Communism has tended to be dogmatic, the Jugoslav revolution was pragmatic from the start.

At the end of the war Tito was a real force backed by a tangible army—unlike the puppets installed elsewhere by the Kremlin. He was able to negotiate with foreign powers on an independent basis. This background made it far easier for him to break with the U.S.S.R. when he felt like it—and to maintain an independent course vis-à-vis the West even when squabbling with the entire Soviet bloc.

When Tito took over the wreckage of postwar Jugoslavia he established a Communist dictatorship with an all-pervasive secret police. This has eased considerably. His Government, however, remains authoritarian. It is certainly not widely popular. But then no prewar Jugoslav Government was widely popular among the mixed Southern Slavs: Serbs, Croats, Slovenes, Macedonians, etc. And its *authority* does keep the lid on a pot of incipient terror which still simmers beneath the surface.

177

During the war all the religious and racial hatreds of the Orthodox, Catholic and Moslem population exploded into bloodshed. Considerably more than one million Jugoslavs killed each other during the occupation. Many Orthodox Serbs who dislike Tito criticize him for not having executed Stepinac. Catholics blame him for ever having arrested the prelate. The scars of fratricide have by no means healed.

The visitor to Jugoslavia, coming from the Soviet orbit, is struck by visible differences in the mode of Communist life. For example, take what Moscow calls "the cult of the individual." Right after the war Tito was played up as heavily as Stalin ever was in Russia: placards, slogans, organized cheering squads. That faded somewhat after the break with the Cominform.

There are still towns and streets named for Tito (although those called after lieutenants such as Rankovic and Kardelj have reverted to their original titles). But, unlike in the satellites, there are no exhortatory Red placards on public buildings, no slogans and picture posters. The reverence for Tito as top man and main war hero is part way between our own public respect for Eisenhower and the Soviet system of iconography —leaning toward the latter.

The press is in no sense free by our standards; neither is it the stultified Soviet version. *Politika*, Belgrade's principal paper, often implies a good deal of criticism by subtlety—as it used to do before the war under another dictatorship. There are even two press agencies, one of which is called "semi-official"; but it at least competes. Books, magazines and newspapers are exchanged with the outside world. American plays and movies draw big crowds.

Although Jugoslavia is still a police state, one does not have that uneasy compulsion to look over one's shoulder as in the satellites. By contrast with Sofia and Budapest one doesn't see Belgrade gendarmes strolling the avenue with Tommy guns on back. Certain telephones are tapped. But one finds no evidence of people being followed. Even some Jugoslavs hostile to the regime are granted passports for travel abroad.

Within the Soviet block the fate of the ideological dissenter has been grim. Most were executed out of hand. A few, like Rumania's Pauker, were put on the shelf. The rest were imprisoned—only now to be allowed to trickle out as political winds change. In Jugoslavia there were sharp attacks on the political heretics Djilas and Dedijer. But their physical freedom was never restricted.

Foreigners in Belgrade have none of that feeling of isolation prevailing behind the Iron Curtain. Jugoslavs—both pro- and anti-regime—tend to mix more freely, to talk with visitors, invite them to their homes. Life, in its usual social sense, is far more normal as we understand that word.

Once it was firmly established after the war, Tito's revolution began to apply orthodox Communist theory as sanctified by Moscow. Factories were nationalized. Private business was backed against the wall. Farming was rapidly and forcibly collectivized. Masses of people were jailed and all murmurs of opposition extinguished. Stalinism, or what the Russians

179

now call the cult of the individual, was the mode.

This began to alter in 1948 when Jugoslavia, refusing to become a Soviet colony, rebelled and was ousted from the Cominform. The Titoist leaders began to look about and explore the outside world. As a result they gradually modified their ideology. Therefore, today, as Moscow proceeds not only to make up its quarrel with Belgrade but to adopt some of Tito's ideas, it finds his ideology considerably different from that of the U.S.S.R. It is impossible to foresee whether eventually the ideological gap will be closed as successfully as has the political gap.

In the field of agriculture the comparison is striking. Virtually, 100 per cent of the land in the U.S.S.R. is socialized (except for miniature family plots). In the East European satellites the trend is persistently toward greater collectivization. In the instance of Bulgaria the figure has probably now exceeded 80 per cent of all acreage. But in Jugoslavia only 17 per cent of arable land is in what is called the "socialized sector." This includes not only collective farms but various forms of co-operatives. For example, peasants, retaining ownership of their land, raise bees or sheep together. Such enterprises are deemed "Socialist."

In 1950, 25 per cent of Jugoslavia's land was socialized; therefore, there has been a *drop* of more than a third in collectivization. If one includes loose co-operatives, it is possible that there is little more "socialized" land today than in prewar Jugoslavia, where there were numerous state farms and voluntary associations called *zadrugas*.

Tito, once he made his break with Moscow, decided to abandon forced collectivization. Inducements are now offered to peasants to join collectives or co-operatives. But anyone who wants to quit such enterprises can, at present, after three years' participation. Will this Communist anomaly be permitted to continue?

Currently Titoism rules out the element of compulsion. One of its principal ideologists, a huge Montenegrin named Veljko Vlahovic, who looks like an immense Alexandre Dumas, explains the prevailing theory accordingly: "Our concept is that you cannot socialize agriculture by force. We allow our peasants to leave co-operatives if they desire. The small landowner can remain a private landowner. Of course we are moving toward socialization of the peasants. But this is voluntary socialization."

A second major difference between Titoism and Soviet Communism is in industrial production. Vlahovic contends: "The U.S.S.R. is highly centralized. But our industry is based on local workers' councils. A council can not only change the directors of its particular factory; it can modify its production program."

What this means in theory is that the workers' council of an enterprise fixes its own output goals. They are not set by the state as in Russia. Furthermore, the council can decide how profits are shared. An interesting example of this occurred in a Serbian factory. The council decided to stimulate productivity and reduce prices by cutting down on inefficiency. It put 60 per cent of any future profits into a bonus fund to be

181

shared out. The remaining 40 per cent was for reinvestment and managerial purposes. The result was vastly improved efficiency. Workers took greater interest. Profits jumped. Production costs fell. So many bonuses were distributed that the plant administration is now embarrassed.

Leading members of the regime, citing this example, admit that Titoism is trying to evolve a theory that seeks to combine incentives of private-enterprise capitalism with state-owner-ship features of traditional Socialism. It is an interesting experiment—enticing the Communist donkey with a capitalistic carrot. Will it continue now that Moscow is again an admired friend?

The kernel of Titoism's economic philosophy at present differs in major degree from that of the Soviet Union. But it still is only a kernel. The Jugoslav revolution has been evolving very rapidly since the war—and since the break with the Cominform. Its program has zigzagged and its application varies greatly in different regions and different enterprises. Will it persevere along its current individualistic and pragmatic course? Or will it tend again toward Communist orthodoxy, now that the political break with Russia has been healed? The answer, at least initially, seems to be that the U.S.S.R. is moving ideologically toward Tito, not vice versa. And, implicit in this trend is acknowledgment of Jugoslavia's political independence.

Even after reconciliation, differences remain between the philosophy evolved, during the years of schism, by Tito and the Communism preached within the U.S.S.R. Jugoslav ideology is not yet either mature or crystallized. But the intensity of its search for pragmatic applications of Marxism during the period of isolation from Moscow produced practices that have, in effect, considerably modified dogma. One of the philosophers of the new credo is Vlahovic, who once represented the Jugoslav Communist party on the Comintern in Moscow. On the basis of his experience both with traditional and Titoist Marxism he says:

"Perhaps the greatest contrast between our own and Soviet Socialism is in the role of the citizen. We try to base state authority upon the individual. There is discussion at the lowest level in our workers' councils, and ideas produced there, at the bottom of the pyramid, funnel upward. In Russia everything is directed downward from the top."

The Jugoslav leadership sees dissimilarity between its own system of political elections and that of the U.S.S.R. even though in both countries there is only a single electoral ticket. It is contended that Soviet Communism selects candidates and imposes them upon the voters. In theory, at any rate, there can be active primary contests for nominations in Jugoslavia.

Anyone who obtains two hundred signatures from supporters can stand as a write-in candidate. Belgrade pretends that voters in any constituency can ignore party favorites. Jugoslavs argue this produces a system somewhat similar to primary contests in our own Southern states; the nomination is all-important even though the actual election afterward is a foregone conclusion.

Any resemblance between Jugoslav politics and what is

183

clearly a particularized feature of our own two-party system can be detected only in theory. Nothing approaching the very real primary battles in the South has yet been seen in Titoist Jugoslavia. Most people would have trouble distinguishing practical dissimilarities in choosing parliaments for Belgrade or Moscow.

However, differences between Jugoslav and Soviet philosophy are considerable. Titoism argues the world is gradually moving toward one single economy, not two systems clearly divided into Socialism and capitalism. As Vlahovic says. "That is artificial. The world has become an indivisible entity even though various roads of progress exist. But the Russians still seem to insist there are two essentially different systems. In this concept there was only *slight* change detectable at the Twentieth Moscow Party Congress."

For seven years a Cominform boycott drove the Jugoslavs to collaborate in many ways with the West. Therefore they have adjusted their ideological outlook. While remaining Communist, they believe many of the objectives they seek are the same as in capitalist lands. For example, Vlahovic says:

"Here we are trying to eliminate bureaucracy. You in America are doing the same thing. You search for efficient management, a managerial revolution. Likewise in West Germany there is a hunt for the same goals through joint worker-management associations."

No doubt the Jugoslavs benefited by being projected into the outside, non-Communist world. Now, they think they are ahead of the Russians in interpreting that world. Vlahovic

184

explains: "We long since discarded classic distinctions between revolutionary and evolutionary Socialism. These have been erased by history. Atomic and electronic developments are altering economic structures. Even in the United States there is a tendency toward Socialism. State intervention in the economy is growing as classic capitalism disappears.

"We not only scrapped Stalinism. We have advanced beyond classical Leninism. Marx and Lenin could not foresee the future. We use their method of analysis. But we are not rigidly bound by their planning. We regard Marx and Lenin as thinkers. But the Russians have tended to view them as deities."

It is extremely difficult to separate what one wishes to see in Titoism from what it wants to see in itself—and to distinguish either category from fact. Since its birth as a pragmatic ideology it has been in a constant state of flux. And there have been frequent variations between theory and practice.

Tito always maintained he was a faithful Communist even when Moscow was calling him capitalism's tool. Yet no doubt three years ago he was politically nearer to the West than to the Soviet Union. Now the reverse is true. As veteran Marxists, Jugoslavia's leaders are pleased to be admired by other Communists. And as Slavs they feel more comfortable on friendly terms with their racial cousins.

Nevertheless, Belgrade has not openly rejoined the Soviet orbit. Instead Khrushchev seems to be practicing our own domestic political adage: "If you can't lick 'em, jine 'em."

185

The big question yet to be resolved is this: Will Moscow's massive diplomatic system in the end engorge Tito; or will he succeed in unfreezing the Soviet icepack?

At this juncture Titoism is less rigidly Communistic than anything else in Eastern Europe. Its workers' councils bear primitive resemblance to stockholders' committees in capitalistic enterprises owned by employees. There is not a great deal more socialization of agriculture than prevailed before the revolution. Jugoslavia's fiscal system is not tied to the ruble bloc; therefore prices are relatively realistic.

The people have benefited from the middle course which enabled Jugoslavia to receive nourishing American aid. In Croatia they joke about a peasant who says his Pater Noster before four ikons—Stalin, Eisenhower, Lollobrigida and Tito. To the first he prays: "Our Father which art in Heaven." To the second: "Give us this day our daily bread." To the third: "Lead us not into temptation." And to the fourth: "Thine is the power and the glory."

Trying to find a way between Muscovite dogma and Western democracy, Titoism watered its Marxist wine. Or rather, as its author learned to do when he visited King Paul of Greece, it mixes claret with champagne. Jugoslav intellectuals traveling in the West have been impressed by techniques and living standards. This led to an ebbing of ideological zeal. Tito is now worried about the tendency to relax. He complains: "Too little attention is being paid to the further ideological building up of cadres. We must have an ideological and organizationally monolithic Communist union. Various ideas and in-

186

fluences which are foreign to us [and by this he means of Western origin] have started to be felt."

Tito insists he wishes only to pursue an actively neutral, independent role free from attachment to either great power bloc. To succeed in this course he must maintain Jugoslavia's political, economic and ideological defenses. And all of these, in a sense, have been obscured since Moscow discarded Stalinism.

Jugoslavia's ideologists wish to tighten their party apparatus. But they continue to preach features heretical to Moscow. Says Edvard Kardelj, the chief philosopher: "Self-administration of the producer is the starting point. The quality of production and low prices are of decisive importance. A well-framed wage system certainly stimulates the struggle for greater labor productivity."

Such emphasis on competition and incentive represents a barrier between Titoism and its orthodox matrix. By the extent of its application we will be able to gauge the validity of Tito's ideological independence.

It is important for us to judge Titoism and to assay its future accurately. For without American aid it is unlikely that it would have managed to survive its fight with Stalin. Thus Titoism today is in some measure the consequence of our foreign policy.

HERESY BREEDS HERETICS

But, inside Jugoslavia, there is an interesting parallel development within the ranks of Titoism's own adherents, and this,

187

likewise, is a consequence of policy. Such was the protest against the Belgrade party leadership of Milovan Djilas and Vladimir Dedijer, two fanatical Communists who had fought through the savage occupation campaigns of World War II. In an odd way their relationship toward Titoism is algebraically comparable to Titoism's relationship to the orthodoxy of Moscow.

The Djilas-Dedijer protest against Jugoslavia's leadership is entirely without precedent in the Communist world. Both Partisan heroes and Marxists, they have challenged the very meaning of the prevailing ideology. They are rebelling against Titoism in precisely the way Tito rebelled against Stalinism. But—and this is remarkable—they remained free despite the fact that they violated the monolithic law.

No purge in the usual meaning of the word resulted from their little heresy. Tito had one swift clean-up of Moscow sympathizers in 1948 right after the Cominform break. Colonel General Jovanovic, the haughty chief of staff, was shot while trying to flee to Rumania. Hebrang and Zujovic, Politburo members, were arrested. Later Zujovic was freed and has since led an anonymous life. Hebrang, a one-eyed bravo who had been in the employ of the Gestapo and then of the Soviet secret police, strangled himself on the pipes of a prison radiator.

The Djilas-Dedijer faction tends ideologically toward Western democracy. Therefore it represents a split from the Leninist structure of government in Belgrade. But the curiously anarchic spirit of the Serbs infects most Jugoslavs. This carefree and savagely independent outlook enabled Tito to lead the war's most effective guerrilla movement. It allowed him to thumb his nose at the mightiest military bloc in Europe, situated right upon his borders. Likewise it has inspired Djilas and Dedijer to assert schismatic views because, as Djilas said, "one cannot go on without some risk."

The two heretics are an extraordinary pair. Dedijer is a great lump of a man, 225 pounds of bone and muscle. He is still an eager athlete although wounded often and seriously. His mother was for long Communist Jugoslavia's most prominent woman. Between the two world wars she taught at a women's college and as a lad Vladimir was teased as "the boy from the girls' school." This scarcely inhibited him; he became renowned for toughness in a land where this is not easy.

Dedijer joined Communism at eighteen. Before the war Tito used to stay at his house. Later he was a colonel on the Partisan general staff. He was desperately wounded in the spring of 1943, losing a large piece of skull. Despite this he kept up with the retreating army. He had to bury his own wife, killed by a bomb. scraping a grave with his knife. He survived, became official Partisan historian and biographer of Tito. Like Djilas he was among the Marshal's really intimate friends who called him *stari,* the old man.

Djilas is different: a moody, sensitive, poetic Montenegrin. He also adopted Communism as a youngster. He was caught by the royal police, imprisoned, tortured and attempted suicide. Later he acquired renown as a writer. During the Partisan retreat from Montenegro Djilas was left behind in charge of a tiny rearguard. He rejoined the main body days

189

later, displaying a bayonet caked with German blood which he refused to clean. When he met Stalin, the Georgian was fascinated by the young Montenegrin mountaineer.

Toward the end of the war, I first encountered Djilas. Tito introduced me to the dour Partisan. "Ah," said Djilas, "so you are the man who writes that our Tito is slaughtering Serbian peasants with American rifles." He turned his back. Said Tito, patting my shoulder, "Don't pay any attention to him." Later Djilas admitted: "Tito remembers the good as well as the bad. Maybe I just remember the little things." In October, 1946, when Jugoslav-United States relationships were critical after two American planes had been shot down, Djilas announced he would have me hanged as "a friend of Mihajlovic" if I entered the country. He didn't. Long afterwards he said, engagingly: "Things have changed."

Djilas was one of four top Jugoslav leaders including Tito specifically denounced by the Cominform. For some years he was regarded as a likely successor to the Marshal and was certainly one of the most popular Communists. To the Jugoslav hierarchy the schism of Djilas and Dedijer is equivalent, in our terms, to Messrs. Nixon and Brownell joining the New York Liberal party. But such political heresy is criminal in Belgrade.

Tito, while at odds with Moscow, nevertheless insisted he was a better Marxist than Stalin. The new Kremlin team admits as much today. But just as it made amends to Belgrade not only Stalinism but Leninism and Titoism were being repudiated there.

190

Djilas was the intellectual of this heresy. Dedijer's role was was more that of loyal friend than rebel. He refused to join the party's condemnation of Djilas, saying, "I am no robot." Dedijer is neither deeply thoughtful nor original. But even he, as long ago as 1949, began to see certain values in the Western world. That year he inquired in detail how press conferences were conducted in Washington, London and Paris. He wished to initiate similar meetings in Belgrade. Two months later, returning from a United Nations Assembly where he and Djilas were delegates, Dedijer admitted they had been immensely impressed by the United States.

During the next two years Djilas and Dedijer, with the approval of other Jugoslav leaders, were groping their way toward democracy. The convenient steppingstone appeared to be British Socialism. In this connection enemies of Djilas are correct in saying that Aneurin Bevan helped influence him. As early as April, 1951, Djilas spoke openly to me of his friendship for the United States and proclaimed the necessity of a Jugoslav alliance with Greece and Turkey.

On his visit to England Djilas was astonished to find far less "bureaucracy" in British trade unions than in the Jugoslav labor movement. This puzzled and disturbed him. "Bureaucracy" contains a special meaning for Jugoslav Communists. This fault, they hold, tainted Leninism under Stalin and led to Tito's break with the Cominform.

The result of Djilas' deliberations was a series of articles in the official organ of Jugoslav Communism, *Borba,* during late 1953 and early 1954. At first they excited only mild in-

191

terest. Djilas did not encounter trouble until he criticized the "caste system" and the development of a privileged Communist "aristocracy." This precipitated an uproar and he was expelled from positions of authority. Later he resigned from the party—the unforgivable Communist sin.

Djilas' *Borba* articles evolved the following theory: Jugoslavia's class struggle is over; therefore the enemy is no longer capitalism but party bureaucracy; bureaucrats are blocking progress by preventing free expression; all forms of despotism, whether Stalinist or Leninist, must be abandoned. This of course is as dangerous to Titoist dogma as the latter was vis-à-vis Stalinism. Djilas reasoned that Communism would come about spontaneously, not by being imposed, because it "is not the product of geniuses or of noble wishes and purposes but of social necessity." He concluded: "The possibility of two Socialist parties emerging in our country cannot be discounted. . . . The Leninist type of both party and state (dictatorship by means of the party) has become and must become obsolete everywhere and always."

It is astounding that such vigorously unorthodox concepts should have been published in the official newspaper of a Communist party. But in Jugoslavia anything can happen. Djilas observed: "The party is depressed and without an ideology. Its dogma was taken from it through the democratization trend and nothing has replaced it. . . . The name Communism is good but it has been compromised. It is a synonym for totalitarianism in this country as well as in Russia."

One must fully comprehend the profound depths of Com-

192

munist psychology to appreciate what a soul-shattering acknowledgment this was for Djilas, who had worshiped Tito and almost died for Communism. Yet he concluded that the very essence of Titoism is illogical; that there is no middle path between orthodox Communism and democracy. This, uttered with precisely reverse emphasis, is what the Cominform said.

The ideological rebellion of Djilas is more fascinating intellectually than significant politically. Most Jugoslavs remain hostile to Communism. Theirs is the deep-rooted hostility of peasant capitalism plus anarchic tendencies among the South Slavs, who seem to resent order. Djilas and Dedijer have little contact with such mass sentiment although, by advocating creation of a multiparty system, they edged toward it.

Tito was challenged to demonstrate that there is in fact a Communist middle way. Since 1952 he has encouraged "democratic" trends within his party. Evidence of this can be seen in the treatment of Djilas and Dedijer as contrasted with heretics in the Soviet bloc. But the quintessential paradox was posed: In an authoritarian system is it possible to ration out democracy and avoid the consequences of its inherent freedom?

Heresy, as was discovered by the Christian world during the Reformation era, encourages heresy. What happens to the Titoist heretic, the independent Communist who agrees neither with Stalin nor with Khrushchev nor with protestant Tito himself?

Jugoslavia being a Communist country, the administrative apparatus could effectively isolate the rebels. Friends were asked to ostracize them and most did. Pressure was placed

193

upon their families. But, being Jugoslavia, the results were otherwise than within the orbit.

There were none of those ghastly family denunciations that featured Stalinism. The Dedijers, a tight and willful clan, stuck together. It was suggested to Vladimir's mother that she turn against her son. She told the regime to go boil its collective head. Veronica, his lovely second wife—a Partisan in schoolgirl days—remained loyally beside him. The entire family has been fired from the party.

For a long time the rebels had a tough life. But it was a free life—because they made it so and because the state, despite its disapproval, permitted this. They kept few friends. Vlado, as everyone calls him, nodded first to people who used to outrank him in the party if he met them in the street. Afterward he cut those who ignored him—one chance for a man, three for a woman. His telephone was tapped. But his mail arrived unopened. He tested this by writing himself frequent letters under phony signatures. None disappeared.

Dedijer's authorized biography, *Tito Speaks,* was a best seller abroad. He used early royalties to build hospitals honoring his first wife. But the price of rebellion meant a drastic change in the family's living standards. Life was no more that of a party big shot—villa, car, travel. When long-delayed Italian payments on his book arrived in 1956, Vlado told me with relief: "Now we can live throughout this year. I don't think beyond into the future. When you start worrying about what's going to happen tomorrow you're finished."

He always sought to dress neatly on his threadbare budget.

"Not like Djilas," said Dedijer. "When we take walks together he goes around without a necktie and with a suitcase on his back. He's a crazy Montenegrin. I tell him: 'Don't be a beggar when you used to be a lord. One must die like an aristocrat when one is ready to die.' "

Dedijer learned much as a rebel. "I have acquired humility," he told me in 1956, two years after his split. "I was arrogant when I lived the life of an important bureaucrat. I did not even know the price of bread. After my downfall, when I went for the first time to ride in a bus I entered by the wrong door. This has been a marvelous and true lesson for me. I was a stupid lug.

"Now for the first time I have plenty of time to study. It is a good experience. And it is wonderful for my children. I assure you they were little bureaucrats. When Branko was six he used to go to the door and shout: 'Where is the car?' Now they know the value of money. They take part in our family councils to discuss accounts. I am finance minister. And I am more criticized than poor Rab Butler ever was in England. But I haven't yet been fired."

Dedijer learned the Platonic concept that nothing is perfect but can only be sought after. "There is," he admitted, "not yet any real Socialism on this earth. The nearest thing is the *kibbutz* collective farm in Israel. If Israel is attacked I shall volunteer into their army even though I admire Nasser's fight against Egyptian feudalism."

The Titoist heretic, who has now been partially rehabilitated —as a university professor—still considers himself a Commu-

195

nist. He explains: "I didn't learn Marx from textbooks but from practice, from our revolution. Our revolution succeeded only when it abandoned Marxist textbooks. What you take only from dogma is bad; it must be balanced against the good learned through experience. That is Titoism in its essence.

"This philosophy saved me. There are certain basics in ethics and I claim that ethics cannot be destroyed. Every society has its ethics and these are constant in European society. Recently in hospital having my war wounds treated, I went to a local performance of *Hamlet*. After the play five members of the local youth club came up and invited me to a party. They said to me: 'We are Communists. We do not agree with your politics. But you are a man and therefore you are our friend.' That is Europe. And I am a European."

There is something symbolic about this strange political aberration within the ranks of Jugoslav Communism. The very emphasis on permanent ethical values contradicts Leninism. Surely it must remind Tito constantly that the struggle for individual rights is, to humanity, as important a force as was the struggle for national rights which he himself came to represent. And, in Jugoslavia where currents of individuality are so powerful, as long as there exists a Titoism there will also exist an equivalent of Djilasism. The *hajduk* spirit is not dead. And the heresy of individualism is inherently powerful among all Southern Slavs, few of whom are Communist by choice.

VI

The Third Rome—Eastern Empire

W E TEND to think of the U.S.S.R. as a Slavic state. But it also has immense importance in the Turkic, Iranic, Moslem and Middle Eastern worlds. And only in Central Asia and the Transcaucasus has Soviet influence so far failed to advance beyond the limits of old Czarist Russia.

It required centuries before Russian colonization had established itself across the Asiatic plains, on the shores of the Pacific and along the mountain ranges that border India and China. The process is not yet complete. The Kremlin is still shipping thousands of European Slavs to the huge flatland belt between Karaganda and Kolyma, to replace forced-labor gangs being gradually released, to cultivate huge new agricultural projects, and to bulwark with *Russian* racial outposts a frontier shared with Asian nations now commencing to grow powerful.

Moscow is not only populating its eastern reaches with Slavs in the manner customary since the days of Catherine the Great. It is also encouraging the germs of pan-Tartar sentiments among its Asiatic subject peoples. Someday, these may be used the way both Czars and Commissars employed Pan-

197

Slavism in Europe for purposes of territorial expansion. The seeds of nationalism are being fertilized upon the Asian steppe.

When Genghis, the first terrible Mongol Khan, clattered into Tartary he proclaimed: "The greatest joy a man can know is to conquer his enemies and drive them before him. To ride their horses and take away their possessions. To see the faces of those who were dear to them bedewed with tears."

As his cavalry rode to the west, frightened Russians reported: "His army is as numerous as ants and locusts. His warriors are as brave as lions, so that none of the fatigues or hardships of war can injure them. They satisfy hunger with dried meat and sour milk. They open a vein in their horses and drink the blood.

"When the Mongols effect a conquest they leave nothing alive, either large or small, and they even rip up the bellies of women with child. No mountain or river can arrest their progress. They cross every ravine and swim their horses over the rivers, themselves holding on to the mane or tail."

The Mongol-Tartar Khans marched toward Europe beneath horse-tail standards. They were described as hounds: "These hounds have skulls of brass, their teeth are hewn from rock, their tongues are shaped like awls, their hearts are of iron. In place of horsewhips they carry curved swords. They drink the dew and ride upon the wind. In battle they feed on human flesh. Now they are loosened from the chain. Their spittle runs; they are full of joy."

Vassaf, the Slavic chronicler, recounted: "An army of Mongols—filthy as demons, devils for savagery, and numerous as the falling raindrops—rolled in waves across the frozen river with the speed of the wind and of fire. The rattling of their chariots and the clashing of their horses' hoofs were like thunder and lightning. With their wrath in full flame, they advanced."

One by one the tribes trotted out of the Altai and Tien Shan Mountains until the Uzbeks populated Central Asia's flatlands, further from the sea than any other region of the earth. Their poets boasted: "Our country is a good country. The winters in it are like spring. Gardeners watch over its gardens and its trees are rich with fruit."

What has become of these Tartar horsemen? Today Tashkent, a sprawling jerry-built city of a million, is their capital and the largest town of Central Asia. The fierce-appearing wiry little Uzbeks still look like cavalrymen. They strut about in pliant kidskin boots. But over these are rubbers. Their herds have dwindled. Their swords are put away. No longer do they subject others but are themselves subject.

They shuffle through muddy market places hawking tawdry manufactured goods, machine-embroidered caps, gourd snuff containers and powdered green tobacco. A steadily shrinking number of faithful Moslems gather in the handful of remaining mosques. They genuflect to Mecca and the *imam* shrieks with quavering voice: "*Allah akbar* [God is great]." But outside the impassive radio blares livestock information.

An old way of life is gone. Horse herds are vanishing and it is almost impossible to obtain the ancient drink *kumyss* made from fermented mare's milk. Factories and tractor sta-

199

tions are gradually tying the nomads into a new social system. Folk arts have vanished in favor of shabby machine-made goods. Workers of Tashkent's new textile plant still wear boots and tribal skullcaps. But they file into bars and get drunk on beer their previous faith forbade them. Oriental peddlers with faces like Eskimos, like Chinese sages, like Mongol lords and like Persian poets trade pathetic manufactured articles in the open markets of Bukhara. A few timid Kirghiz women still wearing forbidden horsehair veils peep at jet fighters clustered on Samarkand's muddy airstrip.

The new Soviet Central Asia is typified by cocky Uzbek youths with trick modern haircuts (clipped save for a disk-shaped lock) ordering and consuming six beers at a time; by dreary radio loudspeakers blaring cheap music or propaganda in every public place; by jazz ensembles beating out old Western tunes, by Russian conscripts in the Kagan railway station, machine pistols strapped to back, admiring boastful recruiting posters.

Unromantic and authoritarian as these changes are, they have undoubtedly brought to this remote area a higher living standard. An illiterate population has been given tools to learn, even if what its collective mind is fed has rigid Marxist limits. In 1927 the veil for Moslem women was abolished. "We were slaves before," a Tadzhik woman says. "Now we are free." Together with the trappings of independence, antediluvian barbarity in such erstwhile free states as Bukhara was erased. Old cities crumbled but new industrial towns like Stalinabad have been constructed.

The Central Asian peoples are being absorbed into Communism and a Russian-dominated state. There is no natural frontier between their domain and Slavdom. Russianization proceeds rapidly across the Asiatic plain. The Bandung spirit preaching self-determination and free development for peoples of the East is absent. Soviet dynamism pushes ever outward— toward Iran, toward Afghanistan, and ultimately toward India. And it uses all the tools of empire to expand: Russian power, Asiatic nationalism, and the massive propaganda of material revolution.

Stifling Islam

To render Central Asia suitably pliable for Moscow's imperial requirements it was necessary to squash resistant forces. First among these was the Islamic creed.

Deliberate ideological conversion is not a new phenomenon in Asia. As long ago as 1570 a shrewd Chinese statesman named Wan-chun-hu memorialized the Ming Emperor suggesting the Buddhist religion be spread among the menacing Mongolians to the north.

Wan reasoned: "Buddhism forbids bloodshed, prescribes confession, recommends a virtuous life; for this reason we should do our utmost to diffuse that faith among the nomads." His advice was followed. Lamaism gradually became the state religion of Mongolia. Military spirit faded; potential warriors became celibate monks; and, as a result, population declined. Eventually "there was no need to light a watch-fire on the boundaries of China."

201

Moscow is now using Communism to convert the U.S.S.R.'s Central Asian tribes—descendants of the same Mongol horsemen—from traditions of bellicose Islam and a vague Turanian nationalism. By force and by suasion the peoples of what are now Uzbekistan, Kazakhstan, Tadzhikistan, Kirghizstan and Turkmenistan are being molded into new patterns to serve Communist dynamism and Soviet empire.

The region was renowned during centuries for its fanaticism and Koranic learning. Before the revolution Tashkent had dozens of *medressehs* or religious seminaries. Now there are none. Samarkand boasted over one hundred mosques. Today there are said to be seventeen; but a search during prayer hour found but one functioning. Samarkand had twenty-five *medressehs*. One is closed for repairs. The rest are gone.

Not four decades ago Bukhara, almost as remote and famed as Mecca, contained 360 mosques and 103 *medressehs* where young Moslems studied for the priesthood. Today there is but one combined mosque and *medresseh* in that crumbling town.

Koranic texts have been replaced by exhortatory slogans: "If you get drunk you cannot fulfill your norm." Mosques are used for sweet shops, barbering establishments and rooming houses. Below Bukhara's famous Kalan Minaret, from which, since the twelfth century, prisoners were hurled to death, is the Mir Arab *medresseh*—the last in Soviet Central Asia training Islamic priests. There is far more bustle and activity across the street at Agitpunkt No. 7, a Communist propaganda center.

The Kremlin has had to alter both thinking habits and living

202

modes of these nomadic peoples. Marxist materialism is being substituted for the Mohammedan religion. Thousands of mullahs were exterminated and most mosques closed or converted. What is left of Moslem appurtenances remains firmly under state control.

Tribal society has been chopped up and peoples divided among gerrymandered Soviet "republics" to keep them from uniting in common aspirations. Just as the French in Morocco encouraged differences between indigenous Arabs and Berbers, the Russians have developed divergencies in language and customs among Uzbeks, Kazakhs and Tadzhiks. To separate them from Turkish and Iranian kinsfolk across the border they are taught to read and write only in Russia's Cyrillic script.

When Bolshevism assumed control of the former independent emirates of Central Asia it brought with it the Communist's unabashed prejudice against religion. Therefore, although early manifestoes assured Moslems: "Henceforth your faith and customs are proclaimed free and inviolable," the vigor of Islam has been waning ever since.

It is doubtful if anyone can say precisely how many Moslems worship in the U.S.S.R. Cairo's *Economic and Political Review* claims there are 20,660,525. But this is merely a tabulation of the last available census figures for this land's traditionally Moslem minorities. The Acting Mufti of Central Asia estimates 30,000,000. That is gross exaggeration.

The hammer and sickle have superseded the crescent as emblem for the Republics of Uzbekistan, Tadzhikistan, Kazakhstan, Kirghizstan and Turkmenistan, an area larger than

India and Pakistan combined. The red Soviet flag has ousted the green banner of the prophet even though Islam retains a skeletal organization. There are four regional Chief Muftis in the U.S.S.R.—at Tashkent (for Central Asia), at Ufa (for the Siberian Bashkirs), at Baku (for the Caucasus) and at Bujnak (for the North Caucasus). But monthly their parishioners diminish.

The ancient Mufti of the Central Asian tribes, Ishan Babahan Ibn Abdul Mejid Khan, sits in his modest Tashkent house fingering a toothless jaw. Ninety-five years ago, when he was born, this was still part of the emirate of Kokand, an independent principality. The Mufti is too old to help his flock. Now his son, Al-Hafiz Ghazi Zia-ud-Din Babahanoff, officiates over the shrinking Moslem population of the region.

Less than twenty pilgrims from the U.S.S.R. go to Mecca every year, says Babahanoff. "Mecca is hard to get to. The trip is expensive. Mecca is far, far away." Forty years ago there were three hundred mosques in Tashkent. Now there are eighteen. "Some of the younger generation still go to mosque occasionally," says the acting Mufti; "but many not at all." Sadly he consoles himself that this is not only because of atheism's spread. "For," says he, "it is not obligatory to attend the mosque if a man still worships Allah in his heart."

Nodding his white turban, with a gesture of impeccable courtesy, Babahanoff invites the guest to a table laden with withered sweet grapes, sugar crystals, pomegranates, round flat loaves of Uzbek bread, soup from the fat-tailed sheep and pilaff of rice, mutton, raisins and pepper, innumerable bowls of tea.

Between 1927 and 1932, when militant atheism was at its height, Islam's priestly hierachy disintegrated. Simultaneously the traditional Arabic script of the Koranic world was replaced —first by Latin letters as in Turkey, then by Russia's Cyrillic alphabet. Religious texts were impounded. New editions of the Koran ceased.

No longer are there overland pilgrimages to Mecca across Afghanistan or Iran. Only a driblet of holy men, equipped by Moscow with permits and foreign exchange, are allowed to fly to sacred Middle Eastern shrines. The ritual of five daily prayers has all but vanished; laborers in factory or field take no time off. Friday, Islam's Sabbath, is a regular working day.

Dozens of Uzbeks, Tadzhiks, Persians from the old Bukhara emirate and Kirghiz from the steppes were questioned by this writer in 1956 and admitted disbelief or disinterest in Islam. Said one: "I am an atheist. I drink. I don't worship old rituals." Said another: "Now not even my parents attend mosque." And a Tadzhik added: "The young are encouraged to play games or go to theaters—not to mosques."

The month-long fast of Ramadan, each dawn to dusk, is scarcely a memory. Hungry workers cannot fulfill norms. The *zakat,* or fixed alms-giving, has lapsed. And only a tiny fraction of the mullahs who once led prayers now function. Hassim Zadeh, vice-director of Bukhara's lone *medresseh,* says there are 105 students there—all the youth of Central Asia preparing for the Moslem priesthood. Only three Soviet Moslems study religion abroad—at Cairo's Al Azhar Theological Seminary.

Hassim Zadeh is not himself a mullah. And he enunciates a

205

new creed for Islam—that "One can be both a good Moslem and also a party member; we don't divide people by religion; all are brothers." Yet Communism preaches atheism openly and proudly. And Communism, in Central Asia, rules.

It rules with a purpose—to use the area as a springboard for further Soviet expansion. And this role is not historically strange to Central Asia. More than five centuries ago Samarkand, the capital of Tamerlane, was one of the world's great power seats.

It is interesting that Arnold Toynbee should see in Central Asia potentially again a geographical focal point. In this air age, he reasons, a gravitational center may again develop there, equidistant from the principal population poles.

Certainly the peoples of this obscure, often forgotten region retain strong ties with nations and movements far off on the map. The Kazakhs have a poet named Maghjan Jumabay. He writes of his distant Turkish kinsmen in the West: "My brother, far away, my brother, like a tulip broken, is not Altai [Central Asia's mountain massif] our common mother? Have we Turks lost the heart of the lion, become cowards and weary of war? Come, let us go again to the Altai and mount the golden throne of our fathers."

The hill Tadzhiks, separated by only ten craggy miles of Afghanistan from Pakistan and Kashmir, belong to the Ismaili sect that venerates the Aga Khan. Kalmyk herders, Buddhists of the Greater Way, take inspiration from the Tibetan Dalai Lama. The orthodox population of fading Islam owes spiritual allegiance to Mecca. Firdausi, the classic Persian poet from

206

this area, invented the terms "Iran" and "Turan" that later fathered so many pan-Iranian and pan-Turanian movements. As recently as the 1920's Turkish adventurers were seeking to build here a great Turanian state.

Despite their isolated position these peoples have not lost touch with the outer world. The Mufti of Central Asia speaks of the "very warm" relationship of Soviet Uzbeks with their cousins in Afghanistan. Saida Khalikova, Vice-President of Soviet Tadzhikistan, comes from the new city of Stalinabad near the Afghan border. She says: "We feel close to the Tadzhiks in Afghanistan; they are our brothers."

A position of great potential political strength is being established on the bounds of the former Kokand and Bukhara emirates, where British diplomacy once contested Russia. Britain's imperialism has been ousted from the Indian sub-continent. But Bolshevism dominates down to the Oxus border. And advancing Soviet rule undoubtedly brings slowly into Central Asia the techniques of Europe and higher rather than lower living standards.

On both sides of the frontier, among Turanian and Iranian peoples, are germs of relationships like those between Western and Russian Slavs. Already, by diplomatic vigor, the impact of Soviet influence has reached into Afghanistan. That country, isolated by a Pakistani blockade from both India and the ocean, is turning increasingly to the U.S.S.R. for commerce and assistance. Like the old state of Bukhara its economy is adjusting to its Russian neighbor's.

Clearly, like Toynbee, Moscow's planners see the future

207

importance of Central Asia. Already the area provides many raw materials for European Russia. Its agriculture is gradually developing along massive canal systems in Fergana, Bukhara, Turkmenistan, Karakorum and the upper Oxus. Plans—so gigantic they may never be realized—have been discussed to reroute the Arctic-flowing rivers Ob and Yenisei toward the Caspian and Aral seas.

This part of the enormous Soviet Eurasian empire is backward and remote. But its role must inevitably increase. The impact of Bolshevism upon a feudal civilization where women wore the veil and squalor rivaled illiteracy has only begun to spread its shock. Even sordid cities like Bukhara contrast favorably with Afghanistan. And the Tashkent radio, beamed all over Asia, daily carries Communism's gospel.

It speaks across the great Tien Shan range that extends south to Afghanistan and eastward into China. As Genghis discovered, this is the land that leads to everyhere: Europe, Asia, the Danube or the Indus; the land of which all Turkic peoples dream: "where the first Turk, born of the gray wolf, saw the light of the world." The vistas are the same today as always, flat and endless and in all directions. But the dynamism is political as well as military.

MOSCOW'S ASIAN ASPIRATIONS

No longer does Moscow seem concerned about Central Asia as a political soft underbelly subject to inroads of pan-Islam or pan-Turanianism. Bolshevism, more mature and confident since World War II, has submerged the Koran and

208

is expanding outward. Its message is not that carried by the singing battalions of Russian infantry that swing nightly through the streets of garrison towns. Instead it is a message of ideological ferment, of political change in the East, advancing toward India.

For Soviet diplomacy and Communist revolution are pushing across Central Asia toward India with more vigor, more skill and more chance of success than imperial Russia ever demonstrated in its drive against the British Raj. Bolshevism ended any remaining vestiges of independence in the feudal appanage of Bukhara. It squashed short-lived insurrectionary states north of the Oxus, absorbed, communized and Russianized them. And it is heading immutably south of that river into tottering Afghanistan.

That ancient kingdom, which survived Greek, Mongol, Persian and British conquests, now seems doomed. On December 18, 1955, the Afghan Premier agreed to accept a Soviet credit of $100,000,000. This amounts to almost five times total state revenues during the previous fiscal year. Computed at Government-tolerated free-market rates of exchange, the 1955 national income was $21,340,206.

How can Afghanistan's backward economy absorb or repay this loan? How much will find its way into the pockets of the royal clan that governs in the name of Shah Mohammed Zahir? Even Nehru, who resisted similar blandishments in India, concluded that Afghanistan must now be under Soviet domination to accept such an immense sum.

Moscow is sending technicians and engineers south of the

209

Oxus to consolidate the advance. Gradually the country is to be overhauled. The *Agitator's Notebook,* a manual for Communist propaganda agents, explains the party line accordingly:

> The economy of Afghanistan is poorly developed. Its development was hampered in every way by British capital and in recent times by American capital. . . . The Government of Afghanistan is taking steps to liquidate the economic and cultural backwardness of the country. In this respect it is receiving support from its northern neighbor, the Soviet Union. . . .
>
> Afghanistan has no outlet to the sea. . . . Until recently a large proportion of its goods went through the territory of Pakistan. . . . As a result of the increased tension in Afghan-Pakistani relations this route has been closed for Afghanistan. A transit agreement between the U.S.S.R. and Afghanistan provides the right of free transport of goods over the territory of both countries under the most favored conditions for both Afghanistan and the U.S.S.R. . . . The friendship and collaboration between the U.S.S.R. and Afghanistan has firm ground under it as both countries carry on a peace-loving foreign policy.

This extension of Soviet influence toward the Khyber Pass is a logical development. Miserable as is the life of Central Asian peoples in the U.S.S.R., it compares favorably with the feudal squalor of Afghanistan. And the advance has been facilitated by jealousy and stupidity. While rising tides of nationalism pushed Britain out of India and artificially partitioned that subcontinent, Soviet revolution brought European techniques down to the Oxus border. Meanwhile New Delhi and Karachi squabbled over Kashmir.

Seeing a chance for territorial gain, Kabul (the Afghan capital) sought to raise revolt among Pakistan's Pathan tribes. India—with short-sighted folly—and Russia—with long-term ambition—secretly financed the idea and publicly encouraged it. Pakistan thereupon isolated Afghanistan by closing its common frontier. No wonder Bulganin says: "We think the demands of Afghanistan to give the population of bordering 'Pathanistan'[1] an opportunity of freely expressing their will are justified."

Just what is the "Pathanistan" movement? It is the hangover of ancient tribal wars on the northwest frontier of old British India (now Pakistan). It is fostered by a fanatical Moslem mullah who, in his day, has been paid by Germany, Japan, Italy, Russia, Afghanistan, and now Nehru's India, to foment trouble.

Hadji Sahib, Mirza Ali Khan, Faqir of Ipi and the man who would be king, is a little old Pathan with orange turban, baggy trousers and skin the color of tobacco juice. His eyes squint and his beard is turning gray; but across his slight frame drapes a heavy bandoleer of cartridges. For Mirza Ali considers himself at war—with Pakistan.

His capital, called Gorwekht, is deep in the mountainous lair of the Wazir tribe of Pathans along the North-West Frontier country adjoining Afghanistan. Gorwekht is only a name. Goats and camels graze in clefts between the rocks. There are no habitations save for caves scooped from conglomerate cliffsides. These caves, whitewashed within, sparsely furnished and carpeted with dull red Afghan rugs, are head-

[1] Also called "Pushtunistan" or "Pakhtoonistan."

211

quarters and palace for the little Faqir of Ipi.

There, guarded by picked sentries, is the slim remnant of foreign funds he has received at various times to make himself a nuisance first to Britain, now to Pakistan. There he grinds out manifestoes on a hand-run Persian printing press. There he assembles and pays off threadbare *lashkars,* or military levies. And there, on a rickety radio transmitter, he broadcasts claims to be the Emir of Pathanistan.

Pathanistan, or Pakhtoonistan, or Pushtunistan, depending on who describes this dream, is a geopolitical invention of Afghan propaganda. It envisions an independent nation of Pathan tribes from Chinese Sinkiang down to the Indian Ocean. But, being an Afghan concept, it refers only to Pakistan's 7,000,000 Pathans—not to the 5,000,000 comprising Afghanistan's ruling minority. In fact, *Afghan* and *Pathan* are synonymous, and Kabul is trying to use the Pathanistan idea to slice Pakistan apart.

Pathanistan was proclaimed by tribal council in the craggy hamlet of Tirah after India's partition. This announced: "The Islamic democratic free and strong state of the entire people of Pathanistan . . . will grow into a firm-rooted and fruitful tree under the shadow of which will assemble all the people of Pathanistan inhabiting this area from Chitral to Baluchistan and from the Khyber Pass to the banks of the River Indus."

The obvious man to head this movement was the indomitable Faqir of Ipi. A mullah, from the village of Ipi, Mirza Ali is renowned for devotion and made the pilgrimage to Mecca. In April, 1954, Faiz Muhammad Khan, Governor of South

Afghanistan, gave Mirza Ali a handout to replenish his ammunition. The Faqir demanded a written pledge that he be recognized as Emir of Pathanistan, a title frequently accorded him by Kabul radio. That July his lieutenants conferred with three Russian agents who promised support.

The Pathan tribesmen haven't the faintest idea they are being used as pawns in power politics. For them it is sport to abandon flocks and, for the princely sum of $10 a month in *afghanis*, go off on *dacoity* raids to steal telephone wire for use in stringing beds. Their poetic vainglory is stirred by appeals from Kabul or the Faqir's cave.

"The *bulbul* is complaining regarding his life," they are told. "The cruel foreigner does not allow the bee to come near . . . heaven, does not permit the lovers to have a sound sleep. . . . I am lying on my sickbed and they do not apply ointment to my wound. . . . My sweet friend, I am not allowed to see you. You are a flower and I am a *bulbul*. They do not allow us to meet. . . . Ah, Pathan, I am addressing you. Arise. Arise with all your gallantry, you who are renowned throughout the world as a warrior, whose heritage is a sharp sword."

Few Pathans arise. Nevertheless, Kabul continues to encourage insurrection, sublimely unaware of the folly of such policy with Russia greedily regarding Afghanistan's own Uzbeks Tadzhiks and Turkmenians, bordering Soviet republics of those same peoples.

This movement is convenient to the new Soviet Asian policy. In the past, for many years, Moscow feared it might lose its hold on Central Asia. The Soviet encyclopedia complained

213

that after World War II "reactionary circles of Iran, relying on the support of the American imperialists, are reviving pan-Iranism to foster a huge Persian state including Soviet Azerbaijan, Uzbekistan and Tadzhikistan." It warned that "foreign imperialists, mainly American and British, are seeking to use pan-Islamism for the struggle against the national liberation movement in the countries of the East." It deplored pan-Turanian elements in Turkey that sought to "wrest from Russia her national outlying districts."

But the shoe is shifting to the other foot. A more confident regime no longer fears foreign incursions. On the contrary, a new political offensive has begun. No real natural border exists between the U.S.S.R. and Afghanistan—only the sluggish Oxus flatlands. Uzbek and Tadzhik cousins of Soviet subject peoples inhabit the area down to the Hindu Kush massif.

If Moscow could succeed in partitioning Pakistan by carving out a Pathan state, it would establish a precedent for direct absorption of northern Afghanistan's population into kindred Soviet republics. Russian penetration continues steadily south. How far off is the day when what is now Afghanistan suffers the fate of its former neighbors, the emirates of Kokand and Bukhara?

Clearly one goal of Moscow's South Asian policy is to neutralize Pakistan, thus destroying SEATO and the Baghdad, or Northern Tier, alliance. For Pakistan, through its eastern segment, pertains to the former coalition and through its western segment to the latter. It is thus the keystone of a strategical arch erected by diplomatic mapmakers along the

214

southern reaches of the Communist bloc. It is the largest pro-Allied country in Asia and the connecting link between our Mediterranean and Southeast Asia defense commitments.

Should the Kremlin succeeed in prying Pakistan loose from these arrangements it would immensely damage Western prestige in the whole wide area between the Mediterranean and South China seas. An avenue to penetration of India would be unbarred. From Suez to Singapore what is left of the sagging Allied position would be still further menaced.

This Soviet thrust through the middle of Asia has already extended into Afghanistan. Afghanistan was a member of that original Northern Tier, the prewar Saadabad pact, which also included Iran, Iraq and Turkey. This lapsed even in the absence of particular Russian pressure because it represented little more than a cartographical exercise embellished by communiqués.

Unfortunately there is danger such could be the eventual fate of SEATO and the Baghdad Pact. Their geographical inadequacy is symbolized by Pakistan. The western portion of that country is not even on the "Northern Tier." That is to say it does not border the Communist bloc and will not until political subjection of Afghanistan has been completed by the U.S.S.R. And East Pakistan is separated from Southeastern Asia by neutral Burma.

Moscow now suggests to Pakistan neutrality, which, as *Pravda* says, is "on the agenda of contemporary life." Soviet policy is prepared to accept almost any definition of this attitude: Nehru's "areas of peace," Tito's "active coexistence,"

215

Indonesia's "active neutrality" or that of Paris's *Le Monde,* "virile neutrality." For Pakistan the cardinal qualification would be withdrawal from its regional alliances.

Moscow offers in exchange expanded trade and might well be prepared to revise its attitudes on Indian and Afghan claims in Kashmir and Pathanistan—which irk the Pakistanis. But the present regime in Karachi is unlikely to fall for such inducements. The U.S.S.R. attributes this to "domination of foreign capital in Pakistan's financial system." Therefore, the underground Communist party has been instructed by its bosses to organize "the anti-imperialist struggle" in Pakistan. It summons "the people to unite in a single national front for the creation of a popular democratic state."

While reassuring Pakistan against these Soviet threats and blandishments the United States must simultaneously soothe India. Yet the two countries, evolved from the same colonial womb, hate each other bitterly. There is a story of the Moslem peasant who was offered any favor but told that twice as much would be accorded to his Hindu neighbor across the border. Said he: "Take out one of my eyes."

Nehru has his own internal problem. Ten years ago he said the Indian Communist party "speaks in a language which finds no echo in the hearts of the people." He cannot believe this now. In the 1955 important Andhra province elections Communism doubled its previous vote. The huge crowds that turned out for Khrushchev and Bulganin in December of that year were not just paying tribute to the Pandit.

India is in a difficult financial position which we cannot

216

ignore despite our alliance commitments to Pakistan. There is no real need for these to conflict. Over the next five years India requires about $250,000,000 for its internal investment program and about $1,000,000,000 in foreign exchange.

India wants trade, not aid; loans, not grants, from both ourselves and Moscow. Deshmukh, while he was Nehru's Finance Minister, insisted on this in negotiations with the Russians. He had a hard time keeping reference to Soviet "aid" out of the joint communiqué published after the Bulganin-Khrushchev visit.

Our task is immensely difficult. We must not only shore up Pakistan in the face of mounting menaces. We must also help keep India's economy viable so that country can maintain its independence—even though we do not like its attitude. Meanwhile, the U.S.S.R. is prepared to play both sides against the middle.

Its shadow already looms dark in Afghanistan. Pressure on Pakistan has begun. And, as India's economic troubles start to squeeze, Moscow acts an ambidextrous role. One hand offers solace and diplomatic help. The other tells Indian Communists to exploit internal weaknesses wherever they occur. For Soviet Central Asian policy, begun at the frontier of Afghanistan, aims ultimately at Calcutta.

With this carefully in mind, the message taken to South Asia by Khrushchev and Bulganin was calculated to appeal. Indians schooled in the nonviolent tradition of Gandhi and Burmese Buddhists were told the Bolshevik revolution would have been bloodless—save for intervention of what is now

217

called the Western bloc. Soviet Russia, by implication, associates itself with Asia in the unfortunately named East-West struggle. And SEATO, disliked both by Rangoon and New Delhi, is lambasted together with the Northern Tier, that other alliance of India's *bête noire*, Pakistan.

Moscow at present supports Nehru's claims in Goa and Kashmir. It has nothing to lose by such an attitude. It is free to align itself with India on these most passionate issues without apparently demanding any *quid pro quo*. However, were further trouble to develop in Korea or Vietnam, Nehru might find it more embarrassing to play a strictly neutral role. And what will be his attitude if other crises explode?

Bulganin, in a speech to New Delhi's Parliament, gave a clue on India's desired international role. He praised "joint efforts by India, the Chinese People's Republic and the Soviet Union" in securing Korean and Vietnam truces. He added: "The foreign policy of our states has much in common." Khrushchev assured the same body: "We have never forced our ideas on the transformation of society on anyone, nor are we doing so now." All this may ring strangely in American ears. But the remarks were addressed to Indians, not us.

Soviet diplomacy crudely claimed credit for allowing a shattered French army to retain half of Vietnam in 1954. In return it secured the death of E.D.C. But this was followed by the Paris agreements to rearm West Germany. Iran, likewise, did not react to Moscow advances. Teheran's gold, seized during the war, was returned and the fluctuating frontier fixed. Nevertheless, Iran joined the Northern Tier. Finally, Finland

218

was pleased to get back Porkkala. But it has not aligned itself more closely with the U.S.S.R.

How will Burma, Afghanistan and above all India respond to the jovial assurances of high-powered Soviet traveling salesmen? The answer must be speculative until tested by future fact. In the end, as far as India is concerned, the all-important reaction will be Nehru's. For, in a curiously amorphous way, Nehru *is* political India today.

And he still has basic differences with the Soviet Union. He doesn't wish to be associated with any bloc—even by implication. He cannot risk cutting himself off from the great sea powers upon whose navies and commercial fleets India depends in time of crisis. He has his own bitter battle with internal Communists who, while turning out in droves for Russian visitors, demand "armed revolution." And, finally, Nehru does not agree with Khrushchev that heavy industrialization is the best primary social policy.

He once told me: "There are many people here who admire the cultural achievements of the Soviet Union but who do not like at all the tendency toward suppression of individual freedom." Another time he said: "We based our five-year plan upon what I might call present advantage. The choice is between that and future development. The Russians in their plans have chosen the latter. But to do this requires an authoritarian government." In other words, Nehru prefers what we call democratic Socialism, more Fabian than Marxist. He wants to improve the lot of the living rather than demanding greater sacrifices in the name of unborn generations. India has been emphasizing

219

construction of cement, fertilizer, textile and glass factories quite as much as steel.

These are fundamental dissimilarities. They need not interfere with the temporary play of purely political problems such as Goa and Kashmir. But ultimately they are important. And perhaps because of such basically antipodal views, Nehru disassociated himself from Khrushchev's criticism of other nations.

Politically and economically, however, Nehru remains an opportunist. Surely he must be pleased by Russia's diplomatic support. And this will be further enhanced by technical and financial assistance. The centralized Soviet system can mobilize aid far more swiftly than our own.

The U.S.S.R.'s appeal to former colonial peoples is unsubtle and straightforward. Its long-range political aims aspire to eliminate current ideological differences. And in the meantime India and Burma hope, like Egypt and Jugoslavia, to receive aid from both power blocs by playing them against each other. That is their interpretation of Competitive Coexistence.

Soviet foreign policy wants to capitalize on such psychology. At present this policy is somewhat static in Europe, probing for soft spots. To the west, where living standards contrast favorably with those of the U.S.S.R., Moscow concentrates on freezing positions and digesting previous gains. But to the south and east, in Asia, where endemic conditions are deplorable, policy remains dynamic. Bolshevik ideology and Russian power continue to push outward.

This Asian program has three facets. In the center it drives from the Oxus frontier over Afghanistan and toward India. To the east it adjusts to the new Communist behemoth, China. And to the southwest it turns into the Levant. There, by pressure, by guile, by diplomacy and by maneuver it seeks to extend its influence toward Suez and the Persian Gulf.

Convinced of Communism's inevitable global triumph, Moscow practiced its own "brink of war" strategy in the restless Middle East. All the inherent contradictions that Marxism sees in the capitalist world are unfortunately prevalent there: Anglo-American-French rivalries; psychopathic legacies of past colonial empires; dynastic strife and ugly religious fervor.

We may resent the Kremlin's intervention. But surely we should not be surprised. Since Czarist days Russia has looked eagerly to warm-water ports and oil. Molotov told Hitler in 1940: "The area south of Batum and Baku in the general direction of the Persian Gulf should be recognized as the center of the aspirations of the Soviet Union." Moscow asked of the Allies bases in the Dardanelles and Bosporus, positions in the Red Sea and a voice in northern Africa. The Montreux Convention that governed the Turkish straits has expired. U.S.S.R. diplomacy, aided by Egyptian and Arab nationalism, is lining up a new deal in that region.

The Russians previously faltered in the Middle East. Even a weak Iran was able to eject them from its northern provinces. Ankara's obstinacy frustrated the Soviets in Turkey. But the situation that arose in 1955 was too favorable for the Kremlin to neglect. An unnecessary crisis was permitted to develop in Cyprus creating a gap between the Greeks and Turks and

221

opening the road for penetration. Simultaneously we challenged the U.S.S.R. by fostering the Baghdad Pact. Communist reaction was to leapfrog across this Northern Tier, already split at Turkey's western border, and peddle arms and influence among the Arab states.

This left us in a highly embarrassed position. Colonel Nasser, who aspires to Arab leadership, used his new weapons successfully to blackmail the West and nationalize Suez. To me he once confided great admiration for Tito, who showed him how to get help from both power blocs without joining either. Nasser is an apt pupil. The satellite arms deal with Cairo changed a strategic Arab-Israeli balance the Allies sought uneasily to preserve. Jingoes on both sides have steadily urged war. Meanwhile the West, insisting Russia could have no say in Palestine, tried unsuccessfully to assume responsibility for a peace it could not keep alone.

Cairo is just as intent as Moscow on destroying the Baghdad Pact. Feudal Saudi Arabia presses its vendetta against the Hashimite dynasties in Jordan and Iraq. To obtain funds for subversion and propaganda King Saud has borrowed in advance on future oil royalties. From Cairo to Damascus underground Communism gains strength. Three North Lebanese trade unions are already controlled by party agents. Syria's labor federation has succumbed. An agent of Britain's Iraq Petroleum Company predicts that by 1961 Communism may take over Syria.

Already it has penetrated the colonies of miserable Arab refugees who are not allowed to work in the states that harbor

222

them. It has managed to make great headway among Moslem nationalists. Nasser says: "We know there are underground Communists here. If they can convince the people that we are agents of the West they can gain control."

Even in Turkey new pressures are commencing. Unwise investment policies brought that country to the verge of bankruptcy. Ankara asked us for an emergency loan of $300,000,-000. We refused unless planning was revised. Now Moscow tells the Turks: Your economy sags because American pressure forces you to maintain a wartime footing.

The Soviets gamble on an audacious Middle Eastern policy. They cold-bloodedly encouraged the area to the verge of Palestine war and a crisis on Suez. Why? At the Geneva summit meeting in 1955 Moscow became convinced world conflict is excluded as too dangerous. A little holocaust was therefore worth the risk. And the prize is so rich that Moscow is ready to play high. If it can deprive Europe of Middle Eastern oil, Britain's straitened economy may collapse and the continental powers of NATO will be subject to economic strangulation or political blackmail.

Finally, while in Western and Southern Asia Soviet foreign policy seeks first to neutralize and then to communize key centers, the problem is otherwise in the Far East. For there the ideological revolution has already triumphed on the vitally important battlefield of China. Communization of that huge country is no longer the task at hand. And politically Peiping and Moscow are working as a team.

Nevertheless, it is fair to ask whether their national as distinct from philosophical interests may not eventually conflict. Certainly in some spheres the aspirations of Chinese dynamism already collide with those of the U.S.S.R. Will the Kremlin discover to its embarrassment that Marxism-Leninism can contain within itself those same "inherent contradictions" it likes to see in capitalism?

The development of revolutionary China surprised all Soviet previsions. Stalin had tended to discount Mao Tse-tung. The Soviet dictator seemed to think that Chiang Kai-shek would triumph in the wake of Japanese collapse. He sidetracked Mao in dealings with the Allies. He looted Manchuria and set back Chinese Communism's industrial base.

Moscow perhaps misjudged the vigor of its Chinese brainchild. Or perhaps it disliked development of a powerful neighboring force. In either case, there is no doubt that Khrushchev and Bulganin patched up matters when they visited Peiping in 1954. To do so they had to acknowledge implicitly acceptance of China as a peer. Thus, even before they went to Belgrade and professed to endorse Tito's doctrine that Socialism can develop along different lines in different lands, they were forced to admit as much in China.

This added to Mao's luster in Asian eyes. At the Bandung conference, where, to their discomfiture, the Russians were edged into the shadow, the Chinese symbolized the cause of Eastern revolution. Since then the Kremlin has been seeking to refurbish its prestige in the Orient. By attacking the "cult of the individual," Moscow not only demotes the dead Stalin but, by inference, the living Mao Tse-tung. It wants to join the

Afro-Asian "Bandung bloc," but has not yet succeeded. Why? Because of opposition from Peiping.

Within the U.S.S.R. itself a move of demographical significance is taking place. Thousands of Slavs are being settled near the Chinese border areas to cultivate new lands. Is this a revival of traditional Czarist practice—establishment of European strongpoints along the dilating Asian frontier of the Russian state? Does Khrushchev foresee a day when overpopulated China looks outward to expand? The only adjacent vacant lots are Soviet.

Assuredly the possibility of Sino-Soviet trouble is not imminent. Peiping depends for sustenance upon the U.S.S.R. Yet, in global politics, geography remains an inescapably important factor. Moscow's understanding of history stresses such abstract forces. Therefore it urges the attentions of its Chinese partner southward and eastward away from Russia.

As long ago as 1936 Mao stated that when his projected revolution has succeeded "the Outer Mongolian Republic will automatically become a part of the Chinese federation." But today it is totally a Soviet fief. This fact does not escape the Chinese people. Despite police controls and censorship, they still disseminate strange rumors. They even spread the crazy tale in 1955 that Moscow planned to retrocede its maritime provinces.

It obviously suits the Kremlin book when Chinese popular ambitions focus in an entirely different direction like Formosa and Vietnam. Yet this is a relatively new development. In 1936 Mao said: "It is the immediate task of China to regain

225

all our lost territories." But what did these comprise? Mao specified: "We do not however include Korea, formerly a Chinese colony. . . . The same thing applies to Formosa." Only after Chiang took refuge on that island did Peiping discover it to be "Chinese."

Moscow is pleased to see uncertainty perpetuated in Southeast Asia. Therefore, it is imperative for us to seal off and attempt to stabilize that general area. We have sponsored military alliances to insure great-power action against aggression. But these alliances are fragile. The frontiers to be protected are not specified by commonly accepted definition.

Nor is military cover enough to save the situation. Economic aid and political reform remain continuously needed. A perceptive American officer reported to the Pentagon after touring Southeast Asia: "For the greater mass of the people there is no hope, either for themselves or for their children, ever to free themselves from want and hunger."

Our problem is not merely to protect this region from assault. We must champion social progress. Only by patient democratic revolution can we frustrate the advance of Communism's counter-revolution. And only by success in this incredibly complex task can we insure that China ceases looking outward—and turns inland toward Russia.

This must be a cardinal feature of any grand political strategy of the West. Wherever the course of Communism can be checked abroad it will ultimately develop within itself frictions and inherent cleavages as Titoism, Maoism and the other nationalistic Socialist philosophies mature. Or it must

226

revert to monolithic Stalinist forms and crack. For its empire is too large for any single autocratic center.

But our diplomatic task is immensely difficult. Not only does the Soviet Union have an initial economic advantage of bringing with it, wherever it spreads in Asia, a living standard relatively higher than what it finds upon the scene. It can promise by dictatorial methods a swifter industrializing pace than anything democracy holds forth. To the impoverished Asian masses, knowing and caring little for abstract freedom, the appeal of Jeffersonian liberty is scant. And wherever it moves in the Orient, no matter what its new motives are, the West must suffer from its past record of colonialism and its present vestiges of racial prejudice. We like to think of ourselves as great powers in a Free World. But, for the determined agents of the new imperial Moscow, we are an unholy coalition of the America of the Autherine Lucy case, the Britain of Cyprus, and the France of Vietnam and Algeria. This befuddles the peoples we would aid. Meantime the empire containing Tamerlane's old capital of Samarkand pushes immutably toward Suez, toward the Persian Gulf and toward Bengal Bay.

227

VII

The New Imperial Age

Destruction of Fascism and the Rome-Berlin-Tokyo axis was by no means the most important result of World War II. Far more significant to history were the rise of Communism as a great world ideology, the doom of overseas colonial empires such as those of Britain, France and Holland, and the growing ascendancy of a new imperial form, the vast land empires of Russia, China and the United States.

This is not a novel historical development. The Arabs and Romans tended to link their imperial possessions more by overland than overseas connections. The empires of Greece and Carthage were, like Britain's, maritime. But the new power age, evolving in the second half of our century, sees dynamism spreading from the heart of great land masses. What has begun in North America, Eurasia and East Asia may unfold elsewhere.

India, although it dislikes the word, has what historians will call imperial aspirations. Egypt is trying to inspire a new Moslem-Arab empire comparable to that of Mohammed's successors. Even Turkey might, before the century is over,

228

revive pan-Turanian aspirations of the past. Today a man on horseback could ride from Albania on the Adriatic Sea, across the Balkans, through the Caucasus, right over Soviet Central Asia, through Sinkiang and into China; and, if he spoke Turkish, he would make himself understood along the entire route. Someday, as they acquire the tools of reading and writing and a knowledge of their dim historical heritage, the backward Turanian peoples may group around some magnetic nationalist movement of their own.

Empire has not always been a nasty word. The unity of Rome was for long considered a model for Western political thought. When the United States began to mature after our revolution we spoke proudly and hopefully of our empire. French revolutionaries proclaimed their imperial expansion. Until very recently it was considered a moral duty of higher civilizations to bring their knowledge and moral standards to the stagnant, backward corners of the world. Many of the fledgling powers of our time such as India, Pakistan, Indonesia and even Egypt have benefited from their years of foreign tutelage. In fact, it is only in instances where colonialism brought with it education and the knowledge of new opportunities that anti-colonialism developed as a flourishing political doctrine and threw off foreign rule. Does Moscow contemplate this when viewing its own muted Caucasus and Asian reaches?

The United States, by wars with Mexico and different Indian tribes, created a huge land empire after vying European powers were expelled. Russia similarly spread

229

gradually across Siberia to the Pacific and down Central Asia to Afghanistan and India. China today has gobbled up Tibet. It looks southward into Vietnam and eastward into Korea. The day will inevitably come when Peiping presses toward the only underpopulated area on its borders—that now possessed by the U.S.S.R. The Russians seem dimly aware of this.

Surely there must be men in Moscow who now wonder if they have not created a Frankenstein monster in the China that Communism labors to industrialize. Forced by the lagging pace of its revolution, China has had to remain Stalinist in method and ideology far longer than the rest of the Marxist orbit. This leads to a potential ideological clash, an inherent cleavage of interests within the Communist world similar to that which Lenin liked to see in capitalism. Does Marxism contain within itself the seeds of its own destruction? When tied to national interests it most assuredly does.

Who could have foreseen as World War II was ending in 1945 that ten years thence the United States would have been allied with Germany and Japan? Is it possible that in another decade or so Moscow's interest will find the Soviet Government seeking closer relations with the West against new Oriental challenges?

In the often forgotten past of both Russia and America there have been moments when curious basic similarities between those expanding imperial nations have been noted. It may strike us as startling to read today the observations on our own early society by Paul Svinin, Russian diplomat and

230

artist, who visited the new American nation between 1811 and 1813. Svinin, who made his journey during a relatively liberal epoch of Czardom, then engaged in the war against Napoleon, concluded: "No two countries bear a more striking resemblance than Russia and the United States."

He was struck not only by the physical likeness of two nations groping toward distant ocean frontiers but by certain political similarities which might astonish us. He wrote: "In Russia, as in the United States, the unfortunate and the persecuted find asylum and a home." And, he added: "The country is glutted with bust portraits of Washington." (Was this an early form of what Khrushchev calls "the cult of the individual"?) Svinin remarked: "It is noteworthy that every American considers it his sacred duty to have a likeness of Washington in his home just as we have images of God's saints. He would fain keep before him the simulacrum of the man to whom he owes independence, happiness and wealth. Washington's portrait is the finest and sometimes the sole decoration of American homes." And with curiously prescient confidence in the future of the two great continental empires, Svinin boasted: "It is little more than a century since from the bosom of impenetrable forests and marshes, inhabited by bears and wolves, rose the superb cities of St. Petersburg, Philadelphia and New York."

Land empires have been gradually gaining power as their maritime counterparts burgeoned and declined. President Roosevelt seemed aware of this historical transition before the end of World War II. He recognized that a death knell had

231

sounded for overseas colonial possessions; that the huge political assemblages of foreign peoples dominated from Britain, France and the Netherlands were shrinking and changing form. Yet we ourselves have not entirely shed such transmaritime imperial trappings. We have granted independence to Cuba and the Philippines. But the day must come when we dissolve our holdings in such distant points as Okinawa.

Professor Hans Kohn has made an interesting study of present imperial trends. He writes:

The American propaganda distinguishing between expansion across land masses and across separating waters was strengthened among Asian intellectuals by the Leninist theory that imperialism and colonialism were the product of late and over-capitalized capitalism seeking new outlets. On the one hand the colonial relationship was regarded as primarily "capitalistic exploitation"; on the other hand a non-capitalistic nation by definition could not be imperialistic or exploiting. Thus the U.S.S.R., in spite of having subjected so many peoples in Europe and Asia to a process of Russification and absolute control from Moscow, and Communist China, in spite of not liberating Tibet or Sinkiang from its imperial control and trying to restore its control over Korea, Annam, Burma, etc., do not appear as imperialist countries to the Asian nations.

The issue of anti-colonialism has been used for some time in the international power struggle, and not only by the U.S.S.R. Anti-imperialism and anti-colonialism are widespread among the independent nations of Latin America, which have seen for a long time in the United States the leading imperialist and colonial nation, American imperialism being chiefly though not exclusively "dollar imperialism." Argentina, an independent nation for over a century, very proud of its independence and hardly in danger

232

of imperialist aggression, has used the issue of anti-colonialism as a weapon in her struggle against the United States for leadership at least in the southern and middle parts of the western hemisphere. The United States has used the issue of colonialism in its rivalry with, or dislike of, Britain for very many decades. Now the Soviet Union is using the same issue in her rivalry with, and hatred of, the United States. But there is hardly anything fundamentally new in it except that the Western nations, especially Britain, have by now set many nations in Asia and Africa free, and that it is above all among these nations which are now independent that the issue of anti-colonialism is raised.

In pressing imperial aspirations eastward and southward, the U.S.S.R. has one immense historical advantage. This is the indisputable fact that, with few exceptions, wherever it extends into Asia, the Soviet system brings with it a higher rather than a lower standard of living, no matter how relatively small the improvement may appear. This is nowhere more strikingly demonstrated than along the frontier between backward Soviet Tadzhikistan and still more backward Afghanistan. But, when Moscow moves westward into Europe, it suffers a relative disadvantage. For in most of the orbit countries we call satellites the traditions of liberty, the standards of living and of culture, are higher than within neighboring districts of the U.S.S.R.

BUREAUCRACY MINUS PEPPER

Terminating a journey through the Soviet empire from the River Oxus to the River Oder, the traveler observes four features surprisingly common to all countries within Moscow's

233

orbit: (1) a housing crisis in the cities; (2) an agricultural crisis on the land; (3) an administrative crisis except at the highest levels; (4) and an absence of pepper from the table. Why?

The answer to this question is not profoundly difficult to discover. Communism, although in many ways a remarkably successful system, does everything the hard way. In order to develop industrial production it creates a working proletariat by fiat and moves it into urban areas. But this is done so swiftly that housing programs never keep pace. That is as true within the U.S.S.R., where the ideology has been practiced almost four decades, as it is in Czechoslovakia, which was communized in 1948.

The famous cities of Eastern Europe are woefully over-crowded. Only the new aristocracy—party bosses, scientists, technocrats and artists—live in comfort. For the rest it is established by universal norm that at least two people shall dwell in each available room.

Not that the orbit governments are unaware of the problem. They simply have proved incompetent to face this issue of their own creation. New buildings keep going up; but not enough to house the people whom planners are moving in. One result is that in Moscow the civil administration has decided to freeze the local population.

The second problem is that of feeding the Soviet empire. After thirty-eight years of Communism this is still the greatest headache in the U.S.S.R. itself, as Khrushchev admits. In the United States about seven million field workers produce so much that we have huge, unexportable surpluses and encourage the leaving of land fallow. In the U.S.S.R. more than fifty million farmers produce insufficient food.

The basic answer to this problem is purely ideological. Farmers throughout the world work better for themselves than for the state. Despite all Stalin's human engineering, collectivization has not been a psychological success. There is insufficient individual incentive.

Curiously enough, the relative degree of freedom can almost be measured by the extent of private land ownership in the Communist world. Jugoslavia, the sole independent state in Marxist Eastern Europe, has only 17 per cent of its land socialized. Poland, where craving for liberty simmers on the surface, is 24 per cent collectivized. Hungary and Rumania, more subservient to Moscow, have about 33 per cent of their acres under the state. Then comes sullen Czechoslovakia with 44 per cent and utterly submissive Bulgaria with about 80 per cent. Of course in Soviet Russia the figure is virtually 100 per cent—and political individuality doesn't exist.

Bureaucracy, inept and often impolite, is a symptom of Communism wherever it prevails. During the first phase of each Marxist revolution a vast proportion of the existing old regime administrative personnel was destroyed, killed or imprisoned. Then the system immediately created need for a new officialdom many times the size. For by making the state omnipotent and putting it in charge of all business, industry, transportation and other features previously in private hands,

235

it multiplied the bureaucratic task after decimating the bureaucracy. This may make sense ideologically to Marxists; but it eviscerates efficiency.

Because of bureaucracy people wait in queues in Poland for permits to buy coal. Because of bureaucracy in Bulgaria it takes about eight hours to purchase a railway ticket and get an exit visa—and occupies the time of perhaps ten state officials. Bureaucracy forces the traveler to break the law. Currency restrictions prevent one from taking money out of one country into another—or make it unreasonably difficult. Train officials therefore exploit their own black market. And all too often the minor bureaucrats, underpaid and overworked, are sullen and discourteous. Meanwhile the voyager, like Alice, must run hard to stay in the same place.

And pepper—why are there no longer pepper shakers on the tables between the Black Sea and the Baltic? Have the people in this area lost their taste for highly seasoned food? Not at all. Pepper is a luxury. Therefore pepper is missing. For in the brave new world of Communism luxury is still a future dream. The practice of Moscow's mode of Marxism has brought with it some notable triumphs in terms of engineering prowess, mass industrialization, scientific advances and the sinews of immense power. But comforts in the sense of a pleasant abode, variety of food, smooth and affable administration and the simple pleasures of life—these are still missing.

With little research and less effort one discovers that the key word in the Soviet empire is *they*. *They* are the apparatus of control, the stultifying bureaucracy that embraces life. *They* are the top dictators of Communist government and the anonymous machinery that dictates even to *them*. There is a *they* at every level of existence, and *they* are invisible.

From the Oxus to the Oder one hears reference to *they: They* might not like this. *They* do not understand. *They* are planning better things. A highly intelligent Czech says: "Nobody knows who or what *they* really are. *They* are bureaucracy. *They* are the system. *They* are the bosses themselves. But *they* are also something else. *They* are the excuse for refusing to take responsibility and for inaction. That is when one hears '*They* may object.' Once I was talking to a member of our Politburo. He apologized for something, saying '*They* would not approve.' 'My God,' I said, 'You don't mean to tell me that even you have a *they*?' "

The most poignant struggle in Communist lands is that between individual human beings and *them*. New winds, perhaps prescient of more liberty, are indeed blowing westward out of Russia. But these have yet to whisk away the deadening gray atmosphere of *they*. A Rumanian confides: "*They* are everywhere and everything. None of us dares speak frankly any more. I talk freely to no one. I don't even trust my brother and sister. All of us have been degraded. Prison doors are opening—but thousands are still inside. We trust nobody. That is the heritage *they* gave us."

The American Minister in Bucharest, sorry for the sentry assigned to guard his legation during the freezing winter, arranged to install an electric heater in his hut. *They* refused

237

permission. The Argentine envoy in the same capital employs three private "tails" to see if he is being followed by police. It is rumored that *they* pay his detectives.

On a Polish train from Wroclaw to Cracow two men asked: "Why don't you Americans like our system?" I read them, in German, excerpts from Pericles' funeral oration. One leaned forward whispering: "Ninety-nine per cent of our people agree with that. But we don't dare talk. *They* might overhear."

They censor mail. Hotel visitors to foreigners are registered on *their* behalf. In Czechoslovakia a citizen wishing to send a letter abroad must first file his name and address for *their* benefit. In Prague a state employee complains: "For the people life is poor. Everything is too expensive. Pawnshops are full of goods. I can't get enough for my three children. Food is dear. But I know that *they* live well. *They* have ham and champagne."

The little man practices shrewd deceptions against *them*. In Poland, Government ministry cars pick up passengers on the sly and taxi them at fixed black-market rates. In Rumania, on the road between Bucharest and Sinaia, state trucks sell seats to hitchhikers. In Warsaw, one night club is patronized by profiteers who earn their living by outwitting *them*.

They have not yet proven able to administer efficiently. A bartender complains: "*They* have a fixed norm for me; I must sell a minimal number of drinks or face a dock in pay." So he waters alcohol and fakes receipts. Hungarian customs officials take away one's Czechoslovakian crowns and refuse to change them, apologizing: "We are not robbers. But *they* do not permit it."

A party boss went to a satirical performance in Prague. He reported to a friend: "I suppose it is all right. *They* have decided to have satire. Since we must have satire, I approve it." Throughout Eastern Europe trains are late. Why? At every frontier point soldiers inspect each car to see that nobody escapes the local heaven. Militiamen search behind curtains and on the roofs. *They* wish to insure that no one can get out.

Says a veteran Communist in Czechoslovakia: "*They* and their bureaucracy are destroying us. When I joined the party here before the war we were all Socialists—the Communists, the Social Democrats, The Beneš National Socialists. This country was rich, well industrialized and had a real tradition of democracy. We all thought and boasted that we would make this such an example of Socialism that we could really demonstrate the value of our ideology to America and Europe. But everybody was deceived. *They* deceived us."

They remain all-pervasive in the realm of Communism. *They* are entrenched in Eastern Europe. *They* are rooted deep in Moscow. *They* are the system, the bureaucracy, the unbottled jinni that surely neither Marx nor Lenin ever dreamed of. And, as Herodotus wrote: "They who mutually injure the state, mutually support each other."

COMPETITIVE PROPAGANDA

Yet, it cannot be disputed, we have been no match for the Russians in playing the great game of psychological warfare

239

that is bound to preoccupy the world in coming decades. We have allowed our own interests to be skillfully and persistently attacked and our own position weakened without adequate riposte. We have halfheartedly defended our declining imperial allies against charges of colonialism without pointing out that, as their empires falter and decline, they are being replaced by new but equally imperial substitutes.

The greatest proof of the fallacy of Marxism is, curiously enough, the existence of the Soviet Union. For Karl Marx foresaw the triumph of his theory first in highly industrial countries like Germany or England. Yet what we call Communism came initially to power in underdeveloped Russia, where it assumed the form, not of Socialism but of the most massive state capitalism known to history. And the next outstanding triumph of the Marxist legend was in backward China.

Despite such glaring inconsistencies, Marx's latter-day prophets extol the "scientific" immutability of their dialectical materialism and insist it must logically inherit the earth. But the Communists themselves continually modify this "proven" doctrine. Lenin, Stalin, Trotsky, Tito and Mao Tse-tung have each reinterpreted the credo. Now Khrushchev is the latest to amend accepted dogma.

Nevertheless, by blandly ignoring these constant fluctuations, Soviet propaganda seeks to convey the impression of a basic logic that progresses unalterably toward an inescapable end. Lenin, who brilliantly grasped what was helpful to him in Marx, taught that "propaganda is of crucial importance."

Modern means of applying this dictum have been carefully coordinated by Moscow.

F. Bowen Evans, in a study of the subject, concludes that the U.S.S.R. employs 375,000 full-time and 2,100,000 part-time propagandists. He says the Bolshevik party maintains 6,000 special schools for training professional agents in that field. Former Senator William Benton, who recently visited the Soviet Union, prepared some observations on "the voice of the Kremlin" for the *Encyclopaedia Britannica's 1956 Book of the Year*. He writes:

At its most ambitious, the aim of Soviet propaganda is so daring that we in the West can hardly comprehend it: so to condition its citizens that they think of their personal freedom and their personal ambitions as identical with the purposes of Soviet society . . . in Russia the rulers seek to convert the total culture into a giant propaganda apparatus. . . .

This is a struggle of a new type, to be waged with new weapons. It is a struggle for which the Western World is little prepared. It boils down to an effort by two great opposing forces to win the faith and confidence of the world's peoples. . . . Russia cannot match us in the export of automobiles, tractors or business machines. She proposes to beat us with her ideas and her trained manpower.

But it is questionable whether our propaganda has successfully faced this challenge. The West German Government has published a commentary complaining that we emphasize material things too much. We have allowed the initiative in the realm of spiritual ideas to remain largely in the very materialistic hands of Communism.

241

Are we [asks Bonn] ready for this spiritual competition? Do we understand the system of thought, belief and ideology of the East? Do we have any certitude about the basis of our lives and our faith? Ideological faith in the collectivist idea makes the Soviet man capable of achievements and sacrifices that surpass human strength. Only a faith that in no way is dependent on material events, that does not live in expectation of future well-being, can resist this ideology. This faith, this conviction must inspire Western man to risk his life for the ultimate values that cannot be abandoned— freedom, personal dignity, the lives of other men, the truth of religion.

There is no sign that the powers of the West have sought seriously to analyze the problem of their propaganda and to co-ordinate efforts in presenting their case abroad. We remain constantly on the defensive, permitting the Kremlin's experts to exploit the very evident chinks in our imperfect armor. Thus the tragic convolutions of the United States' attempt to obliterate segregation feature on the world's front page. What has already been accomplished in the name of Jeffersonian democracy remains forgotten. Britain's embarrassing attitude on Cyprus erases from popular memory her deeds in India, Burma and Ceylon.

Only when Moscow acts openly with brutal menace do the free powers respond in concert and remember that the essential contradictions of our times are those between themselves and Communism. In periods of relaxation we tend to forget the need to constantly reassert the inner meaning of our ideology. This is a dangerous lack. Surely there are enough beneficial aspects in the democratic system, whatever imperfections it may have, to merit retelling to a redundant point.

Simple facts bear frequent repetition. As Pericles told Athens: "We are superior to our enemies . . . our city is open to the world . . . we live freely, and yet we face the same dangers as readily as they . . . those men surely should be deemed bravest who know most clearly what danger is and what pleasure is and are not made thereby to flinch."

In this era of political uncertainty and uneasy coexistence, propaganda becomes increasingly important in maintaining the views and prestige of the United States among captive peoples of Eastern Europe. Yet, despite millions of dollars spent, we are not successful.

This is not for lack of technical ingenuity. Both Government and privately sponsored organizations have demonstrated imagination in getting our ideas across barbed-wire frontiers and a wall of radio jamming. Programs beamed by stations of the Voice of America and Radio Free Europe manage to circumvent these barriers and are heard. Pamphlets dropped from airplanes and wind-borne balloons have so saturated some countries that not even efficient sweeping operations of the security police have kept them from wide circulation. The criticism one hears is of the ideas themselves, not their means of distribution.

One American envoy in the area complains: "Our propaganda is utterly ineffective. Frequently our radios put out 'intelligence' information that is entirely inaccurate or ridiculously late—information that could be verified within ten minutes by any embassy or legation. Much that we broadcast no longer has any bearing on reality."

243

A highly intelligent Czech with pro-American sympathies adds: "All too often your radio either misses events; or it is late; or it is wrong. Once you get through to it you'd like to know something. But the things your propaganda speaks about are frequently silly. Broadcasters give fifteen minutes of statistics. Whom do they think they are talking to, professors of mathematics? Who cares about comparative steel production figures in 1952? Sometimes our emigrants working for you will denounce a man as a traitor when it simply isn't true. They are careless. This happened to a friend of mine and was infuriating."

One of our Eastern European envoys says: "The United States has always encouraged these people to overthrow the Government. Our propaganda still implies this purpose. We have done nothing or said nothing to give the impression that we will ever make our peace with this regime. Yet we *must* do business with it—and do. This schizophrenic attitude puzzles the local population."

Perhaps we should concentrate more on telling our own story, stressing forever the ideals we believe. Objective commentary and calm, straightforward news are durable psychological commodities. We cannot afford to lose touch with changing realities within the satellites. Nor should we be so blinded by emotion that we occasion resentment among those we court.

American political prestige is being sapped by skillful Soviet diplomacy and propaganda. Our attitude is made to appear static and unreasonable. Communist leaders in the satellites argue: "You kept insisting that Moscow's policy must change. You set out a bill of particulars to be met: an Austrian peace treaty, concrete moves toward disarmament. You denounced Stalinism as a threat to the world and proclaimed fears of military force.

"But now the Kremlin has dropped Stalin and outlawed the 'inevitability' of war. Yet you announce the U.S.S.R. is more dangerous than it ever was before. The Russians agreed on Austria. They are demobilizing hundreds of thousands of soldiers. What have you people done to meet them halfway?"

The answer to this question is not simple. To respond that we mistrust Moscow on the basis of its record is inadequate if true. To imply that we fear the outcome of Competitive Coexistence with a monolithic ideology merely weakens our psychological position.

We should do some rethinking. The Russians have changed their line. We must therefore offer something new. We cannot afford indefinitely to pursue a Fabian policy if we are to retain any influence in Eastern Europe.

One way to face the situation is to cease treating the satellite countries as an unimportant, uniform bloc, a mere adjunct of Soviet empire, and to discuss with them their separate problems. These interests, beneath the gray uniformity of Communism, remain disparate. Can we not explore diversities more skillfully?

Czechoslovakia and Bulgaria retain strong pan-Slavic feeling of kinship for Russia, but the Poles, despite blood ties, harbor a traditional dislike. Bulgaria and Rumania are

245

religiously Orthodox. But Hungary, Czechoslovakia and Poland are strongly Roman Catholic. Czechoslovakia and Hungary border on the West—the German Federal Republic and Austria. Bulgaria touches Turkey, Greece and Jugoslavia. Even Rumania has contact with the independent Communistic Jugoslavs. Only Poland is completely sandwiched between segments of the Soviet empire.

The Poles and Czechs have deep concern in East German rearmament. The Poles speak sneeringly of the "Dove's Head Hussars"—successors to Hitler's Death's Head Regiments. The stronger this German satellite becomes the more, automatically, Poland and Czechoslovakia look to Moscow for protection. Both countries fear that someday Teuton refugees will return to Silesia and Sudetenland.

The Hungarians and Rumanians have historical and racial mistrust of their Slavic neighbors. The Bulgarians are deeply interested in Macedonia but care nothing about Germany's future. To them foreign policy revolves about closer relations with Jugoslavia and possible federation with that country.

There are different levels of freedom, of initiative and even of Communist organization among the satellites. The Poles by nature insist upon more liberty of action. "Our party is in better shape than others," say their Communists, "because we fought the Germans. Poland was never tainted with collaboration as in Hungary. Make no mistake, even we Communists prize our liberty. Throughout our history Poles have joined many liberation movements—in Italy, France and even America. Ours will inevitably and must inevitably be a different form of Communism from Russia's. It is not our destiny to be satellites."

Now that Stalin is outmoded the Russians try to blame all past mistakes upon his dictatorship. But a new cry for liberty is rising. Said a Communist intellectual recently in Warsaw: "Now we should publish Koestler's *Darkness at Noon*. After all, what it condemns is Stalinism. And Hemingway's *For Whom the Bell Tolls*? We ban it only because it attacked the brutality of André Marty's butchers in Spain. Now we agree that what Marty did was wrong."

Let us take advantage of this ferment and press for publication of such provocative books. The thoughts they contain are still electrifying. There is a deep-seated craving within the satellites to travel to the West and test comparative freedoms. Do we fear to let them satisfy this appetite?

Hankering for happiness is one of mankind's most contagious diseases. Russian youngsters visiting the Polish ski resort of Zakopane were astonished by the relative freedom from inhibition and the sophistication of the Poles. "Why can't our girls be attractive?" asked young Russian men. Meanwhile their girls locked themselves in rooms to smoke European cigarettes and arranged sly deals with friends to send them lipstick and powder.

Let us remind the East of the mere existence of life's simpler pleasures. Now that there is talk of greater freedom, let us again intrude our Western culture. The yeast of liberty must be encouraged while we wait to measure the sincerity, depth and durability of the Soviet New Look.

The West has shown itself embarrassingly disorganized in combatting the Communist drive for world ascendancy. Even NATO, an alliance that must evolve politically and mature diplomatically in order to survive, has proven an inadequate clearing house for exchanging views and preparing statesman-like actions.

It is astonishing how differently Allied foreign ministries interpret Soviet policy developments. NATO conferences disclose every shade of opinion from outright acceptance of Moscow's sincerity to blank skepticism. Yet these divergent attitudes are based upon a common pool of diplomatic information.

The NATO Council is apparently ill prepared for thoughtful discussion of the Khrushchev-Bulganin new look. By the time joint reports on Soviet intentions are worked out by the alliance's small body of experts they are watered down to cautionary platitudes. This demonstrates one aspect of the need to revise NATO's political machinery.

Surely the West need not have been surprised by all the Russians have done. It was apparent for months that the U.S.S.R. could make many propaganda moves that would not, at the same time, weaken its fundamental position. By July, 1955, it was possible to forecast, in *The New York Times* ways by which "without relinquishing anything but appearances of control, Moscow could retain the realities of its imperial position while conveying an impression of goodwill and compromise." These included: dissolution of the Cominform (abolished on April 24, 1956); reduction of the unwieldy and redundant Soviet army (August 13, 1955, Moscow announced it was demobilizing 640,000 of its troops. In 1956 the release of another 1,200,000 conscripts was promised); evacuation of foreign bases (January 26, 1956, the U.S.S.R. left the Porkkala Peninsula base in Finland; Deputy Premier Pervukhin stated: "The Soviet Union no longer has a military base on the territory of a foreign country").

Yet the West, apparently confused by the effects of Soviet policy, made little effort to co-ordinate reactions in advance through NATO. This sort of needless confusion might be avoided if NATO's consultative machinery is strengthened. It should provide for continual high-level exchanges and consolidation of views. Not only must the alliance be given more authority to manage internal disputes such as the crudely unnecessary Cyprus argument. It must keep a constant, sharp eye upon the Soviet bloc, preparing to adjust ahead of time to Moscow's shifting tactics. This business of confused disagreement after the event is embarrassing and avoidable. To remain viable the alliance will have to be made politically more concerted, supple and alert.

Neither in application nor in announced purpose have we adapted to new realities and potential opportunities in the area between the Black Sea and the Baltic. Our procedure is rigid and unimaginative. We continue to delude both ourselves and our friends with pat slogans. Madison Avenue salesmanship techniques are an inadequate substitute for wisdom.

Such phrases as "liberation" and "roll-back" were politically popular in the United States and ideally to be desired. But this is not an ideal world. Under prevailing conditions the satellite states are not going to change their form of government because of any diplomatic methods we apply. Whether we like it or not, the revolution is a fact in Eastern Europe.

But revolution is not a static thing. The situation in the satellites need not remain static. Already the reign of terror appears to be drawing toward an end. As Moscow commences to ease the tightness of its controlling reins it is up to us to exploit differences, divergent interests and cravings among the Eastern peoples.

A New Policy Approach

There are only two feasible ways of liberating countries within the Soviet orbit. One is by force. The other is by aiding them gradually to extricate themselves. History has tested both methods. Communist Hungary, in 1919, was freed by Allied intervention employing Rumanian troops. Titoist Jugoslavia, while retaining its ideology, broke away from Soviet control in 1948 without a war.

When Secretary Dulles took charge of the State Department in 1953 his talk of "liberation" implied that the United States was prepared to support with force if necessary any counter-revolution in East Europe. But later that year an uprising in East Germany proved this implication wrong. The Western world, led by ourselves, sat back and watched the insurrection being crushed. This was a lesson to the satellites, repeated at Poznan in 1956.

250

Nevertheless, discontented populations continued to believe that someday war might come, a war that ultimately would change their governmental systems. Added credence was given by public utterances of some of our statesmen and our radio stations. This thought, too, faded after the Geneva summit conference. Whatever else that meeting may or may not have accomplished, it convinced Europe that war was finished as a form of political disagreement.

Yet we have not adjusted to the profound changes caused by these events. Nor has our policy in Eastern Europe so far reflected the situation brought about by Stalin's death, Khrushchev's "collective leadership" and the new Communist endorsement of Titoism.

What, we must ask ourselves, is the aim of our policy? What proportion of it is founded upon selfish aspirations such as weakening our enemy's strength and what on altruism? How much are we thinking of aiding East Europe in terms of improving our own global position and how much are we thinking of aiding the people who live there?

The greatest fault of our satellite policy, both as announced and applied, is that it has not concentrated upon the attainable. It has persistently worked for what is patently impossible except in the event of the war that we ourselves rule out. But there is a realizable goal. That is Titoism.

This is a form of ideology abhorrent to us because it is avowedly Communist, against religion, private property and liberty as we conceive it. But as a form of government it is acceptable to us as long as it represents independence and

251

national freedom of action. Philosophically it is a kind of decompression chamber between the Russian empire and the Western world. In Jugoslavia we worked with it closely as it suited our self-interest. Surely the same principle would apply in the rest of Eastern Europe if it serves to thaw the Soviet ice pack.

And it is attainable. Political forces are working in that direction. Most people of the satellites, both the broad anti-Communist masses and a great many Communists themselves, would prefer Titoism to what they have right now. Belgrade, a curiously influential little capital, naturally pushes its brain-child. Even Moscow implies readiness to accept change.

What Titoism means to the subjected satellite populations is not escape from existing Communist forms. Rather it signifies development of national independence and easier contact with the West. It implies liberty of political as distinct from ideological action. And even if Jugoslavia should ever fully rejoin the Soviet orbit this abstract concept of Titoism will remain. The *idea* of Protestantism would have continued even if Luther and Calvin had recanted. Heresy, once initiated, is difficult to limit. Tito found this out with Dedijer and Djilas.

Plainly we must practice different forms of foreign policy toward captive states and toward free states, of which there are not yet any in Moscow's sphere. With regard to the former the primary objective is to release them from foreign control. In this respect our initial aims in Eastern Europe coincide with those proclaimed by Tito.

Our first aspiration is to split the U.S.S.R.'s European

252

empire into individual segments. Even if each retains its present ideology, nothing in terms of ultimate goals is sacrificed by such procedure. The United States will be no less popular or influential with the masses of independent Communist nations than it now is with the masses of subjected Communist nations. That is demonstrable in Jugoslavia.

Is it the task of United States foreign policy to oppose Communism as an ideology? Our tradition is to allow any country to choose its own form of government. What we oppose is enslavement by outside powers. We object to Soviet imperialism enslaving peoples clamoring to be free.

In practice this has been confirmed in our attitude toward Jugoslavia, an independent Communist state allied with two of our NATO partners. Unfortunately, however, we have not exploited the logical development of this policy elsewhere. The current American attitude toward the satellites started in 1953 with a verbal bang of "liberation" slogans. But this dissolved into a whimper of inaction.

It seemed in the autumn of 1955 as if the United States was going to extricate itself from this position. Secretary Dulles called on Tito at Brioni and solicited his views on Eastern Europe. According to an American participant in the discussion:

Tito made no wild asseverations. He argued that changes now occurring in the U.S.S.R. would inevitably bring about changes in the satellites.

Tito knows about these things. He has always been ahead on such occurrences. He maintained it was impossible to sit still in the satellites and act as if nothing had happened in the U.S.S.R.

253

He said the changes he foresaw would not occur overnight; nevertheless they would occur. Popular pressure inside the satellites made this inevitable. And he agreed to an important declaration of principle that was difficult for him because of the American policy background in Eastern Europe.

Dulles made a statement while Tito stood by nodding approval. To avoid misunderstandings it was formulated in advance with great care by both sides. Dulles said: "We discussed the problems of the states of Eastern Europe. We were of common accord on recognizing the importance of independence for these states, non-interference from the outside in their internal affairs, and the right to develop their own social and economic order in ways of their own choice."

This was interpreted by the Jugoslavs and by American diplomats in East Europe with whom I since have talked as implying United States encouragement for any moves toward Titoism among the satellites. But what has happened? We have not followed up.

The Brioni conference was followed by a silent treatment. As one of our interested envoys says: "Clearly Washington was afraid to follow up so highly unconventional an idea—encouraging Titoism. Maybe it feared Congressional opposition during an election year." Meanwhile, diplomats, recalling the witch hunt against "Communists" inside the State Department, are reluctant to volunteer suggestions. One of them reminded me "Remember the John Davies case."

Encouraging Titoism's spread in Eastern Europe would be for ourselves a policy of heads I win, tails you lose. For if Moscow relaxes controls sufficiently to permit political independence among its satellites we gain room for political maneuver even while they remain Communist. And if it refuses, we can fix the onus where it belongs.

If some national freedom of choice is allowed these countries the West might offer reasonable opportunities of trade. Such commerce need not be sought with the U.S.S.R. itself. But increased exchanges with the satellites would afford them a chance to develop gradual economic independence from the Soviet bloc. Without economic independence there can never be political independence. Tito himself discovered this. Despite his more affable relationships with Moscow, he continues to work out business deals with the West. Orbit trade is controlled by the U.S.S.R. But how will it benefit, for example, if Norwegian herring and Greek olives are exchanged for Polish coal?

If the Russians refuse to allow such commerce we should proclaim this fact. If they do, trade must, of course, be carried out at realistic price levels. This in itself could ultimately produce strains in existing money relationships. Right now satellite fiscal systems are tied totally to artificial ruble levels.

Our ultimate hope is that captive peoples may someday be able to choose governments they desire as promised at Yalta. But this is not presently attainable. Our initial goal is to loosen up the bloc. Even in this restricted sense there are foreseeable diplomatic consequences.

Tito pretends to neutralism, an "active neutralism" separated from either power coalition. Until now neutralism has been moving outward from Moscow like ripples from a stone dropped in the Soviet pond. Let us seek to reverse the trend. Lord knows the satellite populations long to be freed from their present ties. We cannot expect subservient governments to scrap the Warsaw Pact. But we can attempt to prepare for Eastern Europe new political positions from which, someday, they might venture demands for withdrawal of Soviet missions and troops. Could a Titoist Hungary imitate Iceland in Anti-NATO?

In Poland are signs of uneasy disquietude since President Bierut's death. Bulgaria is fumbling with change. Hungary's old boss, Rakosi, is out. Czechoslovakia's leadership is neither ruthlessly competent nor strongly situated.

Will the Kremlin permit its newest team of puppets to be unseated? Or can unpopular Communism maintain its Eastern European hold only through Soviet-supported force? Let us help blow away the smoke of "collective leadership" now being generated as a screen and find whether, after all, it is only through modified forms of Stalinism that Moscow can hold its satellites.

Some people fear endorsing this experiment in policy. They argue that encouragement of Titoism in Eastern Europe might boomerang by spreading it through the West. This is specious logic. We are contemplating an attitude toward captive states, not free states. The risk of national Communism always prevails in independent countries, such as Italy and France, where there are large Communist parties. But there are means of facing that threat now; and those means will remain.

East Europe is an unnatural slave of Russia. It is more inherently European and accustomed to higher standards of living and freer standards of thinking. Its normal geopolitical pull is westward, not eastward. This tendency must be exploited. More liberty of political action should be engendered there; and if this is not permitted we can demonstrate that this is Moscow's fault.

The best we can presently hope for in satellite Eastern Europe is to encourage the genesis of new forms within the Marxist fold, to remind that area there are circumstances in which heresy is profitable and independent thinking acceptable to Moscow. Any pragmatic deviation from orthodoxy is a step in the right direction—away from the monolithic imperial system which seems to be all that Moscow has hitherto understood.

If we do not adjust our approach to the satellites we risk losing a valuable diplomatic opportunity. For it is just as incumbent upon our statesmen to seek to loosen the unwilling pieces of Soviet empire as it is desirable from Moscow's viewpoint to break up the Western democratic coalition that opposes Communism and Russian imperial strength.

Not only must we exploit chances presented to us by the post-Stalin development. We must also offer to political refugees from that governmental form a new and better life, a more optimistic opportunity, than the West has so far been willing to give *émigrés* in search of freedom. Why is it that the great expanses of America's own West, Canada's huge reaches, Alaska's undeveloped resources, Australia and New Zealand, are still unavailable to thousands of pathetic in-

257

dividuals who sought promised freedom in the democratic world and found nothing but blind alleys, displaced persons' camps, and disillusionment?

Few Americans know the name of Hugon Hanke; nor is this fact surprising. For Hugon Hanke is an undistinguished figure, one of the innumerable bits of tragic human flotsam to drift on the tides of destiny that rolled across Eastern Europe during the last sixteen years. But during the summer of 1955 he became Prime Minister of the little London Government of *émigré* Poles. And one month later, while still Premier, he decided to go home. Thus he assumed a role in history: the first distinguished expatriate to return to a Communist country after World War II.

In 1955, as a feature of its new coexistence policy, the Soviet bloc began a drive to attract former citizens back. This was a logical move. For surely it is a propaganda weakness in any political system when thousands of the people it would encompass flee abroad. Despite the barbed-wire line running from the Black Sea to the Baltic, men and women still risk death and court unhappiness in an effort to escape. This is no advertisement for social benefits.

Therefore, Moscow sponsored a Committee for the Return of Displaced Persons to the Homeland. This was not without precedent. Twice before, during periods of relaxed relations with the West, the U.S.S.R. fostered similar appeals—once at the time of Lenin's New Economic Policy and again during the era of the last war's alliance.

This maneuver was swiftly echoed by the satellites, who

offered amnesties and benefits to those who would come back. Agents circulated appeals among unhappy emigrant colonies and in the sordid huts where thousands of fugitives still live in anonymity as displaced persons. Radio stations started to beam luring programs.

The return to Warsaw of Hugon Hanke is one consequence. After his country's occupation, he joined the Polish army formed first in France, then in England. When peace came he resolved to stay in London. Says he: "I heard that Poland was a dictatorship, that people were deported to Siberia. I signed a protest to the United Nations complaining ours was an 'occupied country.' "

As time went on the London Polish colony shrank. Some became British subjects. Others journeyed overseas to new careers. In 1953 Hanke, the little-known and unaspiring fugitive, became a minister. In August, 1955, he was chosen Premier. This was a grandiose position. But for sixteen years he had not seen his wife or three children. He lived in a dreary flat on £28 a month. His Cabinet was feuding. His colleagues, he complains, contended that only by war could Poland again be freed. Then came the Geneva summit conference. "I saw," he says, "that there wouldn't be a war."

Hanke asked his ministers how they felt about new Warsaw offers of amnesty and aid to those who would return. His Government took no decision. But Hugon Hanke did. He went to Rome and sought to see the Pope. The London Poles' envoy to the Vatican blocked his audience. So he went to Warsaw's Embassy in Rome and was persuaded. He resigned his office and boarded a train for Poland. The Communists arranged to have his family meet him.

As a prize exhibit, Hanke has been treated kindly. Despite the housing shortage he has a five-room apartment. He was made vice-president of Polonia, an organization to develop contacts with Poles abroad. He earns 4,000 zlotys a month, good pay in Poland. He is studying Marxism and plans to join P.A.X., a fellow-traveling church and political movement.

For Poland's regime the return of Hanke was a triumph. His appeal to expatriates is bound to wring nostalgic hearts. And unless the free world can make greater opportunities for *émigrés* from Communism, the number to go back may well increase. For abstract freedom alone is insufficient. This the Communists calculate. And, during any relaxation era, time and propaganda may abet their efforts.

CONSEQUENCES OF THE THAW

Neither the Western nor the so-called Eastern world is static. Since immemorial time empires, maritime or terrestrial, have grown and shrunk. The evolution, during this mid-century, both of democracy's coalition and what we call the Soviet orbit, are natural developments when viewed across the span of time. It is illogical for Moscow to blame us for protecting our wealth and political aspirations; and it is equally illogical for us to blame their ideological and territorial dynamism. There is nothing inherently abnormal in either development. These, whether we like to think so or not, are traditional, human, rational ambitions. But, just as

260

the Russians try to split up and dislodge our forces, whether by blandishment or threat, it is our duty to counteract in similar fashion. This is an obligation of our own political system as long as we consider it valid and viable.

A West German periodical called *Europa* wrote in April, 1955:

> In the course of European history there has evolved what we can call a common culture despite all dissimilarities. The awareness of this common culture has often been dimmed by political confusion, but it has never been lost, so that basically it has been the most vigorous factor in what Europe has given out to the world. . . . Bolshevism may introduce into its power area any cultural measures whatever by means of administrative enforcement. We in the West, however, cannot do that. We have to work with conviction and argument; we have to unite by finding areas of agreement for diverging opinions.

The United States belongs to that portion of the world called "European" whether in a political, a psychological or an emotional sense. Our enemies, in the burgeoning colored lands of Asia and Africa attack us as "European" in the meaning of white-supremacy prejudices. This is a label we must escape by eliminating more swiftly the terrible vestiges of racial complexes that are our heritage from colonial plantation days. Our friends think of us as "European" in the sense of culture, of liberalism, of democracy; as the legatees of what was best in Athens, in Renaissance Italy and eighteenth-century France, Germany and England. Where we have gone wrong is in forgetting the testament of beauty and of tolerance handed down to us by the thinkers of those times. Where we

261

have gone right is in abiding by them.

The Soviet empire is apparently in a new phase of development. Some of the revolution's own children, before being devoured by it, foresaw an end to Stalin's brutal aberrations. Leon Trotsky wrote: "Nero, too, was a product of his epoch. Yet after he perished his statues were smashed and his name was scraped off everything. The vengeance of history is more terrible than the vengeance of the most powerful General Secretary. I venture to think that this is consoling."

The tyrant of the first Rome was followed by a tumultuous war of succession. It is indeed unlikely that any such strife will gnaw the post-Stalin state. Nevertheless, that massive empire is bound to experience convulsive throes if it truly experiments with freedom. Therefore, in the ideological contest of our time, we have an inherent advantage. For freedom, both explicit and implicit, is already native to our political system. If we can but hold together with our friends, we will observe the results of Khrushchev's anachronism—trying to mix liberty and Leninism. Ultimately, this is unlikely to work. For liberty means individualism; and individualism abhors dictatorship in any form.

Moscow, with great audacity, has decreed a Big Thaw in its empire. Should this prove meaningful, its consequences to the Communist system are far more dangerous than to ourselves. Let us attempt by every means to stimulate it.

Postscript

THIS essay derives from a series of visits to the Soviet orbit, the latest of which were in the winter and spring of 1956. It is based on my columns in *The New York Times* and acknowledgment is made to that newspaper for permission to reprint many articles. Several readers had suggested that a book be compiled from these dispatches; the above is the result. Necessarily, it suffers from the limitations of journalism, above all in terms of time. Nevertheless, since I have traveled on various trips between the Oxus and the Oder and between the Caucasus and the Baltic and Adriatic seas, it is thought these impressions are worth compiling.

That many of them will soon be dated by future developments cannot be avoided. The scene is shifting. New and unforeseeable events may erupt before these pages are published. Statesmen mentioned here may suddenly fall from power or vanish from the scene.

Furthermore, our State Department's attitude on travel to those areas, when visas became possible, has forced me to limit my observations on Communist China and the less important

263

segments of the Marxist domain: North Korea, North Vietnam, Mongolia, Tibet. This becomes particularly unfortunate since, to a considerable degree, I have sought to base my remarks upon personal reflections and discussions. It is my only hope that these opinions may stimulate thinking on the immense problems posed by Competitive Coexistence.

Along with millions of others on both sides of the Iron Curtain I share hopes that there will develop a real change in Communism's outlook now that Stalinism is officially discountenanced. But I agree with those Western leaders who advocate a cautious approach. Leninism remains the official doctrine and it is replete with authoritarian tendencies. It scoffs at morality and ethics. Furthermore, there are deep currents in Russia's past history that may not safely be disregarded no matter what Moscow's present rulers tell us. Time and again, in that great country's past, movements toward liberalization have ended in tyrannical agony. Therefore, to calculate that the new Soviet junta is manufacturing a brave new world is hazardous; to base policy upon such calculations would be folly. But to allow our policy to remain static in a changing situation is obviously insane.

264

Index

265

269

271

An Unsuitable Job for a Woman

An Unsuitable Job

for

a Woman

P. D. JAMES

CHARLES SCRIBNER'S SONS
New York

For Jane and Peter
who kindly allowed two of
my characters to live at
57 Norwich Street.

Author's Note

❖❖❖

A crime novelist, by virtue of his unpleasant craft, has the duty to create at least one highly reprehensible character in each book and it is perhaps inevitable that from time to time their sanguinary misdeeds should impinge upon the dwellings of the just. A writer whose characters have chosen to act out their tragicomedy in an ancient university city is in particular difficulty. He can, of course, call it Oxbridge, invent colleges named after improbable saints and send his characters boating on the Camsis, but this timid compromise merely confuses characters, readers and the author alike, with the result that no one knows precisely where he is and two communities are offered opportunities for offence instead of one.

The greater part of this story is unrepentantly set in Cambridge, a city in which, undeniably, there live and work policemen, coroners, doctors, students, college servants, flower sellers, Dons, scientists, and even, no doubt, retired Majors. None of them, to my knowledge, bears the slightest resemblance to his counterpart in this book. All the characters, even the most unpleasant, are imaginary; the city, happily for us all, is not.

P. D. J.

Chapter One

On the morning of Bernie Pryde's death—or it may have been the
morning after, since Bernie died at his own convenience, nor did he
think the estimated time of his departure worth recording—Cordelia was caught in a breakdown of the Bakerloo Line outside Lam-
beth North and was half an hour late at the office. She came up from
Oxford Circus underground into the bright June sunshine, sped past
the early morning shoppers scanning the windows of Dickins and
Jones and plunged into the cacophony of Kingly Street threading
her way between the blocked pavement and the shining mass of cars
and vans which packed the narrow street. The hurry she knew was
irrational, a symptom of her obsession with order and punctuality.
There were no appointments booked; no clients to be interviewed;
no case outstanding; not even a final report to be written. She and
Miss Sparshott, the temporary typist, at Cordelia's suggestion were
circulating information about the Agency to all the London solicitors in the hope of attracting custom; Miss Sparshott would probably
be busy with it now, eyes straying to her watch, tapping out her staccato irritation at every minute of Cordelia's lateness. She was an un-
prepossessing woman with lips permanently taut as if to prevent the
protruding teeth from springing from her mouth, a receding chin
with one coarse hair which grew as quickly as it was plucked, and
fair hair set in stiff corrugated waves. That chin and mouth seemed
to Cordelia the living refutation that all men are born equal and
she tried from time to time to like and sympathize with Miss Sparshott, with a life lived in bedsitting rooms, measured in the five-
penny pieces fed to the gas stove and circumscribed by fell seams
and hand hemming. For Miss Sparshott was a skilled dressmaker, an
assiduous attender at the G.L.C. evening classes. Her clothes were
beautifully made but so dateless that they were never actually in
fashion; straight skirts in grey or black which were exercises in how
to sew a pleat or insert a zip fastener; blouses with mannish collars
and cuffs in insipid pastel shades on which she distributed without
discretion her collection of costume jewellery; intricately cut dresses

with hems at the precise length to emphasize her shapeless legs and thick ankles.

Cordelia had no premonition of tragedy as she pushed open the street door which was kept perpetually on the latch for the convenience of the secretive and mysterious tenants and their equally mysterious visitors. The new bronze plaque to the left of the door gleamed brightly in the sun in incongruous contrast to the faded and dirt-encrusted paint. Cordelia gave it a short glance of approval:

Pryde's Detective Agency
(*Props*: Bernard G. Pryde   Cordelia Gray)

It had taken Cordelia some weeks of patient and tactful persuasion to convince Bernie that it would be inappropriate to append the words "ex-C.I.D. Metropolitan Police" to his name or prefix "Miss" to hers. There had been no other problem over the plaque since Cordelia had brought no qualifications or relevant past experience to the partnership and indeed no capital, except her slight but tough twenty-two-year-old body, a considerable intelligence which Bernie, she suspected, had occasionally found more disconcerting than admirable, and a half exasperated, half pitying affection for Bernie himself. It was obvious very early to Cordelia that in some undramatic but positive way life had turned against him. She recognized the signs. Bernie never got the enviable front left hand seat in the bus; he couldn't admire the view from the train window without another train promptly obscuring it; the bread he dropped invariably fell buttered side downwards; the Mini, reliable enough when she drove it, stalled for Bernie at the busiest and most inconvenient intersections. She sometimes wondered whether, in accepting his offer of a partnership in a fit of depression or of perverse masochism, she was voluntarily embracing his ill-luck. She certainly never saw herself as powerful enough to change it.

The staircase smelt as always of stale sweat, furniture polish and disinfectant. The walls were dark green and were invariably damp whatever the season as if they secreted a miasma of desperate respectability and defeat. The stairs, with their ornate wrought-iron balustrade, were covered with split and stained linoleum patched by the landlord in various and contrasting colours only when a tenant complained. The Agency was on the third floor. There was no clatter of typewriter keys as Cordelia entered and she saw that Miss Sparshott was engaged in cleaning her machine, an ancient Imperial which was a constant cause of justified complaint. She looked up,

her face blotched with resentment, her back as rigid as the space bar.

"I've been wondering when you would turn up, Miss Gray. I'm concerned about Mr. Pryde. I think he must be in the inner office but he's quiet, very quiet, and the door's locked."

Cordelia, chill at heart, wrenched at the door handle:

"Why didn't you do something?"

"Do what, Miss Gray? I knocked at the door and called out to him. It wasn't my place to do that, I'm only the temporary typist, I've no authority here. I should have been placed in a very embarrassing position if he had answered. After all, he's entitled to use his own office I suppose. Besides, I'm not even sure if he's there."

"He must be. The door's locked and his hat is here."

Bernie's trilby, the stained brim turned up all round, a comedian's hat, was hanging on the convoluted hatstand, a symbol of forlorn decrepitude. Cordelia was fumbling in her shoulder bag for her own key. As usual, the object most required had fallen to the bottom of the bag. Miss Sparshott began to clatter on the keys as if to disassociate herself from impending trauma. Above the noise she said defensively:

"There's a note on your desk."

Cordelia tore it open. It was short and explicit. Bernie had always been able to express himself succinctly when he had something to say:

"I'm sorry, partner, they've told me it's cancer and I'm taking the easy way out. I've seen what the treatment does to people and I'm not having any. I've made my will and it's with my solicitor. You'll find his name in the desk. I've left the business to you. Everything, including *all* the equipment. Good luck and thank you." Underneath with the inconsiderateness of the doomed he had scribbled a final unfair plea:

"If you find me alive, for God's sake wait before calling help. I rely on you for this, partner. Bernie."

She unlocked the door of the inner office and went inside, closing the door carefully behind her.

It was a relief to see that there was no need to wait. Bernie was dead. He lay slumped over the desk as if in an extremity of exhaustion. His right hand was half-clenched and an open cut-throat razor had slithered over the desk top leaving a thin trail of blood like a snail's track and had come to rest precariously poised on the extreme edge of the desk. His left wrist, scored with two parallel cuts, lay palm upwards in the enamel bowl which Cordelia used for the

3

washing-up. Bernie had filled it with water but it was now brimfull with a pale pinky liquid smelling sickly sweet, through which the fingers, curved as if in supplication and looking as white and delicate as those of a child, gleamed as smooth as wax. The blood and water had overflowed on to the desk and floor soaking the oblong of garish rug which Bernie had recently bought in the hope of impressing visitors with his status but which Cordelia privately thought had only drawn attention to the shabbiness of the rest of the office. One of the cuts was tentative and superficial but the other had gone deep as the bone and the severed edges of the wound, drained of blood, gaped cleanly like an illustration in an anatomy text book. Cordelia remembered how Bernie had once described the finding of a prospective suicide when he was first on the beat as a young constable. It was an old man huddled into a warehouse doorway who had slashed his wrist with a broken bottle—but who had later been dragged back to reluctant half-life because an immense clot of blood had blocked the severed veins. Bernie, remembering, had taken precautions to ensure that his blood would not clot. He had, she noticed, taken another precaution; there was an empty tea cup, the one in which she served his afternoon tea, on the right of the desk with a grain or two of powder, aspirin perhaps or a barbiturate, staining the rim and side. A dried trickle of mucus, similarly stained, hung from the corner of his mouth. His lips were pursed and half open like those of a sleeping child, petulant and vulnerable. She put her head round the office door and said quietly:

"Mr. Pryde is dead; don't come in. I'll ring the police from here."

The telephone message was taken calmly, someone would come round. Sitting beside the body to wait and feeling that she needed to make some gesture of pity and comfort Cordelia laid her hand gently on Bernie's hair. Death had as yet no power to diminish these cold and nerveless cells and the hair felt roughly and unpleasantly alive like that of an animal. Quickly she took her hand away and tentatively touched the side of his forehead. The skin was clammy and very cold. This was death; this was how Daddy had felt. As with him, the gesture of pity was meaningless and irrelevant. There was no more communication in death than there had been in life.

She wondered when exactly Bernie had died. No one now would ever know. Perhaps Bernie himself had not known. There must, she supposed, have been one measurable second in time in which he had ceased to be Bernie and had become this unimportant but embarrassingly unwieldy weight of flesh and bone. How odd that a mo-

ment of time so important to him should pass without his knowledge. Her second foster mother, Mrs. Wilkes, would have said that Bernie did know, that there was a moment of indescribable glory, shining towers, limitless singing, skies of triumph. Poor Mrs. Wilkes! Widowed, her only son dead in the war, her small house perpetually noisy with the foster children who were her livelihood, she had needed her dreams. She had lived her life by comfortable maxims stored like nuggets of coal against the winter. Cordelia thought of her now for the first time in years and heard again the tired, determinedly cheerful voice "If the Lord doesn't call on his way out, He'll call on his way back." Well, going or coming, He hadn't called on Bernie.

It was odd but somehow typical of Bernie that he should have retained a dogged and invincible optimism about the business even when they had nothing in the cash box but a few coins for the gas meter and yet had given up hope of life without even a struggle. Was it perhaps that he had sub-consciously recognized that neither he nor the Agency had any real future and had decided that this way he could yield up both life and livelihood with some honour? He had done it effectively but messily, surprisingly so for an ex-policeman versed in the ways of death. And then she realized why he had chosen the razor and the drugs. The gun. He hadn't really taken the easy way out. He could have used the gun, but he had wanted her to have it; he had bequeathed it to her together with the rickety filing cabinets, the antique typewriter, the scene-of-crime kit, the Mini, his shock-proof and waterproof wrist watch, the blood-soaked rug, the embarrassingly large stock of writing paper with the ornate heading *Pryde's Detective Agency—We take a Pride in our Work. All* the equipment; he had underlined all. He must have meant to remind her about the gun.

She unlocked the small drawer at the base of Bernie's desk to which only she and he had a key and drew it out. It was still in the suede draw-string bag which she had made for it, with three rounds of ammunition packed separately. It was a pistol, a .38 semi-automatic; she had never known how Bernie had come by it but she was certain that he had no licence. She had never seen it as a lethal weapon, perhaps because Bernie's boyishly naive obsession with it had reduced it to the impotence of a child's toy. He had taught her to become—at any rate in theory—a creditable shot. They had driven for practice into the depths of Epping Forest and her memories of the gun were linked with dappled shade and the rich smell of de-

caying leaves. He had fixed a target to a convenient tree; the gun was loaded with blanks. She could still hear the excited staccato orders. "Bend your knees slightly. Feet apart. Arm full length. Now place the left hand against the barrel, cradling it. Keep your eyes on the target. Arm straight, partner, arm straight! Good! Not bad; not bad; not bad at all." "But, Bernie," she had said, "we can never fire it! We haven't a licence." He had smiled, the sly self-satisfied smile of superior knowledge. "If we ever fire in anger it will be to save our lives. In such an eventuality the question of a licence is irrelevant." He had been pleased with this rotund sentence and had repeated it, lifting his heavy face to the sun like a dog. What, she wondered, had he seen in imagination? The two of them crouching behind a boulder on some desolate moor, bullets pinging against the granite, the gun passed smoking from hand to hand?

He had said: "We'll have to go carefully with the ammunition. Not that I can't get it of course . . ." The smile had become grim, as if at the memory of those mysterious contacts, those ubiquitous and obliging acquaintances whom he had only to summon from their shadow world.

So he had left her the gun. It had been his most prized possession. She slipped it, still shrouded, into the depths of her shoulder bag. It was surely unlikely that the police would examine the drawers of the desk in a case of obvious suicide but it was as well to take no risk. Bernie had meant her to have the gun and she wasn't going to give it up easily. With her bag at her feet she sat down again by the body. She said a brief convent-taught prayer to the God she wasn't sure existed for the soul which Bernie had never believed he possessed and waited quietly for the police.

The first policeman to arrive was efficient but young, not yet experienced enough to hide his shock and distaste at the sight of violent death nor his disapproval that Cordelia should be so calm. He didn't spend long in the inner office. When he came out he meditated upon Bernie's note as if a careful scrutiny could extract some inner meaning from the bald sentence of death. Then he folded it away.

"I'll have to keep this note for the present, Miss. What did he get up to here?"

"He didn't get up to anything. This was his office. He was a private detective."

"And you worked for this Mr. Pryde? You were his secretary?"

6

"I was his partner. It says so in the note. I'm twenty-two. Bernie was the senior partner; he started the business. He used to work for the Metropolitan Police in the C.I.D. with Superintendent Dalgliesh."

As soon as the words were spoken, she regretted them. They were too propitiatory, too naive a defence of poor Bernie. And the name Dalgliesh, she saw meant nothing to him. Why should it? He was just one of the local uniformed branch. He couldn't be expected to know how often she had listened with politely concealed impatience to Bernie's nostalgic reminiscences of his time in the C.I.D. before he was invalided out, or to his eulogies on the virtues and wisdom of Adam Dalgliesh. "The Super—well, he was just an Inspector then—always taught us . . . The Super once described a case . . . If there was one thing the Super couldn't stand . . ."

Sometimes she had wondered whether this paragon had actually existed or whether he had sprung impeccable and omnipotent from Bernie's brain, a necessary hero and mentor. It was with a shock of surprise that she had later seen a newspaper picture of Chief Superintendent Dalgliesh, a dark, sardonic face which, on her closer scrutiny, disintegrated into an ambiguity of patterned micro dots, giving nothing away. Not all the wisdom Bernie so glibly recalled was the received gospel. Much, she suspected, was his own philosophy. She in turn had devised a private litany of disdain: supercilious, superior, sarcastic Super; what wisdom, she wondered, would he have to comfort Bernie now.

The policeman had made discreet telephone calls. He now prowled around the outer office, hardly bothering to hide his puzzled contempt at the shabby second-hand furniture, the battered filing cabinet with one drawer half-open to reveal teapot and mugs, the worn linoleum. Miss Sparshott, rigid at an ancient typewriter, gazed at him with fascinated distaste. At last he said:

"Well, suppose you make yourselves a nice cup of tea while I wait for the police surgeon. There is somewhere to make tea?"

"There's a small pantry down the corridor which we share with the other tenants on this floor. But surely you don't need a surgeon? Bernie's dead!"

"He's not officially dead until a qualified medical practitioner says so." He paused: "It's just a precaution."

Against what, Cordelia wondered—judgement, damnation, decay? The policeman went back into the inner office. She followed him and asked softly:

7

"Couldn't you let Miss Sparshott go? She's from a secretarial agency and we have to pay for her by the hour. She hasn't done any work since I arrived and I doubt whether she will now."

He was, she saw, a little shocked by the apparent callousness of concerning herself with so mercenary a detail while standing within touching distance of Bernie's body, but he said willingly enough:

"I'll just have a word with her, then she can go. It isn't a nice place for a woman."

His tone implied that it never had been.

Afterwards, waiting in the outer office, Cordelia answered the inevitable questions.

"No, I don't know whether he was married. I've a feeling that he was divorced; he never talked about a wife. He lived at 15, Cremona Road, S.E.2. He let me have a bedsitting room there but we didn't see much of each other."

"I know Cremona Road; my aunt used to live there when I was a kid—one of those streets near the Imperial War Museum."

The fact that he knew the road seemed to reassure and humanize him. He ruminated happily for a moment.

"When did you last see Mr. Pryde alive?"

"Yesterday at about five o'clock when I left work early to do some shopping."

"Didn't he come home last night?"

"I heard him moving around but I didn't see him. I have a gas ring in my room and I usually cook there unless I know he's out. I didn't hear him this morning which is unusual, but I thought he might be lying in. He does that occasionally when it's his hospital morning."

"Was it his hospital morning to-day?"

"No, he had an appointment last Wednesday but I thought that they might have asked him to come back. He must have left the house very late last night or before I woke early this morning. I didn't hear him."

It was impossible to describe the almost obsessional delicacy with which they avoided each other, trying not to intrude, preserving the other's privacy, listening for the sound of flushing cisterns, tip-toeing to ascertain whether the kitchen or bathroom was empty. They had taken infinite trouble not to be a nuisance to each other. Living in the same small terraced house they had hardly seen each other outside the office. She wondered whether Bernie had decided to kill

8

himself in his office so that the little house would be uncontaminated and undisturbed.

❖❖❖

At last the office was empty and she was alone. The police surgeon had closed his bag and departed; Bernie's body had been manoeuvred down the narrow staircase watched by eyes from the half-opened doors of other offices; the last policeman had left. Miss Sparshott had gone for good, violent death being a worse insult than a typewriter which a trained typist ought not to be expected to use or lavatory accommodation which was not at all what she had been accustomed to. Alone in the emptiness and silence Cordelia felt the need of physical action. She began vigorously to clean the inner office, scrubbing the blood stains from desk and chair, mopping the soaked rug.

At one o'clock she walked briskly to their usual pub. It occurred to her that there was no longer any reason to patronize the Golden Pheasant but she walked on unable to bring herself to so early a disloyalty. She had never liked the pub or the landlady and had often wished that Bernie would find a nearer house, preferably one with a large bosomy barmaid with a heart of gold. It was, she suspected, a type commoner in fiction than in real life. The familiar lunch-time crowd was clustered around the bar and, as usual, Mavis presided behind it wearing her slightly minatory smile, her air of extreme respectability. Mavis changed her dress three times a day, her hair style once every year, her smile never. The two women had never liked each other although Bernie had galumphed between them like an affectionate old dog, finding it convenient to believe that they were great mates and unaware of or ignoring the almost physical crackle of antagonism. Mavis reminded Cordelia of a librarian known to her in childhood who had secreted the new books under the counter in case they should be taken out and soiled. Perhaps Mavis's barely suppressed chagrin was because she was forced to display her wares so prominently, compelled to measure out her bounty before watchful eyes. Pushing a half pint of shandy and a Scotch egg across the counter in response to Cordelia's order, she said:

"I hear you've had the police round."

Watching their avid faces, Cordelia thought, they know about it,

9

of course; they want to hear the details; they may as well hear them. She said:

"Bernie cut his wrists twice. The first time he didn't get to the vein; the second time he did. He put his arm in water to help the bleeding. He had been told that he had cancer and couldn't face the treatment."

That, she saw, was different. The little group around Mavis glanced at each other, then quickly averted their eyes. Glasses were momentarily checked upon their upward way. Cutting one's wrist was something which other people did but the sinister little crab had his claws of fear into all their minds. Even Mavis looked as if she saw his bright claws lurking among her bottles. She said:

"You'll be looking for a new job, I suppose? After all, you can hardly keep the Agency going on your own. It isn't a suitable job for a woman."

"No different from working behind a bar; you meet all kinds of people."

The two women looked at each other and a snatch of unspoken dialogue passed between them clearly heard and understood by both.

"And don't think, now he's dead, that people can go on leaving messages for the Agency here."

"I wasn't going to ask."

Mavis began vigorously polishing a glass, her eyes still on Cordelia's face.

"I shouldn't think your mother would approve of you staying on alone."

"I only had a mother for the first hour of my life, so I don't have to worry about that."

Cordelia saw at once that the remark had deeply shocked them and wondered again at the capacity of older people to be outraged by simple facts when they seemed capable of accepting any amount of perverse or shocking opinion. But their silence, heavy with censure, at least left her in peace. She carried her shandy and the Scotch egg to a seat against the wall and thought without sentimentality about her mother. Gradually out of a childhood of deprivation she had evolved a philosophy of compensation. In her imagination she had enjoyed a lifetime of love in one hour with no disappointments and no regrets. Her father had never talked about her mother's death and Cordelia had avoided questioning him, fearful of learning that her mother had never held her in her arms, never regained consciousness, never perhaps even known that she had a daughter.

This belief in her mother's love was the one fantasy which she could still not entirely risk losing although its indulgence had become less necessary and less real with each passing year. Now, in imagination, she consulted her mother. It was just as she expected: her mother thought it an entirely suitable job for a woman.

The little group at the bar had turned back to their drinks. Between their shoulders she could see her own reflection in the mirror above the bar. Today's face looked no different from yesterday's face; thick, light brown hair framing features which looked as if a giant had placed a hand on her head and the other under her chin and gently squeezed the face together; large eyes, browny-green under a deep fringe of hair; wide cheek bones; a gentle, childish mouth. A cat's face she thought, but calmly decorative among the reflection of coloured bottles and all the bright glitter of Mavis's bar. Despite its look of deceptive youth it could be a secret, uncommunicative face. Cordelia had early learnt stoicism. All her foster parents, kindly and well-meaning in their different ways, had demanded one thing of her—that she should be happy. She had quickly learned that to show unhappiness was to risk the loss of love. Compared with this early discipline of concealment, all subsequent deceits had been easy.

The Snout was edging his way towards her. He settled himself down on the bench, his thick rump in its appalling tweed pressed close to hers. She disliked the Snout although he had been Bernie's only friend. Bernie had explained that the Snout was a police informer and did rather well. And there were other sources of income. Sometimes his friends stole famous pictures or valuable jewellery. Then the Snout, suitably instructed, would hint to the police where the loot could be found. There was a reward for the Snout to be subsequently shared, of course, among the thieves, and a payoff, too, for the detective, who after all, had done most of the work. As Bernie had pointed out, the insurance company got off lightly, the owners got their property back intact, the thieves were in no danger from the police and the Snout and the detective got their payoff. It was the system. Cordelia, shocked, had not liked to protest too much. She suspected that Bernie too had done some snouting in his time, although never with such expertise or with such lucrative results.

The Snout's eyes were rheumy, his hand around the glass of whisky was shaking.

"Poor old Bernie, I could see he had it coming to him. He'd been losing weight for the last year and he had that grey look to him, the cancer complexion, my dad used to call it."

At least the Snout had noticed; she hadn't. Bernie had always seemed to her grey and sick-looking. A thick, hot thigh edged closer.

"Never had any luck, poor sod. They chucked him out of the C.I.D. Did he tell you? That was Superintendent Dalgliesh, Inspector at the time. Christ, he could be a proper bastard; no second chance from him, I can tell you."

"Yes, Bernie told me," Cordelia lied. She added: "He didn't seem particularly bitter about it."

"No use, is there, in being bitter? Take what comes, that's my motto. I suppose you'll be looking for another job?"

He said it wistfully as if her defection would leave the Agency open for his exploitation.

"Not just yet," said Cordelia. "I shan't look for a new job just yet."

She had made two resolutions: she would keep on Bernie's business until there was nothing left with which to pay the rent, and she would never come into the Golden Pheasant again as long as she lived.

This resolution to keep the business going survived the next four days—survived discovery of the rent book and agreement which revealed that Bernie hadn't, after all, owned the little house in Cremona Road and that her tenancy of the bedsitting room was illegal and certainly limited; survived learning from the Bank Manager that Bernie's credit balance would barely pay for his funeral and from the garage that the Mini was shortly due for an overhaul; survived the clearing up of the Cremona Road house. Everywhere was the sad detritus of a solitary and mismanaged life.

The tins of Irish stew and baked beans—had he never eaten anything else?—stacked in a carefully arranged pyramid as if in a grocer's window; large tins of floor and metal polish, half-used, with their contents dried or congealed; a drawer of old rags used as dusters but stiff with an amalgam of polish and dirt; a laundry basket unemptied; thick woollen combinations felted with machine washing and stained brown about the crotch—how could he have borne to leave those for discovery?

She went daily to the office, cleaning, tidying, rearranging the filing. There were no calls and no clients and yet she seemed always busy. There was the inquest to attend, depressing in its detached

almost boring formality, in its inevitable verdict. There was a visit to Bernie's solicitor. He was a dispirited, elderly man with an office inconveniently situated near Mile End Station who took the news of his client's death with lugubrious resignation as if it were a personal affront, and after a brief search found Bernie's will and pored over it with puzzled suspicion, as if it were not the document he himself had recently drawn up. He succeeded in giving Cordelia the impression that he realized that she had been Bernie's mistress—why else should he have left her the business?—but that he was a man of the world and didn't hold the knowledge against her. He took no part in arranging the funeral except to supply Cordelia with the name of a firm of undertakers; she suspected that they probably gave him a commission. She was relieved after a week of depressing solemnity to find that the funeral director was both cheerful and competent. Once he discovered that Cordelia wasn't going to break down in tears or indulge in the more histrionic antics of the bereaved, he was happy to discuss the relative price and the merits of burial and cremation with conspiratorial candour.

"Cremation every time. There's no private insurance, you tell me? Then get it all over as quickly, easily and cheaply as possible. Take my word, that's what the deceased would want nine times out of ten. A grave's an expensive luxury these days—no use to him—no use to you. Dust to dust, ashes to ashes; but what about the process in between? Not nice to think about, is it? So why not get it over as quickly as possible by the most reliable modern methods? Mind you, Miss, I'm advising you against my own best interests."

Cordelia said:

"It's very kind of you. Do you think we ought to have a wreath?"

"Why not, it'll give it a bit of tone. Leave it to me."

So there had been a cremation and one wreath. The wreath had been a vulgarly inappropriate cushion of lilies and carnations, the flowers already dying and smelling of decay. The cremation service had been spoken by the priest with carefully controlled speed and with a suggestion of apology in his tone as if to assure his hearers that, although he enjoyed a special dispensation, he didn't expect them to believe the unbelievable. Bernie had passed to his burning to the sound of synthetic music and only just on time, to judge by the impatient rustlings of the cortège already waiting to enter the chapel.

Afterwards Cordelia was left standing in the bright sunlight, feeling the heat of the gravel through the soles of her shoes. The air was

rich and heavy with the scent of flowers. Swept suddenly with desolation and a defensive anger on Bernie's behalf, she sought a scapegoat and found it in a certain Superintendent of the Yard. He had kicked Bernie out of the only job he had ever wanted to do; hadn't troubled to find out what happened to him later; and, most irrational indictment of all, he hadn't even bothered to come to the funeral. Bernie had needed to be a detective as other men needed to paint, write, drink or fornicate. Surely the C.I.D. was large enough to accommodate one man's enthusiasm and inefficiency? For the first time Cordelia wept for Bernie; hot tears blurred and multiplied the long line of waiting hearses with their bright coronets so that they seemed to stretch in an infinity of gleaming chrome and trembling flowers. Untying the black chiffon scarf from her head, her only concession to mourning, Cordelia set off to walk to the tube station.

She was thirsty when she got to Oxford Circus and decided to have tea in the restaurant at Dickins and Jones. This was unusual and an extravagance but it had been an unusual and extravagant day. She lingered long enough to get full value for her bill and it was after a quarter past four when she returned to the office.

She had a visitor. There was a woman waiting, shoulders against the door—a woman who looked cool and incongruous against the dirty paintwork and the greasy walls. Cordelia caught her breath in surprise, her upward rush checked. Her light shoes had made no sound on the stairway and for a few seconds she saw her visitor unobserved. She gained an impression, immediate and vivid, of competence and authority and an intimidating rightness of dress. The woman was wearing a grey suit with a small stand-away collar which showed a narrow band of white cotton at the throat. Her black patent shoes were obviously expensive; a large black bag with patch pockets was slung from her left shoulder. She was tall and her hair, prematurely white, was cut short and moulded to her head like a cap. Her face was pale and long. She was reading *The Times*, the paper folded so that she could hold it in her right hand. After a couple of seconds, she became aware of Cordelia and their eyes met. The woman looked at her wrist watch.

"If you are Cordelia Gray, then you're eighteen minutes late. This notice says that you would return at four o'clock."

"I know, I'm sorry." Cordelia hurried up the last few steps and fitted the Yale key into the lock. She opened the door.

"Won't you come in?"

The woman preceded her into the outer office and turned to face her without giving the room even a glance.

"I was hoping to see Mr. Pryde. Will he be long?"

"I'm sorry; I've just come back from his cremation. I mean . . . Bernie's dead."

"Obviously. Our information was that he was alive ten days ago. He must have died with remarkable speed and discretion."

"Not with discretion. Bernie killed himself."

"How extraordinary!" The visitor seemed to be struck by its extraordinariness. She pressed her hands together and for a few seconds walked restlessly about the room in a curious pantomime of distress.

"How extraordinary!" she said again. She gave a little snort of laughter. Cordelia didn't speak, but the two women regarded each other gravely. Then the visitor said:

"Well, I seem to have had a wasted journey."

Cordelia breathed an almost inaudible "Oh no!" and resisted an absurd impulse to fling her body against the door.

"Please don't go before talking to me. I was Mr. Pryde's partner and I own the business now. I'm sure I could help. Won't you please sit down?"

The visitor took no notice of the offered chair.

"No one can help, no one in the world. However, that is beside the point. There is something which my employer particularly wants to know—some information he requires—and he had decided that Mr. Pryde was the person to get it for him. I don't know if he would consider you an effective substitute. Is there a private telephone here?"

"In here, please."

The woman walked into the inner office, again with no sign that its shabbiness had made any impression on her. She turned to Cordelia.

"I'm sorry, I should have introduced myself. My name is Elizabeth Leaming and my employer is Sir Ronald Callender."

"The conservationist?"

"I shouldn't let him hear you call him that. He prefers to be called a micro-biologist, which is what he is. Please excuse me."

She shut the door firmly. Cordelia, feeling suddenly weak, sat down at the typewriter. The keys, oddly unfamiliar symbols encircled in black medallions, shifted their pattern before her tired eyes, then at a blink clicked back to normality. She grasped the sides

15

of the machine, cold and clammy to the touch, and talked herself back to calmness. Her heart was thudding.

"I must be calm, must show her that I am tough. This silliness is only the strain of Bernie's funeral and too much standing in the hot sun."

But hope was traumatic; she was angry with herself for caring so much.

The telephone call took only a couple of minutes. The door of the inner office opened; Miss Leaming was drawing on her gloves.

"Sir Ronald has asked to see you. Can you come now?"

Come where, thought Cordelia, but she didn't ask.

"Yes, shall I need my gear?"

The gear was Bernie's carefully designed and fitted out scene-of-crime case with its tweezers, scissors, finger printing equipment, jars to collect specimens; Cordelia had never yet had occasion to use it.

"It depends upon what you mean by your gear, but I shouldn't think so. Sir Ronald wants to see you before deciding whether to offer you the job. It means a train journey to Cambridge but you should get back tonight. Is there anyone you ought to tell?"

"No, there's only me."

"Perhaps I ought to identify myself." She opened her handbag. "Here is an addressed envelope. I'm not a white slaver if they exist and in case you're frightened."

"I'm frightened of quite a number of things but not of white slavers and if I were, an addressed envelope would hardly reassure me. I'd insist on telephoning Sir Ronald Callender to check."

"Perhaps you would like to do so?" suggested Miss Leaming without rancour.

"No."

"Then shall we go?" Miss Leaming led the way to the door. As they went out to the landing and Cordelia turned to lock the office behind her, her visitor indicated the notepad and pencil hanging together from a nail on the wall.

"Hadn't you better change the notice?"

Cordelia tore off her previous message and after a moment's thought wrote:

I am called away to an urgent case. Any messages pushed through the door will receive my immediate and personal attention on return.

"That," pronounced Miss Leaming, "should reassure your clients." Cordelia wondered if the remark was sarcastic; it was impossible to tell from the detached tone. But she didn't feel that Miss Leaming

16

was laughing at her and was surprised at her own lack of resentment at the way in which her visitor had taken charge of events. Meekly, she followed Miss Leaming down the stairs and into Kingly Street.

They travelled by the Central Line to Liverpool Street and caught the 17.36 train to Cambridge with plenty of time. Miss Leaming bought Cordelia's ticket, collected a portable typewriter and a brief-case of papers from the left luggage department and led the way to a first-class carriage. She said:

"I shall have to work in the train; have you anything to read?"

"That's all right. I don't like talking when I'm travelling either. I've got Hardy's *Trumpet Major*—I always have a paperback in my bag."

After Bishops Stortford they had the compartment to themselves but only once did Miss Leaming look up from her work to question Cordelia.

"How did you come to be working for Mr. Pryde?"

"After I left school I went to live with my father on the continent. We travelled around a good deal. He died in Rome last May after a heart attack and I came home. I had taught myself some shorthand and typing so I took a job with a secretarial agency. They sent me to Bernie and after a few weeks he let me help him with one or two of the cases. He decided to train me and I agreed to stay on permanently. Two months ago he made me his partner."

All that had meant was that Cordelia gave up a regular wage in return for the uncertain rewards of success in the form of an equal share of the profits together with a rent-free bedsitting room in Bernie's house. He hadn't meant to cheat. The offer of the partnership had been made in the genuine belief that she would recognize it for what it was; not a good conduct prize but an accolade of trust.

"What was your father?"

"He was an itinerant Marxist poet and an amateur revolutionary."

"You must have had an interesting childhood."

Remembering the succession of foster mothers, the unexplained incomprehensible moves from house to house, the changes of school, the concerned faces of Local Authority Welfare Officers and school teachers desperately wondering what to do with her in the holidays, Cordelia replied as she always did to this assertion, gravely and without irony.

"Yes, it was very interesting."

"And what was this training you received from Mr. Pryde?"

"Bernie taught me some of the things he learnt in the C.I.D.: how

17

to search the scene of a crime properly, how to collect exhibits, some elementary self-defence, how to detect and lift finger prints—that kind of thing."

"Those are skills which I hardly feel you will find appropriate to this case."

Miss Leaming bent her head over her papers and did not speak again until the train reached Cambridge.

❖❖❖

Outside the station Miss Leaming briefly surveyed the car park and led the way towards a small black van. Standing beside it rigidly as a uniformed chauffeur, was a stockily built young man dressed in an open-necked white shirt, dark breeches and tall boots who Miss Leaming introduced casually and without explanation as "Lunn." He nodded briefly in acknowledgement of the introduction but did not smile. Cordelia held out her hand. His grip was momentary but remarkably strong, crushing her fingers; suppressing a grimace of pain she saw a flicker in the large mud-brown eyes and wondered if he had hurt her deliberately. The eyes were certainly memorable and beautiful, moist calves' eyes heavily lashed and with the same look of troubled pain at the unpredictability of the world's terrors. But their beauty emphasized rather than redeemed the unattractiveness of the rest of him. He was, she thought, a sinister study in black and white with his thick, short neck and powerful shoulders straining the seams of his shirt. He had a helmet of strong black hair, a pudgy slightly pox-marked face and a moist petulant mouth; the face of a ribald cherub. He was a man who sweated profusely; the underarms of his shirt were stained and the cotton stuck to the flesh emphasizing the strong curve of the back and the obtrusive biceps.

Cordelia saw that the three of them were to sit squashed together in the front of the van. Lunn held open the door without apology except to state:

"The Rover's still in dock."

Miss Leaming hung back so that Cordelia was compelled to get in first and to sit beside him. She thought: "They don't like each other and he resents me."

She wondered about his position in Sir Ronald Callender's household. Miss Leaming's place she had already guessed; no ordinary secretary however long in service, however indispensable, had quite

that air of authority or talked of "my employer" in that tone of possessive irony. But she wondered about Lunn. He didn't behave like a subordinate but nor did he strike her as a scientist. True, scientists were alien creatures to her. Sister Mary Magdalen was the only one she had known. Sister had taught what the syllabus dignified as general science, a hotch-potch of elementary physics, chemistry and biology unceremoniously lumped together. Science subjects were in general little regarded at the Convent of the Immaculate Conception, although the arts were well taught. Sister Mary Magdalen had been an elderly and timid nun, eyes puzzled behind her steel-rimmed spectacles, her clumsy fingers permanently stained with chemicals, who had apparently been as surprised as her pupils at the extraordinary explosions and fumes which her activities with test tube and flask had occasionally produced. She had been more concerned to demonstrate the incomprehensibility of the universe and the inscrutability of God's laws than to reveal scientific principles and in this she had certainly succeeded. Cordelia felt that Sister Mary Magdalen would be no help to her in dealing with Sir Ronald Callender; Sir Ronald who had campaigned in the cause of conservation long before his interest became a popular obsession, who had represented his country at International Conferences on Ecology and been knighted for his services to conservation. All this Cordelia, like the rest of the country, knew from his television appearances and the Sunday Colour Supplements. He was the establishment scientist, carefully uncommitted politically, who personified to everyone's reassurance the poor boy who had made good and stayed good. How, Cordelia wondered, had he come to think of employing Bernie Pryde?

Uncertain how far Lunn was in his employer's or Miss Leaming's confidence, she asked carefully:

"How did Sir Ronald hear about Bernie?"

"John Bellinger told him."

So the Bellinger bonus had arrived at last! Bernie had always expected it. The Bellinger case had been his most lucrative, perhaps his only, success. John Bellinger was the director of a small family firm which manufactured specialized scientific instruments. The previous year his office had been plagued by an outbreak of obscene letters and, unwilling to call in the police, he had telephoned Bernie. Bernie, taken on the staff at his own suggestion as a messenger, had quickly solved a not very difficult problem. The writer had been Bellinger's middle-aged and highly regarded personal secretary. Bellinger had been grateful. Bernie, after anxious thought and con-

19

sultation with Cordelia, had sent in a bill the size of which had astounded them both and the bill had been promptly paid. It had kept the Agency going for a month. Bernie had said: "We'll get a bonus from the Bellinger case, see if we don't. Anything can happen in this job. He only chose us by picking our name from the telephone directory but now he'll recommend us to his friends. This case could be the beginning of something big."

And now, thought Cordelia, on the day of Bernie's funeral, the Bellinger bonus had arrived.

She asked no more questions and the drive, which took less than thirty minutes, passed in silence. The three of them sat thigh to thigh, but distanced. She saw nothing of the city. At the end of Station Road by the War Memorial the car turned to the left and soon they were in the country. There were wide fields of young corn, the occasional stretch of tree-lined dappled shade, straggling villages of thatched cottages and squat red villas strung along the road, low uplands from which Cordelia could see the towers and spires of the city, shining with deceptive nearness in the evening sun. Finally, there was another village, a thin belt of elms fringing the road, a long curving wall of red brick and the van turned in through open wrought iron gates. They had arrived.

◆◆◆

The house was obviously Georgian, not perhaps the best Georgian but solidly built, agreeably proportioned and with the look of all good domestic architecture of having grown naturally out of its site. The mellow brick, festooned with wisteria, gleamed richly in the evening sun so that the green of the creeper glowed and the whole house looked suddenly as artificial and unsubstantial as a film set. It was essentially a family house, a welcoming house. But now a heavy silence lay over it and the rows of elegantly proportioned windows were empty eyes.

Lunn, who had driven fast but skilfully, braked in front of the porch. He stayed in his seat while the two women got out then drove the van round the side of the house. As she slid down from the high seat Cordelia could glimpse a range of low buildings, topped with small ornamental turrets, which she took to be stables or garages. Through the wide-arched gateway she could see that the grounds dropped slowly away to give a far vista of the flat Cambridgeshire

countryside, patterned with the gentle greens and fawns of early summer. Miss Leaming said:

"The stable block has been converted into laboratories. Most of the east side is now glass. It was a skilful job by a Swedish architect, functional but attractive."

For the first time since they had met her voice sounded interested, almost enthusiastic.

The front door was open. Cordelia came into a wide, panelled hall with a staircase curving to the left, a carved stone fireplace to the right. She was aware of a smell of roses and lavender, of carpets gleaming richly against polished wood, of the subdued ticking of a clock.

Miss Leaming led the way to a door immediately across the hall. It led to a study, a room booklined and elegant, one with a view of wide lawns and a shield of trees. In front of the french windows was a Georgian desk and behind the desk sat a man.

Cordelia had seen his photographs in the press and knew what to expect. But he was at once smaller and more impressive than she had imagined. She knew that she was facing a man of authority and high intelligence; his strength came over like a physical force. But as he rose from his seat and waved her to a chair, she saw that he was slighter than his photographs suggested, the heavy shoulders and impressive head making the body look top-heavy. He had a lined, sensitive face with a high-bridged nose, deep-set eyes on which the lids weighed heavily and a mobile, sculptured mouth. His black hair, as yet unflecked with grey, lay heavily across his brow. His face was shadowed with weariness and, as Cordelia came closer, she could detect the twitch of a nerve in his left temple and the almost imperceptible staining of the veins in the irises of the deep-set eyes. But his compact body, taut with energy and latent vigour, made no concession to tiredness. The arrogant head was held high, the eyes were keen and wary under the heavy lids. Above all he looked successful. Cordelia had seen that look before, had recognized it from the back of crowds as, inscrutable, they had watched the famous and notorious pass on their way—that almost physical glow, akin to sexuality and undimmed by weariness or ill-health, of men who knew and enjoyed the realities of power.

Miss Leaming said:

"This is all that remains of Pryde's Detective Agency—Miss Cordelia Gray."

The keen eyes looked into Cordelia's.

"We take a Pride in our Work. Do you?"

Cordelia, tired after her journey at the end of a momentous day, was in no mood for jokes about poor Bernie's pathetic pun. She said:

"Sir Ronald, I have come here because your secretary said that you might want to employ me. If she's wrong, I would be glad to know so that I can get back to London."

"She isn't my secretary and she isn't wrong. You must forgive my discourtesy; it's a little disconcerting to expect a burly ex-policeman and to get you. I'm not complaining, Miss Gray; you might do very well. What are your fees?"

The question might have sounded offensive but it wasn't; he was completely matter-of-fact. Cordelia told him, a little too quickly, a little too eagerly.

"Five pounds a day and expenses, but we try to keep those as low as possible. For that, of course, you get my sole services. I mean I don't work for any other client until your case is finished."

"And is there another client?"

"Well, not just at present but there very well could be." She went on quickly:

"We have a fair-play clause. If I decide at any stage of the investigation that I'd rather not go on with it, you are entitled to any information I have gained up to that point. If I decide to withhold it from you, then I make no charge for the work already done."

That had been one of Bernie's principles. He had been a great man for principles. Even when there hadn't been a case for a week, he could happily discuss the extent to which they would be justified in telling a client less than the full truth, the point at which the police ought to be brought into an enquiry, the ethics of deception or lying in the service of truth. "But no bugging," Bernie would say "I set my face firmly against bugging. And we don't touch industrial sabotage."

The temptation to either wasn't great. They had no bugging equipment and wouldn't have known how to use it if they had, and at no time had Bernie been invited to touch industrial sabotage.

Sir Ronald said:

"That sounds reasonable but I don't think this case will present you with any crisis of conscience. It is comparatively simple. Eighteen days ago my son hanged himself. I want you to find out why. Can you do that?"

"I should like to try, Sir Ronald."

"I realize that you need certain basic information about Mark. Miss

Leaming will type it out for you, then you can read it through and let us know what else you require."

Cordelia said:

"I should like you to tell me yourself, please."

"Is that necessary?"

"It would be helpful to me."

He settled again into his chair and picked up a stub of pencil, twisting it in his hands. After a minute he slipped it absent-mindedly into his pocket. Without looking at her, he began to speak.

"My son Mark was twenty-one on the 25th April this year. He was at Cambridge reading history at my old college and was in his final year. Five weeks ago and without warning, he left the university and took a job as gardener with a Major Markland, who lives in a house called Summertrees outside Duxford. Mark gave me no explanation of this action either then or later. He lived alone in a cottage in Major Markland's grounds. Eighteen days later he was found by his employer's sister hanging by the neck from a strap knotted to a hook in the sitting-room ceiling. The verdict at the inquest was that he took his life while the balance of his mind was disturbed. I know little of my son's mind but I reject that comfortable euphemism. He was a rational person. He had a reason for his action. I want to know what it was."

Miss Leaming, who had been looking out of the french windows to the garden, turned and said with sudden vehemence:

"This lust always to know! It's only prying. If he'd wanted us to know, he'd have told us."

Sir Ronald said:

"I'm not prepared to go on in this uncertainty. My son is dead. *My* son. If I am in some way responsible, I prefer to know. If anyone else is responsible I want to know that too."

Cordelia looked from one to the other: She asked:

"Did he leave a note?"

"He left a note but not an explanation. It was found in his typewriter."

Quietly Miss Leaming began to speak:

"Down the winding cavern we groped our tedious way, till a void boundless as the nether sky appeared beneath us, and we held by the roots of trees and hung over this immensity; but I said: if you please we will commit ourselves to this void, and see whether providence is here also."

23

The husky, curiously deep voice came to an end. They were silent. Then Sir Ronald said:

"You claim to be a detective, Miss Gray. What do you deduce from that?"

"That your son read William Blake. Isn't it a passage from *The Marriage of Heaven and Hell?*"

Sir Ronald and Miss Leaming glanced at each other. Sir Ronald said:

"So I am told."

Cordelia thought that Blake's gently unemphatic exhortation, devoid of violence or despair, was more appropriate to suicide by drowning or by poison—a ceremonious floating or sinking into oblivion—than to the trauma of hanging. And yet there was the analogy of falling, of launching oneself into the void. But this speculation was indulgent fantasy. He had chosen Blake: he had chosen hanging. Perhaps other and more gentle means were not to hand; perhaps he had acted upon impulse. What was it that the Super always said? "Never theorize in advance of your facts." She would have to look at the cottage.

Sir Ronald said, with a touch of impatience:

"Well, don't you want the job?"

Cordelia looked at Miss Leaming but the woman did not meet her eyes.

"I want it very much. I was wondering whether you really want me to take it."

"I'm offering it to you. Worry about your own responsibilities, Miss Gray, and I'll look after mine."

Cordelia said:

"Is there anything else that you can tell me? The ordinary things. Was your son in good health? Did he seem worried about his work or his love affairs? About money?"

"Mark would have inherited a considerable fortune from his maternal grandfather had he reached the age of twenty-five. In the meantime, he received an adequate allowance from me, but from the date of leaving college he transferred the balance back to my own account and instructed his Bank Manager to deal similarly with any future payments. Presumably he lived on his earnings for the last two weeks of his life. The postmortem revealed no illnesses and his tutor testified that his academic work was satisfactory. I, of course, know nothing of his subject. He didn't confide in me about his love

affairs—what young man does to his father? If he had any, I would expect them to be heterosexual."

Miss Leaming turned from her contemplation at the garden. She held out her hands in a gesture which could have been resignation or despair:

"We knew nothing about him, nothing! So why wait until he's dead and then start finding out?"

"And his friends?" asked Cordelia quietly.

"They rarely visited here but there were two I recognized at the inquest and the funeral: Hugo Tilling from his own college and his sister who is a post-graduate student at New Hall, studying philology. Do you remember her name, Eliza?"

"Sophie. Sophia Tilling. Mark brought her here to dinner once or twice."

"Could you tell me something about your son's early life? Where was he educated?"

"He went to a pre-prep school when he was five and to a prep school subsequently. I couldn't have a child here running unsupervised in and out of the laboratory. Later, at his mother's wish—she died when Mark was nine months old—he went to a Woodard Foundation. My wife was what I believe is called a High Anglican and wanted the boy educated in that tradition. As far as I know, it had no deleterious effect on him."

"Was he happy at prep school?"

"I expect he was as happy as most eight-year-olds are, which means that he was miserable most of the time, interposed with periods of animal spirits. Is all this relevant?"

"Anything could be. I have to try to get to know him, you see."

What was it that the supercilious, sapient, superhuman Super had taught? "Get to know the dead person. Nothing about him is too trivial, too unimportant. Dead men can talk. They can lead you directly to their murderer." Only this time, of course, there wasn't a murderer. She said:

"It would be helpful if Miss Leaming could type out the information you have given to me and add the name of his college and his tutor. And please may I have a note signed by you to authorize me to make enquiries."

He reached down to a left-hand drawer in the desk, took out a sheet of writing paper and wrote on it; then he passed it to Cordelia. The printed heading read: From Sir Ronald Callender, F.R.S., Garforth House, Cambridgeshire. Underneath he had written:

25

The bearer, Miss Cordelia Gray, is authorized to make enquiries on my behalf into the death on 26th May of my son Mark Callender. He had signed and dated it. He asked:

"Is there anything else?"

Cordelia said:

"You talked about the possibility of someone else being responsible for your son's death. Do you quarrel with the verdict?"

"The verdict was in accordance with the evidence which is all one can expect of a verdict. A court of law is not constituted to establish the truth. I'm employing you to make an attempt at that. Have you everything you need? I don't think we can help you with any more information."

"I should like a photograph." They looked at each other nonplussed. He said to Miss Leaming:

"A photograph. Have we a photograph, Eliza?"

"There is his passport somewhere but I'm not sure where. I have that photograph I took of him in the garden last summer. It shows him fairly clearly, I think. I'll get it." She went out of the room. Cordelia said:

"And I should like to see his room, if I may. I assume that he stayed here during his vacations?"

"Only occasionally, but of course he had a room here. I'll show it to you."

The room was on the second floor and at the back. Once inside, Sir Ronald ignored Cordelia. He walked over to the window and gazed out over the lawns as if neither she nor the room held any interest for him. It told Cordelia nothing about the adult Mark. It was simply furnished, a school boy's sanctum, and looked as if little had been changed in the last ten years. There was a low white cupboard against one wall with the usual row of discarded childhood toys; a teddy bear, his fur scuffed with much cuddling and one beady eye hanging loose; painted wooden trains and trucks; a Noah's Ark, its deck a-tumble with stiff-legged animals topped by a round-faced Noah and his wife; a boat with limp dejected sail; a miniature darts board. Above the toys were two rows of books. Cordelia went over to examine them. Here was the orthodox library of the middle-class child, the approved classics handed down from generation to generation, the traditional lore of Nanny and mother. Cordelia had come to them late as an adult; they had found no place in her Saturday comic and television-dominated childhood. She said:

"What about his present books?"

"They're in boxes in the cellar. He sent them here for storage when he left college and we haven't had time to unpack them yet. There hardly seems any point in it."

There was a small round table beside the bed and on it a lamp and a bright round stone intricately holed by the sea, a treasure picked up, perhaps, from some holiday beach. Sir Ronald touched it gently with long tentative fingers then began rolling it under his palm over the surface of the table. Then, apparently without thinking, he dropped it into his pocket. "Well," he said. "Shall we go down now?"

They were met at the foot of the stairs by Miss Leaming. She looked up at them as slowly they came down side by side. There was such controlled intensity in her regard that Cordelia waited almost with apprehension for her to speak. But she turned away, her shoulders drooping as if with sudden fatigue, and all she said was:

"I've found the photograph. I should like it back when you've finished with it, please. I've put it in the envelope with the note. There isn't a fast train back to London until nine thirty-seven, so perhaps you would care to stay for dinner?"

❖·❖·❖

The dinner party which followed was an interesting but rather odd experience, the meal itself a blend of the formal and casual which Cordelia felt was the result of conscious effort rather than chance. Some effect, she felt, had been aimed at but whether of a dedicated band of co-workers meeting together at the end of a day for a corporate meal, or the ritual imposition of order and ceremony on a diverse company, she wasn't sure. The party numbered ten: Sir Ronald Callender, Miss Leaming, Chris Lunn, a visiting American Professor, whose unpronounceable name she forgot as soon as Sir Ronald introduced her, and five of the young scientists. All the men, including Lunn, were in dinner jackets, and Miss Leaming wore a long skirt of patchwork satin below a plain sleeveless top. The rich blues, greens and reds gleamed and changed in the candlelight as she moved, and emphasized the pale silver of her hair and the almost colourless skin. Cordelia had been rather nonplussed when her hostess left her in the drawing room and went upstairs to change. She wished that she had something more competitive than the fawn skirt

and green top, being at an age to value elegance more highly than youth.

She had been shown to Miss Leaming's bedroom to wash and had been intrigued by the elegance and simplicity of the furniture and the contrasting opulence of the adjacent bathroom. Studying her tired face in the mirror and wielding her lipstick, she had wished she had some eye shadow with her. On impulse, and with a sense of guilt, she had pulled open a dressing-table drawer. It was filled with a variety of make-up; old lipsticks in colours long out-of-date; half-used bottles of foundation cream; eye pencils; moisturizing creams; half-used bottles of scent. She had rummaged, and eventually found, a stick of eye shadow which, in view of the wasteful muddle of discarded items in the drawer, she had had little compunction in using. The effect had been bizarre but striking. She could not compete with Miss Leaming but at least she looked five years older. The disorder in the drawer had surprised her and she had had to resist the temptation to see if the wardrobe and the other drawers were in a similar state of disarray. How inconsistent and how interesting human beings were! She thought it astonishing that such a fastidious and competent woman should be content to live with such a mess.

The dining room was at the front of the house. Miss Leaming placed Cordelia between herself and Lunn, a seating which held little prospect of pleasurable conversation. The rest of the party sat where they wished. The contrast between simplicity and elegance showed in the table arrangements. There was no artificial light and three silver branched candlesticks were placed at regular intervals down the table. Between them were set four wine carafes made of thick green glass with curved lips, such as Cordelia had often seen in cheap Italian restaurants. The place mats were of plain cork, but the forks and spoons were antique silver. The flowers were set in low bowls, not skilfully arranged but looking as if they were casualties of a garden storm, blooms which had snapped off in the wind and which someone had thought it kind to place in water.

The young men looked incongruous in their dinner jackets, not ill at ease since they enjoyed the essential self-esteem of the clever and successful, but as if they had picked up the suits second-hand or at a fancy dress costumier and were participating in a charade. Cordelia was surprised at their youth; she guessed that only one was over thirty. Three were untidy, fast talking, restless young men with loud emphatic voices who took no notice of Cordelia after the first introduction. The other two were quieter and one, a tall black-

28

haired boy with strong irregular features, smiled at her across the table and looked as if he would like to have sat within speaking distance.

The meal was brought in by an Italian manservant and his wife who left the cooked dishes on hot plates on a side table. The food was plentiful and the smell almost intolerably appetizing to Cordelia, who hadn't realized until then just how hungry she was. There was a dish heaped high with glistening rice, a large casserole of veal in a rich mushroom sauce, a bowl of spinach. Beside it on the cold table was a large ham, a sirloin of beef and an interesting assortment of salads and fruit. The company served themselves, carrying their plates back to the table with whatever combination of food, hot or cold, they fancied. The young scientists piled their plates high and Cordelia followed their example.

She took little interest in the conversation except to notice that it was predominantly about science and that Lunn, although he spoke less than the others, spoke as their equal. He should, she thought, have looked ridiculous in his rather tight dinner jacket but, surprisingly, he looked the most at ease, the second most powerful personality in the room. Cordelia tried to analyse why this was so, but was defeated. He ate slowly, with finicky attention to the arrangement of the food on his plate, and from time to time, smiled secretly into his wine.

At the other end of the table Sir Ronald was peeling an apple and talking to his guest, his head inclined. The green rind slid thinly over his long fingers and curved down towards his plate. Cordelia glanced at Miss Leaming. She was staring at Sir Ronald with such unwavering and speculative concern, that Cordelia uncomfortably felt that every eye present must be irresistibly drawn to that pale disdainful mask. Then, Miss Leaming seemed to become aware of her glance. She relaxed and turned to Cordelia:

"When we were travelling here together you were reading Hardy. Do you enjoy him?"

"Very much. But I enjoy Jane Austen more."

"Then you must try to find an opportunity of visiting the Fitzwilliam Museum in Cambridge. They have a letter written by Jane Austen. I think you'd find it interesting."

She spoke with the controlled, artificial brightness of a hostess trying to find a subject to interest a difficult guest. Cordelia, her mouth full of veal and mushrooms, wondered how she would manage to get through the rest of the meal. Luckily, however, the American

professor had caught the word "Fitzwilliam" and now called down the table to enquire about the Museum's collection of majolica in which, apparently, he was interested. The conversation became general.

It was Miss Leaming who drove Cordelia to the station, Audley End this time instead of Cambridge; a change for which no reason was given. They didn't speak about the case during the drive. Cordelia was exhausted with tiredness, food and wine and allowed herself to be firmly taken in hand and placed in the train without attempting to gain any further information. She didn't really think she would have got it. As the train drew out, her tired fingers fumbled with the flap of the strong white envelope which Miss Leaming had handed to her and she drew out and read the enclosed note. It was expertly typed and set out, but told her little more than she had already learnt. With it was the photograph. She saw the picture of a laughing boy, his head half-turned towards the camera, one hand shielding his eyes from the sun. He was wearing jeans and a vest and was half lying on the lawn, a pile of books on the grass beside him. Perhaps he had been working there under the trees when she had come out of the french windows with her camera and called imperiously to him to smile. The photograph told Cordelia nothing except, that for one recorded second at least, he had known how to be happy. She placed it back in the envelope; her hands closed protectively over it. Cordelia slept.

Chapter Two

❖❖❖

Next morning Cordelia left Cremona Road before seven o'clock. Despite her tiredness the night before, she had made her major preparations before she went to bed. They hadn't taken long. As Bernie had taught her, she checked systematically the scene-of-crime kit, an unnecessary routine since nothing had been touched since, in celebration of their partnership, he had first set it up for her. She put ready the polaroid camera; sorted into order the road maps from the jumble pushed into the back of his desk; shook out the sleeping bag and rolled it ready; filled a carrier bag with iron rations from Bernie's store of tinned soup and baked beans; considered, and finally decided to take, their copy of Professor Simpson's book on forensic medicine and her own Hacker portable radio; checked the first-aid kit. Finally, she found herself a fresh notebook, headed it *Case of Mark Callender* and ruled up the last few pages ready for her expense account. These preliminaries had always been the most satisfying part of a case, before boredom or distaste set in, before anticipation crumbled into disenchantment and failure. Bernie's planning had always been meticulous and successful; it was reality which had let him down.

Finally, she considered her clothes. If this hot weather continued her Jaeger suit, bought from her savings after much careful thought to see her through almost any interview, would be uncomfortably hot, but she might have to interview the head of a college and the dignified professionalism best exemplified by a suit would be the effect to aim at. She decided to travel in her fawn suede skirt with a short-sleeved jumper and pack jeans and warmer jumpers for any field work. Cordelia enjoyed clothes, enjoyed planning and buying them, a pleasure circumscribed less by poverty than by her obsessive need to be able to pack the whole of her wardrobe into one medium sized suitcase like a refugee perpetually ready for flight.

Once she had shaken free from the tentacles of north London, Cordelia enjoyed the drive. The Mini purred along and Cordelia thought that it had never run so sweetly. She liked the flat East Anglian countryside, the broad streets of the market towns, the way in

which the fields grew unhedged to the edge of the road, the openness and freedom of the far horizons and wide skies. The country matched her mood. She had grieved for Bernie and would grieve for him again, missing his comradeship and his undemanding affection, but this, in a sense, was her first case and she was glad to be tackling it alone. It was one that she thought she could solve. It neither appalled nor disgusted her. Driving in happy anticipation through the sunbathed countryside, the boot of the car carefully packed with her gear, she was filled with the euphoria of hope.

When she finally reached Duxford village she had difficulty at first in finding Summertrees. Major Markland was apparently a man who thought that his importance warranted omitting the name of the road from his address. But the second person she stopped to ask was a villager who was able to point the way, taking infinite trouble over the simple directions as if fearing that a perfunctory answer might have seemed discourteous. Cordelia had to find a suitable place to turn and then drive back a couple of miles, for she had already passed Summertrees.

And this, at last, must be the house. It was a large Victorian edifice of red brick, set well back, with a wide turfed verge between the open wooden gate leading to the drive and the road. Cordelia wondered why anyone should have wanted to build such an intimidatingly ugly house or, having decided to do so, should have set down a suburban monstrosity in the middle of the countryside. Perhaps it had replaced an earlier more agreeable house. She drove the Mini onto the grass but at some distance from the gate and made her way up the drive. The garden suited the house; it was formal to the point of artificiality and too well kept. Even the rock plants burgeoned like morbid excrescences at carefully planned intervals between the terrace paving stones. There were two rectangular beds in the lawn, each planted with red rose trees and edged with alternate bands of lobelia and alyssum. They looked like a patriotic display in a public park. Cordelia felt the lack of a flag pole.

The front door was open, giving a view of a dark, brown-painted hall. Before Cordelia could ring, an elderly woman came round the corner of the house trundling a wheelbarrow full of plants. Despite the heat, she was wearing Wellington boots, a jumper and long tweed skirt and had a scarf tied round her head. When she saw Cordelia she dropped the handle of the wheelbarrow and said:

"Oh, good morning. You've come from the church about the jumble, I expect?"

Cordelia said:

"No, not the jumble. I'm from Sir Ronald Callender. It's about his son."

"Then I expect you've called for his things? We wondered when Sir Ronald was going to send for them. They're all still at the cottage. We haven't been down there since Mark died. We called him Mark, you know. Well, he never told us who he was which was rather naughty of him."

"It isn't about Mark's things. I want to talk about Mark himself. Sir Ronald has engaged me to try to find out why his son killed himself. My name is Cordelia Gray."

This news seemed to puzzle rather than disconcert Mrs. Markland. She blinked at Cordelia rapidly through troubled, rather stupid, eyes and clutched at the wheelbarrow handle as if for support.

"Cordelia Gray? Then we haven't met before, have we? I don't think I know a Cordelia Gray. Perhaps it would be better if you came into the drawing room and talked to my husband and sister-in-law."

She abandoned the barrow where it stood in the middle of the path and led the way into the house, pulling off her head scarf and making ineffective pats at her hair. Cordelia followed her through the sparsely furnished hall, smelling of floor polish, with its clutter of walking sticks, umbrellas and mackintoshes draping the heavy oak hat stand, and into a room at the back of the house.

It was a horrible room, ill-proportioned, bookless, furnished not in poor taste but in no taste at all. A huge sofa of repellent design and two armchairs surrounded the fireplace and a heavy mahogany table, ornately carved and lurching on its pedestal, occupied the centre of the room. There was little other furniture. The only pictures were framed groups, pale oblong faces too small to identify posed in straight innominate lines in front of the camera. One was a regimental photograph; the other had a pair of crossed oars above two rows of burly adolescents, all of whom were wearing low peaked caps and striped blazers. Cordelia supposed it to be a school boating club.

Despite the warmth of the day, the room was sunless and cold. The doors of the french windows were open. On the lawn outside were grouped a large swinging sofa with a fringed canopy, three cane chairs sumptuously cushioned in a garish blue cretonne, each with its footrest, and a wooden slatted table. They looked part of a setting for a play in which the designer had somehow failed to catch

the mood. All the garden furniture looked new and unused. Cordelia wondered why the family should bother to sit indoors on a summer morning while the lawn was so much more comfortably furnished.

Mrs. Markland introduced Cordelia by sweeping her arm in a wide gesture of abandonment and saying feebly to the company in general:

"Miss Cordelia Gray. It isn't about the Church jumble."

Cordelia was struck by the resemblance that husband and wife and Miss Markland bore to each other. All three reminded her of horses. They had long, bony faces, narrow mouths above strong, square chins, eyes set unattractively close, and grey, coarse-looking hair which the two women wore in thick fringes almost to the eyes. Major Markland was drinking coffee from an immense white cup, much stained about the rim and sides, which had been set on a round tin tray. He held *The Times* in his hands. Miss Markland was knitting, an occupation which Cordelia vaguely felt was inappropriate to a hot summer morning.

The two faces, unwelcoming, only partly curious, regarded her with faint distaste. Miss Markland could knit without looking at the needles, an accomplishment which enabled her to fix Cordelia with sharp, inquisitive eyes. Invited by Major Markland to sit, Cordelia perched on the edge of the sofa, half expecting the smooth cushion to let out a rude noise as it subsided beneath her. She found it, however, unexpectedly hard. She composed her face into the appropriate expression—seriousness combined with efficiency and a touch of propitiatory humility seemed about right, but she wasn't sure that she managed to bring it off. As she sat there, knees demurely together, her shoulder bag at her feet, she was unhappily aware that she probably looked more like an eager seventeen-year-old facing her first interview than a mature business woman, sole proprietor of Pryde's Detective Agency.

She handed over Sir Ronald's note of authority and said:

"Sir Ronald was very distressed on your account, I mean it was awful for you that it should happen on your property when you'd been so kind in finding Mark a job he liked. His father hopes you won't mind talking about it; it's just that he wants to know what made his son kill himself."

"And he sent you?" Miss Markland's voice was a compound of disbelief, amusement and contempt. Cordelia didn't resent the rudeness. She felt Miss Markland had a point. She gave what she hoped was a credible explanation. It was probably true.

34

"Sir Ronald thinks that it must have been something to do with Mark's life at university. He left college suddenly, as you may know, and his father was never told why. Sir Ronald thought that I might be more successful in talking to Mark's friends than the more usual type of private detective. He didn't feel that he could trouble the police; after all, this sort of enquiry isn't really their kind of job."

Miss Markland said grimly:

"I should have thought it was precisely their job; that is, if Sir Ronald thinks there's something odd about his son's death . . ."

Cordelia broke in:

"Oh no, I don't think there's any suggestion of that! He's quite satisfied with the verdict. It's just that he badly wants to know what made him do it."

Miss Markland said with sudden fierceness:

"He was a drop-out. He dropped out of university, apparently he dropped out of his family obligations, finally he dropped out of life. Literally."

Her sister-in-law gave a little bleat of protest.

"Oh, Eleanor, is that quite fair? He worked really well here. I liked the boy. I don't think——"

"I don't deny that he earned his money. That doesn't alter the fact that he was neither bred nor educated to be a jobbing gardener. He was, therefore, a drop-out. I don't know the reason and I have no interest in discovering it."

"How did you come to employ him?" asked Cordelia.

It was Major Markland who answered.

"He saw my advertisement in the *Cambridge Evening News* for a gardener and turned up here one evening on his bicycle. I suppose he cycled all the way from Cambridge. It must have been about five weeks ago, a Tuesday I think."

Again Miss Markland broke in:

"It was Tuesday, May 9th."

The Major frowned at her as if irritated that he couldn't fault the information.

"Yes, well, Tuesday the 9th. He said that he had decided to leave university and take a job and that he'd seen my advertisement. He admitted that he didn't know much about gardening but said that he was strong and was willing to learn. His inexperience didn't worry me; we wanted him mostly for the lawns and for the vegetables. He never touched the flower garden; my wife and I see to that ourselves.

35

Anyway, I quite liked the look of the boy and I thought I'd give him a chance."

Miss Markland said:

"You took him because he was the only applicant who was prepared to work for the miserable pittance you were offering." The Major, so far from showing offence at this frankness, smiled complacently.

"I paid him what he was worth. If more employers were prepared to do that, the country wouldn't be plagued with this inflation." He spoke as one to whom economics were an open book.

"Didn't you think it was odd, his turning up like that?" asked Cordelia.

"Of course I did, damned odd! I thought he had probably been sent down; drinks, drugs, revolution, you know the sort of things they get up to at Cambridge now. But I asked him for the name of his tutor as a referee and rang him, a fellow called Horsfall. He wasn't particularly forthcoming but he did assure me that the boy had left voluntarily and to use his own words, his conduct while in college had been almost boringly irreproachable. I need not fear that the shades of Summertrees would be polluted."

Miss Markland turned her knitting and broke into her sister-in-law's little cry of "What can he have meant by that?" with the dry comment:

"A little more boredom of that kind would be welcome from the city of the plains."

"Did Mr. Horsfall tell you why Mark had left college?" asked Cordelia.

"I didn't enquire. That wasn't my business. I asked a plain question and I got a more or less plain answer, as plain as you can expect from those academic types. We certainly had no complaint about the lad while he was here. I speak as I find."

"When did he move into the cottage?" asked Cordelia.

"Immediately. That wasn't our idea, of course. We never advertised the job as residential. However, he'd obviously seen the cottage and taken a fancy to the place and he asked if we'd mind if he camped out there. It wasn't practicable for him to cycle in from Cambridge each day, we could quite see that, and as far as we knew there was no one in the village who could put him up. I can't say I was keen on the idea; the cottage needs a lot doing to it. Actually we have it in mind to apply for a conversion grant and then get rid of the place. It wouldn't do for a family in its present state but the lad seemed keen on roughing it there, so we agreed."

36

Cordelia said:

"So he must have inspected the cottage before he came for the job?"

"Inspected? Oh, I don't know. He probably snooped around to see what the property was like before he actually came to the door. I don't know that I blame him, I'd have done the same myself."

Mrs. Markland broke in:

"He was very keen on the cottage, very keen. I pointed out that there was no gas or electricity but he said that that wouldn't worry him; he'd buy a primus stove and manage with lamps. There's water laid on, of course, and the main part of the roof is really quite sound. At least I think it is. We don't go there you know. He seemed to settle in very happily. We never actually visited him, there was no need, but as far as I could see he was looking after himself perfectly well. Of course as my husband said, he was very inexperienced; there were one or two things we had to teach him, like coming up to the kitchen early every morning for the orders. But I liked the boy; he was always working hard when I was in the garden."

Cordelia said:

"I wonder if I might have a look at the cottage?"

The request disconcerted them. Major Markland looked at his wife. There was an embarrassed silence and for a moment Cordelia feared that the answer would be no. Then Miss Markland stabbed her needles into the ball of wool and got to her feet:

"I'll come with you now," she said.

The grounds of Summertrees were spacious. First there was the formal rose garden, the bushes closely planted and grouped according to variety and colour like a market garden, the name tags fixed at precisely the same height from the earth. Next was the kitchen garden cut in two by a gravel path with evidence of Mark Callender's work in the weeded rows of lettuce and cabbages, the patches of dug earth. Finally they passed through a gate into a small orchard of old and unpruned apple trees. The scythed grass, smelling richly of hay, lay in thick swathes round the gnarled trunks.

At the furthest end of the orchard was a thick hedge, so overgrown that the wicket gate into the rear garden of the cottage was at first difficult to see. But the grass around it had been trimmed and the gate opened easily to Miss Markland's hand. On the other side was a thick bramble hedge, dark and impenetrable and obviously allowed to grow wild for a generation. Someone had hacked a way through,

but Miss Markland and Cordelia had to bend low to avoid catching their hair on its tangled tentacles of thorn.

Once free of this barrier, Cordelia lifted her head and blinked in the bright sunshine. She gave a little exclamation of pleasure. In the short time in which he had lived here Mark Callender had created a little oasis of order and beauty out of chaos and neglect. Old flower beds had been discovered and the surviving plants tended; the stone path had been scraped free of grass and moss; a minute square of lawn to the right of the cottage door had been cut and weeded. On the other side of the path a patch about twelve feet square had been partly dug. The fork was still in the earth, driven deep about two feet from the end of the row.

The cottage was a low, brick building under a slate roof. Bathed in the afternoon sunshine, and despite its bare, rain-scoured door, its rotted window frames and the glimpse of exposed beams in the roof, it had the gentle melancholy charm of age which hadn't yet degenerated into decay. Just outside the cottage door, dropped casually side by side, was a pair of heavy gardening shoes encrusted with earth.

"His?" asked Cordelia.

"Who else's?"

They stood together for a moment contemplating the dug earth. Neither spoke. Then they moved to the back door. Miss Markland fitted the key into the lock. It turned easily as if the lock had been recently oiled. Cordelia followed her into the sitting-room of the cottage.

The air was cool after the heat of the garden but unfresh, with a taint of contagion. Cordelia saw that the plan of the cottage was simple. There were three doors, one straight ahead obviously led to the front garden but was locked and barred, the joints hung with cobwebs as if it hadn't been opened for generations. One to the right led, as Cordelia guessed, to the kitchen. The third door was ajar and she could glimpse through it an uncarpeted wooden stairway leading to the first floor. In the middle of the room was a wooden-topped table, the surface scarred with much scrubbing, and with two kitchen chairs, one at each end. In the middle of the table a blue ribbed mug held a posy of dead flowers, black brittle stems bearing sad tatters of unidentifiable plants, their pollen staining the surface of the table like golden dust. Shafts of sunlight cut across the still air; in their beams a myriad of motes, specks of dust and infinitesimal life danced grotesquely.

To the right was a fireplace, an old-fashioned iron range with ovens each side of the open fire. Mark had been burning wood and papers; there was a mound of white ash in the grate and a pile of kindling wood and small logs placed ready for the next cool evening. On one side of the fire was a low wooden slatted chair with a faded cushion and on the other a wheel-backed chair with the legs sawn off, perhaps to make it low enough for nursing a child. Cordelia thought that it must have been a beautiful chair before its mutilation.

Two immense beams, blackened with age, ran across the ceiling. In the middle of one was fixed a steel hook, probably once used for hanging bacon. Cordelia and Miss Markland looked at it without speaking; there was no need for question and answer. After a moment they moved, as if by common consent, to the two fireside chairs and sat down. Miss Markland said:

"I was the one who found him. He didn't come up to the kitchen for the day's orders so after breakfast I walked down here to see if he had overslept. It was nine twenty-three exactly. The door was unlocked. I knocked, but there was no reply so I pushed it open. He was hanging from that hook with a leather belt round his neck. He was wearing his blue cotton trousers, the ones he usually worked in, and his feet were bare. That chair was lying on its side on the floor. I touched his chest. He was quite cold."

"Did you cut him down?"

"No. He was obviously dead and I thought it better to leave the body until the police arrived. But I did pick up the chair and place it so that it supported his feet. That was an irrational action, I know, but I couldn't bear to see him hanging there without releasing the pressure on his throat. It was, as I've said, irrational."

"I think it was very natural. Did you notice anything else about him, about the room?"

"There was a half-empty mug of what looked like coffee on the table and a great deal of ash in the grate. It looked as if he had been burning papers. His portable typewriter was where you see it now, on that side table; the suicide note was still in the machine. I read it, then I went back to the house, told my brother and sister-in-law what had happened and rang the police. After the police arrived I brought them to this cottage, and confirmed what I had seen. I never came in here again until this moment."

"Did you, or Major and Mrs. Markland, see Mark on the night he died?"

"None of us saw him after he stopped work at about six-thirty. He was a little later that evening because he wanted to finish mowing the front lawn. We all saw him putting the mower away, then walking across the garden towards the orchard. We never saw him alive again. No one was at home at Summertrees that night. We had a dinner party at Trumpington—an old army colleague of my brother. We didn't get home until after midnight. By then, according to the medical evidence, Mark must have been dead about four hours."

Cordelia said:

"Please tell me about him."

"What is there to tell? His official hours were eight-thirty to six o'clock, with an hour for lunch and half an hour for tea. In the evenings he would work in the garden here or round the cottage. Sometimes in his lunch hour he would cycle to the village store. I used to meet him there from time to time. He didn't buy much—a loaf of wholemeal bread, butter, the cheapest cut of bacon, tea, coffee—the usual things. I heard him ask about free-range eggs and Mrs. Morgan told him that Wilcox at Grange Farm would always sell him half a dozen. We didn't speak when we met, but he would smile. In the evenings once the light had faded, he used to read or type at that table. I could see his head against the lamplight."

"I thought Major Markland said that you didn't visit the cottage?"

"They don't; it holds certain embarrassing memories for them. I do." She paused and looked into the dead fire.

"My fiancé and I used to spend a great deal of time here before the war when he was at Cambridge. He was killed in 1937, fighting in Spain for the Republican cause."

"I'm sorry," said Cordelia. She felt the inadequacy, the insincerity of her response and yet, what else was there to say? It had all happened nearly forty years ago. She hadn't heard of him before. The spasm of grief, so brief that it was hardly felt, was no more than a transitory inconvenience, a sentimental regret for all lovers who died young, for the inevitability of human loss.

Miss Markland spoke with sudden passion as if the words were being forced out of her:

"I don't like your generation, Miss Gray. I don't like your arrogance, your selfishness, your violence, the curious selectivity of your compassion. You pay for nothing with your own coin, not even for your ideals. You denigrate and destroy and never build. You invite punishment like rebellious children, then scream when you are pun-

ished. The men I knew, the men I was brought up with, were not like that."

Cordelia said gently:

"I don't think Mark Callender was like that either."

"Perhaps not. At least the violence he practised was on himself." She looked up at Cordelia searchingly.

"No doubt you'll say I'm jealous of youth. It's a common enough syndrome of my generation."

"It ought not to be. I can never see why people should be jealous. After all, youth isn't a matter of privilege, we all get the same share of it. Some people may be born at an easier time or be richer or more privileged than others, but that hasn't anything to do with being young. And being young is terrible sometimes. Don't you remember how terrible it could be?"

"Yes, I remember. But I remember other things too."

Cordelia sat in silence, thinking that the conversation was strange but somehow inevitable and that, for some reason, she didn't resent it. Miss Markland looked up.

"His girl friend visited him once. At least, I suppose she was his girl friend or why should she have come? It was about three days after he started work."

"What was she like?"

"Beautiful. Very fair, with a face like a Botticelli angel—smooth, oval, unintelligent. She was foreign, French, I think. She was also rich."

"How could you tell that, Miss Markland?" Cordelia was intrigued.

"Because she spoke with a foreign accent; because she arrived driving a white Renault which I took to be her own car; because her clothes, although odd and unsuitable for the country, weren't cheap; because she walked up to the front door and announced that she wanted to see him with the confident arrogance that one associates with the rich."

"And did he see her?"

"He was working in the orchard at the time, scything the grass. I took her down to him. He greeted her calmly and without embarrassment and took her to sit in the cottage garden until it was time for him to stop work. He seemed pleased enough to see her but not, I thought, either delighted or surprised. He didn't introduce her. I left them together and returned to the house before he had the chance to. I didn't see her again."

Before Cordelia could speak she said suddenly:

"You're thinking of living here for a time, aren't you?"

"Will they mind? I didn't like to ask in case they said no."

"They won't know, and if they did, they wouldn't care."

"But do you mind?"

"No. I shan't worry you and I don't mind." They were talking in whispers as if in church. Then Miss Markland got up and moved to the door. She turned.

"You've taken on this job for the money, of course. Why not? But if I were you I'd keep it that way. It's unwise to become too personally involved with another human being. When that human being is dead, it can be dangerous as well as unwise."

❖❖❖

Miss Markland stumped off down the garden path and disappeared through the wicket gate. Cordelia was glad to see her go. She was fidgeting with impatience to examine the cottage. This was where it had happened; this was where her job really began.

What was it that the Super had said? "When you're examining a building look at it as you would a country church. Walk round it first. Look at the whole scene inside and out; then make your deductions. Ask yourself what you saw, not what you expected to see or what you hoped to see, but what you saw."

He must be a man then who liked country churches and that at least was a point in his favour; for this, surely, was genuine Dalgliesh dogma. Bernie's reaction to churches, whether country or town, had been one of half-superstitious wariness. Cordelia decided to follow the advice.

She made her way first to the east side of the cottage. Here, discreetly set back and almost smothered by the hedge, was a wooden privy with its latched stable-like door. Cordelia peeped inside. The privy was very clean and looked as if it had been recently repainted. When she pulled the chain, to her relief, the bowl flushed. There was a roll of lavatory paper hanging by a string from the door and nailed beside it a small plastic bag containing a crumpled collection of orange papers and other soft wrappings. He had been an economical young man. Next to the privy was a large dilapidated shed containing a man's bicycle, old but well cared for, a large tin of white emulsion paint with the lid rammed down hard and a clean brush

upended in a jam jar beside it, a tin bath, a few clean sacks, and a collection of gardening tools. All were shining clean and were neatly disposed against the wall or supported on nails.

She moved to the front of the cottage. This was in marked contrast to the southern aspect. Here Mark Callender had made no attempt to tackle the waist-high wilderness of nettles and grass which stifled the small front garden and almost obliterated the path. A thick climbing shrub sprinkled with small white flowers had thrust its black and thorned boughs to bar the two ground floor windows. The gate leading to the lane had stuck and would open only wide enough for a visitor to squeeze through. On each side a holly tree stood sentinel, its leaves grey with dust. The front hedge of privet was head-high. Cordelia could see that on either side of the path there had once been twin flower beds edged with large round stones which had been painted white. Now most of the stones had sunk out of sight among the encroaching weeds and nothing remained of the beds but a tangle of wild and straggling roses.

As she took a last look at the front garden, her eye caught a flash of colour half trodden among the weeds at the side of the path. It was a crumpled page of an illustrated magazine. She smoothed it open and saw that it was a colour photograph of a female nude. The woman had her back to the camera and was bending forward, gross buttocks splayed above booted thighs. She was smiling saucily over her shoulder in a blatant invitation made more grotesque by the long androgynous face which even tactful lighting couldn't make other than repellent. Cordelia noted the date at the top of the page; it was the May edition. So the magazine, or at least the picture, could have been brought to the cottage while he was there.

She stood with it in her hand trying to analyse the nature of her disgust which seemed to her excessive. The picture was vulgar and salacious but no more offensive or indecent than dozens on view in the side streets of London. But as she folded it away in her bag—for it was evidence of a kind—she felt contaminated and depressed. Had Miss Markland been more percipient than she knew? Was she, Cordelia, in danger of becoming sentimentally obsessed with the dead boy? The picture probably had nothing to do with Mark; it could easily have been dropped by some visitor to the cottage. But she wished that she hadn't seen it.

She passed round to the west of the cottage and made one more discovery. Hidden behind a clump of elder bushes was a small well about four feet in diameter. It had no superstructure but was closely

fitted with a domed lid made of strong slatted wood and fitted at the top with an iron hoop. Cordelia saw that the cover was padlocked to the wooden rim of the well and the lock, although rusty with age, held firm at her tug. Someone had taken the trouble to see that there was no danger here to exploring children or visiting tramps.

And now it was time to explore the interior of the cottage. First the kitchen. It was a small room with a window over the sink looking east. It had obviously been recently painted and the large table which took up most of the room had been covered with a red plastic cloth. There was a poky larder containing half a dozen tins of beer, a jar of marmalade, a crock of butter and the mouldy heel of a loaf. It was here in the kitchen that Cordelia found the explanation of the disagreeable smell which had struck her on entering the cottage. On the table was an open bottle of milk about half full, the silver top crumpled beside it. The milk was solid and furred with putrefaction; a bloated fly was sucking at the rim of the bottle and still stuck to its feast as, instinctively, she tried to flick it away. On the other side of the table was a twin-burner paraffin stove with a heavy pot on one burner. Cordelia tugged at the close-fitting lid and it came off suddenly, letting out a rich repulsive smell. She opened the table drawer and stirred the mess with a spoon. It looked like beef stew. Chunks of greenish meat, soapy looking potatoes and unidentifiable vegetables floated up through the scum like drowned and putrefying flesh. Beside the sink was an orange box placed on one side and used as a vegetable store. The potatoes were green, the onions had shrunk and sprouted, the carrots were wrinkled and limp. So nothing had been cleaned up, nothing had been removed. The police had taken away the body and any evidence they required but no one, neither the Marklands nor the boy's family or friends, had bothered to come back to clean up the pathetic leavings of his young life.

Cordelia went upstairs. A cramped landing led to two bedrooms, one obviously unused for years. Here the window frame had rotted, the ceiling plaster had crumbled and a faded paper patterned with roses was peeling away with the damp. The second and larger room was the one in which he had slept. There was a single iron bed with a hair mattress and on it a sleeping bag and a bolster folded in two to make a high pillow. Beside the bed was an old table with two candles, stuck with their own wax to a cracked plate, and a box of matches. His clothes were hung in the single cupboard; a pair of bright-green corduroy trousers, one or two shirts, pullovers and one

44

formal suit. A few underclothes, clean but not ironed, were folded on the ledge above. Cordelia fingered the pullovers. They were hand knitted in thick wool and intricate patterns and there were four of them. Someone, then, had cared enough about him to take some trouble on his behalf. She wondered who.

She ran her hands over his meagre wardrobe, feeling for pockets. She found nothing except a slim, brown leather wallet in the bottom left-hand pocket of his suit. Excitedly she carried it over to the window hoping that it might contain a clue—a letter, perhaps, a list of names and addresses, a personal note. But the wallet was empty except for a couple of pound notes, his driving licence and a blood donor's card issued by the Cambridge blood transfusion service, which showed his group as B rhesus negative.

The uncurtained window gave a view of the garden. His books were arranged on the window shelf. There were only a few of them: several volumes of the *Cambridge Modern History*; some Trollope and Hardy; a complete William Blake; school text book volumes of Wordsworth, Browning and Donne; two paperbacks on gardening. At the end of the row was a white leather-bound book which Cordelia saw was the Book of Common Prayer. It was fitted with a finely wrought brass clasp and looked much used. She was disappointed in the books; they told her little beyond his superficial tastes. If he had come to this solitary life to study, to write or to philosophize he had come singularly ill-equipped.

The most interesting thing in the room was above the bed. It was a small oil painting about nine inches square. Cordelia studied it. It was certainly Italian and probably, she thought, late fifteenth century. It showed a very young tonsured monk reading at a table, his sensitive fingers enleafed between the pages of his book. The long, controlled face was taut with concentration, the heavy lidded eyes were fixed on the page. Behind him, a view from the open window was a miniature of delight. Cordelia thought that one would never tire of looking at it. It was a Tuscan scene showing a walled city with towers enclosed by cypresses, a river winding like a silver stream, a gaudily clad procession preceded by banners, yoked oxen working in the fields. She saw the picture as a contrast between the worlds of intellect and action and tried to remember where she had seen similar paintings. The comrades—as Cordelia always thought of that ubiquitous band of fellow-revolutionaries who attached themselves to her father—had been very fond of exchanging messages in art galleries and Cordelia had spent hours walking slowly from pic-

ture to picture, waiting for the casual visitor to pause beside her and whisper his few words of warning or information. The device had always struck her as a childish and unnecessarily histrionic way of communicating, but at least the galleries were warm and she had enjoyed looking at the pictures. She enjoyed this picture; he had obviously liked it too. Had he also liked that vulgar illustration which she had found in the front garden? Were they both an essential part of his nature?

The tour of inspection over, she made herself coffee using a packet from his store cupboard and boiling the water on the stove. She took a chair from the sitting-room and sat outside the back door with the mug of coffee in her lap, her head stretched back to feel the sun. She was filled with a gentle happiness as she sat there, contented and relaxed, listening to the silence, her half-closed lids impressed with the visage of the sun. But now it was the time to think. She had examined the cottage in accordance with the Super's instructions. What did she now know about the dead boy? What had she seen? What could she deduce?

He had been almost obsessively neat and tidy. His garden tools were wiped after use and carefully put away, his kitchen had been painted and was clean and ordered. Yet he had abandoned his digging less than two feet from the end of a row; had left the uncleaned fork in the earth; had dropped his gardening shoes casually at the back door. He had apparently burnt all his papers before killing himself, yet had left his coffee mug unwashed. He had made himself a stew for his supper which he hadn't touched. The preparation of the vegetables must have been done earlier in the same day, or perhaps the day before, but the stew was clearly intended for supper that night. The pot was still on the stove and was full to the brim. This wasn't a heated-up meal, one left from the evening before. This surely meant that he had only made the decision to kill himself after the stew had been prepared and had been put on the stove to cook. Why should he trouble to prepare a meal that he knew he wouldn't be alive to eat?

But was it likely, she wondered, that a healthy young man coming in from an hour or two of hard digging and with a hot meal waiting should be in that mood of boredom, accidie, anguish or despair which could lead to suicide? Cordelia could remember times of intense unhappiness, but she couldn't recall that they had followed purposeful outdoor exercise in the sun with a meal in prospect. And why the

mug of coffee, the one which the police had taken away to analyse? There were tins of beer in the larder; if he had come in thirsty from his digging, why not open one of those? Beer would have been the quickest, the obvious way of quenching thirst. Surely no one, however thirsty, would brew and drink coffee just before a meal. Coffee came after the food.

But suppose someone had visited him that evening. It wasn't likely to have been someone calling with a casual message as he passed by; it was important enough for Mark to break off his digging even within two feet of the end of a row and invite the visitor into the cottage. It was probably a visitor who didn't like or drink beer—could that mean a woman? It was a visitor who wasn't expected to stay for supper but yet was at the cottage long enough to be offered some refreshment. Perhaps it was someone on his way to his own evening meal. Obviously, the visitor hadn't been invited to supper earlier or why would the two of them have begun the meal by drinking coffee and why would Mark have worked so late in the garden instead of coming in to change? So it was an unexpected visitor. But why was there only one mug of coffee? Surely Mark would have shared it with his guest or, if he preferred not to drink coffee, would have opened a tin of beer for himself. But there was no empty beer can in the kitchen and no second mug. Had it perhaps been washed and put away? But why should Mark wash one mug and not the other? Was it to conceal the fact that he'd had a visitor that evening?

The jug of coffee on the kitchen table was almost empty and the bottle of milk only half full. Surely more than one person had taken milk and coffee. But perhaps that was a dangerous and unwarranted deduction; the visitor might well have had his mug refilled.

But suppose it wasn't Mark who had wished to conceal the fact that a visitor had called that night; suppose it wasn't Mark who had washed and put away the second mug; suppose it was the visitor who had wished to conceal the fact of his presence. But why should he bother to do that since he couldn't know that Mark was going to kill himself? Cordelia shook herself impatiently. This, of course, was nonsense. Obviously the visitor wouldn't have washed up the mug if Mark were still there and alive. He would only have obliterated the evidence of his visit if Mark were already dead. And if Mark had been dead, had been strung up on that hook before his visitor left the cottage, then could this really be suicide? A word dancing at the back of Cordelia's mind, an amorphous half-formed jangle of

47

letters, came suddenly into focus and, for the first time, spelt out clearly the blood-stained word. Murder.

❖❖❖

Cordelia sat on in the sun for another five minutes finishing her coffee, then she washed up the mug and hung it back on a hook in the larder. She walked down the lane to the road to where the Mini was still parked on the grass verge outside Summertrees, glad of the instinct that had led her to leave it out of sight of the house. Letting in the clutch gently, she drove it slowly down the lane looking carefully from side to side for a possible parking place; to leave it outside the cottage would only advertise her presence. It was a pity that Cambridge wasn't closer; she could then have used Mark's bicycle. The Mini was necessary to her task but would be inconveniently conspicuous wherever she left it.

But she was lucky. About fifty yards down the lane was the entrance to a field, a wide grass verge with a small copse at one side. The copse looked damp and sinister. It was impossible to believe that flowers could spring from this tainted earth or bloom among these scarred and mis-shapen trees. The ground was scattered with old pots and pans, the upended skeleton of a pram, a battered and rusty gas stove. Beside a stunted oak a matted heap of blankets were disintegrating into the earth. But there was space for her to drive the Mini off the road and under cover of a kind. If she locked it carefully it would be better here than outside the cottage and at night, she thought, it would be unobserved.

But now, she drove it back to the cottage and began to unpack. She moved Mark's few underclothes to one side of the shelf and set her own beside them. She laid her sleeping bag on the bed over his, thinking that she would be glad of the extra comfort. There was a red toothbrush and half-used tube of toothpaste in a jamjar on the kitchen window ledge; she placed her yellow brush and her own tube beside them. She hung her towel next to his across the cord which he had fixed between two nails under the kitchen sink. Then she made an inventory of the contents of the larder and a list of the things she would need. It would be better to buy them in Cambridge; she would only draw attention to her presence if she shopped locally. The saucepan of stew and the half bottle of milk were a worry. She couldn't leave them in the kitchen to sour the cottage with the stench

48

of decay but she was reluctant to throw the contents away. She considered whether to photograph them but decided against it; tangible objects were better evidence. In the end she carried them out to the shed and shrouded them thickly with a piece of old sacking.

Last of all, she thought about the gun. It was a heavy object to carry with her all the time but she felt unhappy about parting with it, even temporarily. Although the back door of the cottage could be locked and Miss Markland had left her the key, an intruder would have no difficulty in breaking-in through a window. She decided that the best plan would be to secrete the ammunition among her underclothes in the bedroom cupboard but to hide the pistol itself separately in or near the cottage. The exact place cost her a little thought, but then she remembered the thick and twisting limbs of the elder bush by the well; by reaching high, she was able to feel for a convenient hollow near the fork of a branch and could slip the gun, still shrouded in its draw-string bag, among the concealing leaves.

At last she was ready to leave for Cambridge. She looked at her watch; it was half-past ten; she could be in Cambridge by eleven and there would still be two hours of the morning to go. She decided that her best plan would be to visit the newspaper office first and read the account of the inquest, then to see the police; after that she would go in search of Hugo and Sophia Tilling.

She drove away from the cottage with a feeling very like regret, as if she were leaving home. It was, she thought, a curious place, heavy with atmosphere and showing two distinct faces to the world like facets of a human personality; the north, with its dead thorn-barred windows, its encroaching weeds, and its forbidding hedge of privet, was a numinous stage for horror and tragedy. Yet the rear, where he had lived and worked, had cleared and dug the garden and tied up the few flowers, had weeded the path, and opened the windows to the sun, was as peaceful as a sanctuary. Sitting there at the door she had felt that nothing horrible could ever touch her; she was able to contemplate the night there alone without fear. Was it this atmosphere of healing tranquillity, she wondered, that had attracted Mark Callender? Had he sensed it before he took the job, or was it in some mysterious way the result of his transitory and doomed sojourn there? Major Markland had been right; obviously Mark had looked at the cottage before he went up to the house. Had it been the cottage he wanted or the job? Why were the Marklands so reluctant to come to the place, so reluctant that they obviously hadn't

visited it even to clean up after his death? And why had Miss Markland spied on him, for surely such close observation was very close to spying? Had she only confided that story about her dead lover to justify her interest in the cottage, her obsessional preoccupation with what the new gardener was doing? And was the story even true? That ageing body heavy with latent strength, that equine expression of perpetual discontent, could she really once have been young, have lain perhaps with her lover on Mark's bed through the long, warm evenings of long-dead summers? How remote, how impossible and grotesque it all seemed.

Cordelia drove down Hills Road, past the vigorous memorial statue of a young 1914 soldier striding to death, past the Roman Catholic church and into the centre of the city. Again she wished that she could have abandoned the car in favour of Mark's bicycle. Everyone else seemed to be riding one and the air tinkled with bells like a festival. In these narrow and crowded streets even the compact Mini was a liability. She decided to park it as soon as she could find a place and set out on foot in search of a telephone. She had decided to vary her programme and see the police first.

But it didn't surprise her when at last she rang the police station to hear that Sergeant Maskell, who had dealt with the Callender case, was tied up all the morning. It was only in fiction that the people one wanted to interview were sitting ready at home or in their office, with time, energy and interest to spare. In real life, they were about their own business and one waited on their convenience, even if, untypically, they welcomed the attention of Pryde's Detective Agency. Usually they didn't. She hardly expected Sergeant Maskell to welcome it. She mentioned Sir Ronald's note of authority to impress her hearer with the authenticity of her business. The name was not without influence. He went away to enquire. After less than a minute he came back to say that Sergeant Maskell could see Miss Gray at two-thirty that afternoon.

So the newspaper office came first after all. Old files were at least accessible and could not object to being consulted. She quickly found what she wanted. The account of the inquest was brief, couched in the usual formal language of a court report. It told her little that was new, but she made a careful note of the main evidence. Sir Ronald Callender testified that he hadn't spoken to his son for over a fortnight before his death, when Mark had telephoned to tell his father of his decision to leave college and to take a job at Summertrees. He hadn't consulted Sir Ronald before making this decision

50

nor had he explained his reasons. Sir Ronald had subsequently spoken to the Master, and the College authorities were prepared to take his son back for the next academic year if he changed his mind. His son had never spoken to him of suicide and had no health or money worries as far as he was aware. Sir Ronald's testimony was followed by a brief reference to other evidence. Miss Markland described how she had found the body; a forensic pathologist testified that the cause of death was asphyxia due to strangulation; Sergeant Maskell recounted the measures he had thought it proper to take and a report from the forensic science laboratory was submitted which stated that a mug of coffee found on the table had been analysed and found harmless. The verdict was that the deceased died by his own hand while the balance of his mind was disturbed. Closing the heavy file, Cordelia felt depressed. It looked as if the police work had been thorough. Was it really possible that these experienced professionals had overlooked the significance of the unfinished digging, the gardening shoes dropped casually at the back door, the untouched supper?

And now, at mid-day, she was free until half-past two. She could explore Cambridge. She bought the cheapest guide book she could find from Bowes and Bowes, resisting the temptation to browse among the books, since time was short and pleasure must be rationed. She stuffed her shoulder bag with a pork pie and fruit bought from a market stall and entered St. Mary's church to sit quietly and work out her itinerary. Then for an hour and a half she walked about the city and its colleges in a trance of happiness.

She was seeing Cambridge at its loveliest. The sky was an infinity of blue from whose pellucid depths the sun shone in unclouded but gentle radiance. The trees in the college gardens and the avenues leading to the Backs, as yet untouched by the heaviness of high summer, lifted their green tracery against stone and river and sky. Punts shot and curtsied under the bridges, scattering the gaudy water fowl, and by the rise of the new Garret Hostel bridge the willows trailed their pale, laden boughs in the darker green of the Cam.

She included all the special sights in her itinerary. She walked gravely down the length of Trinity Library, visited the Old Schools, sat quietly at the back of King's College Chapel marvelling at the upward surge of John Wastell's great vault spreading into curved fans of delicate white stone. The sunlight poured through the great windows staining the still air, blue, crimson and green. The finely carved Tudor roses, the heraldic beasts supporting the crown, stood

out in arrogant pride from the panels. Despite what Milton and Wordsworth had written, surely this chapel had been built to the glory of an earthly sovereign, not to the service of God? But that didn't invalidate its purpose nor blemish its beauty. It was still a supremely religious building. Could a non-believer have planned and executed this superb interior? Was there an essential unity between motive and creation? This was the question which Carl alone among the comrades would have been interested to explore and she thought of him in his Greek prison, trying to shut her mind to what they might be doing to him and wishing his stocky figure at her side.

During her tour she indulged in small particular pleasures. She bought a linen tea cloth printed with a picture of the chapel from the stall near the west door; she lay on her face on the shorn grass above the river by Kings Bridge and let the cold green water eddy round her arms; she wandered among the book stalls in the market place and after careful reckoning bought a small edition of Keats printed on India paper and a cotton kaftan patterned in greens, blues and brown. If this hot weather continued it would be cooler than a shirt or jeans for wear in the evenings.

Finally, she returned to King's College. There was a seat set against the great stone wall which ran from the chapel down to the river bank and she sat there in the sun to eat her lunch. A privileged sparrow hopped across the immaculate lawn and cocked a bright insouciant eye. She threw him scraps from the crust of her pork pie and smiled at his agitated peckings. From the river floated the sound of voices calling across the water, the occasional scrunch of wood on wood, the harsh call of a duckling. Everything about her—the pebbles bright as jewels in the gravel path, the silver shafts of grass at the verge of the lawn, the sparrow's brittle legs—was seen with an extraordinarily and individual intensity as if happiness had cleared her eyes.

Then memory recalled the voices. First her father's:

"Our little fascist was educated by the papists. It accounts for a lot. How on earth did it happen, Delia?"

"You remember, Daddy. They muddled me up with another C. Gray who was a Roman Catholic. We both passed the eleven plus exam the same year. When they discovered the mistake they wrote to you to ask if you minded my staying on at the Convent because I'd settled there."

He hadn't in fact replied. Reverend Mother had tried tactfully to conceal that he hadn't bothered to answer and Cordelia had stayed

on at the Convent for the six most settled and happy years of her life, insulated by order and ceremony from the mess and muddle of life outside, incorrigibly Protestant, uncoerced, gently pitied as one in invincible ignorance. For the first time she learned that she needn't conceal her intelligence, that cleverness which a succession of foster mothers had somehow seen as a threat. Sister Perpetua had said:

"There shouldn't be any difficulty over your 'A' Levels if you go on as you are at present. That means that we can plan for university entrance in two years' time from this October. Cambridge, I think. We might as well try for Cambridge, and I really don't see why you shouldn't stand a chance of a scholarship."

Sister Perpetua had herself been at Cambridge before she entered the Convent and she still spoke of the academic life, not with longing or regret, but as if it had been a sacrifice worthy of her vocation. Even the fifteen-year-old Cordelia had recognized that Sister Perpetua was a real scholar and had thought it rather unfair of God to bestow a vocation on one who was so happy and useful as she was. But for Cordelia herself, the future had, for the first time, seemed settled and full of promise. She would go to Cambridge and Sister would visit her there. She had a romantic vision of wide lawns under the sun and the two of them walking in Donne's paradise: "Rivers of knowledge are there, arts and sciences flow from thence; gardens that are walled in; bottomless depths of unsearchable councils are there." By the aid of her own brain and Sister's prayers she would win her scholarship. The prayers occasionally worried her. She had absolutely no doubt of their efficacy since God must necessarily listen to one who at such personal cost had listened to Him. And if Sister's influence gave her an unfair advantage over the other candidates—well, that couldn't be helped. In a matter of such importance neither Cordelia nor Sister Perpetua had been disposed to fret over theological niceties.

But this time Daddy had replied to the letter. He had discovered a need for his daughter. There were no "A" Levels and no scholarship and at sixteen Cordelia finished her formal education and began her wandering life as cook, nurse, messenger and general camp follower to Daddy and the comrades.

But now by what devious routes and for what a strange purpose she had come at last to Cambridge. The city didn't disappoint her. In her wanderings she had seen lovelier places, but none in which she had been happier or more at peace. How indeed, she thought,

could the heart be indifferent to such a city where stone and stained glass, water and green lawns, trees and flowers were arranged in such ordered beauty for the service of learning. But as regretfully she rose at last to go, brushing the few crumbs from her skirt, a quotation, untraced and unsought, came into her mind. She heard it with such clarity that the words might have been spoken by a human voice—a young masculine voice, unrecognized and yet mysteriously familiar: "Then saw I that there was a way to hell even from the gates of heaven."

❖❖❖

The police headquarters building was modern and functional. It represented authority tempered with discretion; the public were to be impressed but not intimidated. Sergeant Maskell's office and the Sergeant himself conformed to this philosophy. He was surprisingly young and elegantly dressed, with a square, tough face wary with experience and a long but skilfully cut hair style which, Cordelia thought, could only just have satisfied the Force requirements, even for a plain clothes detective. He was punctiliously polite without being gallant and this reassured her. It wasn't going to be an easy interview, but she had no wish to be treated with the indulgence shown to a pretty but importunate child. Sometimes it helped to play the part of a vulnerable and naive young girl eager for information—this was a role in which Bernie had frequently sought to cast her—but she sensed that Sergeant Maskell would respond better to an unflirtatious competence. She wanted to appear efficient, but not too efficient. And her secrets must remain her own; she was here to get information, not to give it.

She stated her business concisely and showed him her note of authority from Sir Ronald. He handed it back to her, remarking without rancour:

"Sir Ronald said nothing to me to suggest that he was not satisfied with the verdict."

"I don't think that's in question. He doesn't suspect foul play. If he did, he would have come to you. I think he has a scientist's curiosity to know what made his son kill himself and he couldn't very well indulge that at public expense. I mean, Mark's private miseries aren't really your problem, are they?"

"They could be if the reasons for his death disclosed a criminal

54

offence—blackmail, intimidation—but there was never any suggestion of that."

"Are you personally satisfied that he killed himself?"

The Sergeant looked at her with the sudden keen intelligence of a hunting dog on the scent.

"Why should you ask that, Miss Gray?"

"I suppose because of the trouble you took. I've interviewed Miss Markland and read the newspaper report of the inquest. You called in a forensic pathologist; you had the body photographed before it was cut down; you analysed the coffee left in his drinking mug."

"I treated the case as a suspicious death. That's my usual practice. This time the precautions proved unnecessary, but they might not have been."

Cordelia said:

"But something worried you, something didn't seem right?"

He said, as if reminiscing:

"Oh, it was straightforward enough to all appearances. Almost the usual story. We get more than our share of suicides. Here is a young man who gave up his university course for no apparent reason and went to live on his own in some discomfort. You get the picture of an introspective, rather solitary student, one who doesn't confide in his family or friends. Within three weeks after leaving college he's found dead. There's no sign of a struggle; no disturbance in the cottage; he leaves a suicide note conveniently in the typewriter, much the kind of suicide note you would expect. Admittedly, he took the trouble to destroy all the papers in the cottage and yet left the garden fork uncleaned and his work half-completed, and bothered to cook himself a supper which he didn't eat. But all that proves nothing. People do behave irrationally, particularly suicides. No, it wasn't any of those things which gave me a bit of worry; it was the knot."

Suddenly he bent down and rummaged in the left-hand drawer of his desk.

"Here," he said. "How would you use this to hang yourself, Miss Gray?"

The strap was about five feet long. It was a little over an inch wide and was made of strong but supple brown leather, darkened in places with age. One end was tapered and pierced with a row of metal-bound eye holes, the other was fitted with a strong brass buckle. Cordelia took it in her hands; Sergeant Maskell said:

"That was what he used. Obviously it's meant as a strap, but Miss

55

Leaming testified that he used to wear it wound two or three times round his waist as a belt. Well, Miss Gray, how would you hang yourself?"

Cordelia ran the strap through her hands.

"First of all, of course, I'd slip the tapered end through the buckle to make a noose. Then, with the noose round my neck, I'd stand on a chair underneath the hook in the ceiling and draw the other end of the strap over the hook. I'd pull it up fairly tight and then make two half-hitches to hold it firm. I'd pull hard on the strap to make sure that the knot didn't slip and that the hook would hold. Then I'd kick away the chair."

The Sergeant opened the file in front of him and pushed it across the desk.

"Look at that," he said. "That's a picture of the knot."

The police photograph, stark in black and white, showed the knot with admirable clarity. It was a bowline on the end of a low loop and it hung about a foot from the hook.

Sergeant Maskell said:

"I doubt whether he would be able to tie that knot with his hands above his head, no one could. So he must have made the noose first just as you did and then tied the bowline. But that can't be right either. There were only a few inches of strap between the buckle and the knot. If he'd done it that way, he wouldn't have had sufficient play on the strap to get his neck through the noose. There's only one way he could have done it. He made the noose first, pulled it until the strap fitted his neck like a collar and then tied the bowline. Then he got on the chair, placed the loop over the nail and kicked the chair away. Look, this will show you what I mean."

He turned over a new page of the file and suddenly thrust it towards her.

The photograph, uncompromising, unambiguous, a brutal surrealism in black and white, would have looked as artificial as a sick joke if the body were not so obviously dead. Cordelia felt her heart hammering against her chest. Beside this horror Bernie's death had been gentle. She bent her head low over the file so that her hair swung forward to shield her face and made herself study the pitiable thing in front of her.

The neck was elongated so that the bare feet, their toes pointed like a dancer's, hung less than a foot from the floor. The stomach muscles were taut. Above them the high rib cage looked as brittle as a bird's. The head lolled grotesquely on the right shoulder like a

56

horrible caricature of a disjointed puppet. The eyes had rolled upwards under half-open lids. The swollen tongue had forced itself
between the lips.

Cordelia said calmly:

"I see what you mean. There are barely four inches of strap between the neck and the knot. Where is the buckle?"

"At the back of the neck under the left ear. There's a photograph
of the indentation it made in the flesh later in the file."

Cordelia did not look. Why, she wondered, had he shown her the
photograph? It wasn't necessary to prove his argument. Had he hoped
to shock her into a realization of what she was meddling in; to punish
her for trespassing on his patch; to contrast the brutal reality of his
professionalism with her amateurish meddling; to warn her perhaps? But against what? The police had no real suspicion of foul
play; the case was closed. Had it, perhaps, been the casual malice,
the incipient sadism of a man who couldn't resist the impulse to hurt
or shock? Was he even aware of his own motives?

She said:

"I agree he could only have done it in the way you described, if he
did it. But suppose someone else pulled the noose tight about his
neck, then strung him up. He'd be heavy, a dead weight. Wouldn't
it have been easier to make the knot first and then hoist him on to the
chair?"

"Having first asked him to hand over his belt?"

"Why use a belt? The murderer could have strangled him with a
cord or a tie. Or would that have left a deeper and identifiable mark
under the impression of the strap?"

"The pathologist looked for just such a mark. It wasn't there."

"There are other ways, though; a plastic bag, the thin kind they
pack clothes in, dropped over his head and held tight against his
face; a thin scarf; a woman's stocking."

"I can see you would be a resourceful murderess, Miss Gray. It's
possible, but it would need a strong man and there would have to be
an element of surprise. We found no sign of a struggle."

"But it could have been done that way?"

"Of course, but there was absolutely no evidence that it was."

"But if he were first drugged?"

"That possibility did occur to me; that's why I had the coffee analysed. But he wasn't drugged, the P.M. confirmed it."

"How much coffee had he drunk?"

"Only about half a mug, according to the P.M. report and he died

57

immediately afterwards. Sometime between seven and nine p.m. was as close as the pathologist could estimate."

"Wasn't it odd that he drank coffee before his meal?"

"There's no law against it. We don't know when he intended to eat his supper. Anyway, you can't build a murder case on the order in which a man chooses to take his food and drink."

"What about the note he left? I suppose it isn't possible to raise prints from typewriter keys?"

"Not easily on that type of key. We tried but there was nothing identifiable."

"So in the end you accepted that it was suicide?"

"In the end I accepted that there was no possibility of proving otherwise."

"But you had a hunch? My partner's old colleague—he's a Superintendent of the C.I.D.—always backed his hunches."

"Ah, well, that's the Met, they can afford to indulge themselves. If I backed all my hunches I'd get no work done; it isn't what you suspect, it's what you can prove that counts."

"May I take the suicide note and the strap?"

"Why not, if you sign for them? No one else seems to want them."

"Could I see the note now, please?"

He extracted it from the file and handed it to her. Cordelia began to read to herself the first half-remembered words:

a void, boundless as the nether sky appeared
beneath us . . .

She was struck, not for the first time, by the importance of the written word, the magic of ordered symbols. Would poetry hold its theurgy if the lines were printed as prose, or prose be so compelling without the pattern and stress of punctuation? Miss Leaming had spoken Blake's passage as if she recognized its beauty yet here, spaced on the page, it exerted an even stronger power.

It was then that two things about the quotation caught at her breath. The first was not something which she intended to share with Sergeant Maskell but there was no reason why she should not comment on the second.

She said:

"Mark Callender must have been an experienced typist. This was done by an expert."

"I didn't think so. If you look carefully you'll see that one or two

of the letters are fainter than the rest. That's always the sign of an amateur."

"But the faint letters aren't always the same ones. It's usually the keys on the edges of the keyboard which the inexperienced typist hits more lightly. And the spacing here is good until nearly the end of the passage. It looks as if the typist suddenly realized that he ought to disguise his competence but hadn't time to retype the whole passage. And it's strange that the punctuation is so accurate."

"It was probably copied direct from the printed page. There was a copy of Blake in the boy's bedroom. The quotation is from Blake, you know, the Tyger Tyger burning bright poet."

"I know. But if he typed it from the book, why bother to return the Blake to his bedroom?"

"He was a tidy lad."

"But not tidy enough to wash up his coffee mug or clean his garden fork."

"That proves nothing. As I said, people do behave oddly when they're planning to kill themselves. We know that the typewriter was his and that he'd had it for a year. But we couldn't compare the typing with his work. All his papers had been burnt."

He glanced at his watch and got to his feet. Cordelia saw that the interview was over. She signed a chit for the suicide note and the leather belt, then shook hands and thanked him formally for his help. As he opened the door for her he said, as if on impulse:

"There's one intriguing detail you may care to know. It looks as if he was with a woman some time during the day on which he died. The pathologist found the merest trace—a thin line only—of purple-red lipstick on his upper lip."

Chapter Three

❖❖❖

New Hall, with its Byzantine air, its sunken court and its shining domed hall like a peeled orange, reminded Cordelia of a harem; admittedly one owned by a sultan with liberal views and an odd predilection for clever girls, but a harem nonetheless. The college was surely too distractingly pretty to be conducive to serious study. She wasn't sure, either, whether she approved of the obtrusive femininity of its white brick, the mannered prettiness of the shallow pools where the goldfish slipped like blood-red shadows between the water lilies, its artfully planted saplings. She concentrated on her criticism of the building; it helped to prevent her being intimidated.

She hadn't called at the Lodge to ask for Miss Tilling, afraid that she might be asked her business or refused admission; it seemed prudent just to walk in and chance to luck. Luck was with her. After two fruitless enquiries for Sophia Tilling's room, a hurrying student called back at her:

"She doesn't live in college but she's sitting on the grass over there with her brother."

Cordelia walked out of the shadow of the court into bright sunlight and over turf as soft as moss towards the little group. There were four of them, stretched out on the warm-smelling grass. The two Tillings were unmistakably brother and sister. Cordelia's first thought was that they reminded her of a couple of pre-Raphaelite portraits with their strong dark heads held high on unusually long necks, and their straight noses above curved, foreshortened upper lips. Beside their bony distinction, the second girl was all softness. If this were the girl who had visited Mark at the cottage, Miss Markland was right to call her beautiful. She had an oval face with a neat slender nose, a small but beautifully formed mouth, and slanted eyes of a strikingly deep blue which gave her whole face an oriental appearance intriguingly at variance with the fairness of her skin and her long blonde hair. She was wearing an ankle-length dress of fine mauve patterned cotton, buttoned high at the waist but with no other fastening. The gathered bodice cupped her full breasts and the skirt fell open to reveal a pair of tight fitting shorts in the same material.

As far as Cordelia could see, she wore nothing else. Her feet were bare and her long, shapely legs were untanned by the sun. Cordelia reflected that those white voluptuous thighs must be more erotic than a whole city of sunburnt limbs and that the girl knew it. Sophia Tilling's dark good looks were only a foil to this gentler, more entrancing beauty.

At first sight the fourth member of the party was more ordinary. He was a stocky, bearded young man with russet curly hair and a spade-shaped face, and was lying on the grass by the side of Sophie Tilling.

All of them, except the blonde girl, were wearing old jeans and open-necked cotton shirts.

Cordelia had come up to the group and had stood over them for a few seconds before they took any notice of her. She said:

"I'm looking for Hugo and Sophia Tilling. My name is Cordelia Gray." Hugo Tilling looked up:

"What shall Cordelia do, love and be silent."

Cordelia said:

"People who feel the need to joke about my name usually enquire after my sisters. It gets very boring."

"It must do. I'm sorry. I'm Hugo Tilling, this is my sister, this is Isabelle de Lasterie and this is Davie Stevens."

Davie Stevens sat up like a jack-in-the-box and said an amiable "Hi."

He looked at Cordelia with a quizzical intentness. She wondered about Davie. Her first impression of the little group, influenced perhaps by the college architecture, had been of a young sultan taking his ease with two of his favourites and attended by the captain of the guard. But, meeting Davie Stevens's steady intelligent gaze, that impression faded. She suspected that, in this seraglio, it was the captain of the guard who was the dominant personality.

Sophia Tilling nodded and said "Hullo."

Isabelle did not speak but a smile beautiful and meaningless spread over her face. Hugo said:

"Won't you sit down, Cordelia Gray, and explain the nature of your necessities?"

Cordelia knelt gingerly, wary of grass stains on the soft suede of her skirt. It was an odd way to interview suspects—only, of course, these people weren't suspects—kneeling like a suppliant in front of them. She said:

"I'm a private detective. Sir Ronald Callender has employed me to find out why his son died."

The effect of her words was astonishing. The little group, which had been lolling at ease like exhausted warriors, stiffened with instantaneous shock into a rigid tableau as if struck to marble. Then, almost imperceptibly, they relaxed. Cordelia could hear the slow release of held breath. She watched their faces. Davie Stevens was the least concerned. He wore a half-rueful smile, interested but unworried, and gave a quick look at Sophie as if in complicity. The look was not returned; she and Hugo were staring rigidly ahead. Cordelia felt that the two Tillings were carefully avoiding each other's eyes. But it was Isabelle who was the most shaken. She gave a gasp and her hand flew to her face like a second-rate actress simulating shock. Her eyes widened into fathomless depths of violet blue and she turned them on Hugo in desperate appeal. She looked so pale that Cordelia half expected her to faint. She thought:

"If I'm in the middle of a conspiracy, then I know who is its weakest member."

Hugo Tilling said:

"You're telling us that Ronald Callender has employed you to find out why Mark died?"

"Is that so extraordinary?"

"I find it incredible. He took no particular interest in his son when he was alive, why begin now he's dead?"

"How do you know he took no particular interest?"

"It's just an idea I had."

Cordelia said:

"Well, he's interested now even if it's only the scientist's urge to discover truth."

"Then he'd better stick to his microbiology, discovering how to make plastic soluble in salt water, or whatever. Human beings aren't susceptible to his kind of experiment."

Davie Stevens said with casual unconcern:

"I wonder that you can stomach that arrogant fascist."

The gibe plucked at too many chords of memory. Wilfully obtuse, Cordelia said:

"I didn't enquire what political party Sir Ronald favours."

Hugo laughed.

"Davie doesn't mean that. By fascist Davie means that Ronald Callender holds certain untenable opinions. For example, that all men may not be created equal, that universal suffrage may not neces-

62

sarily add to the general happiness of mankind, that the tyrannies of the left aren't noticeably more liberal or supportable than the tyrannies of the right, that black men killing black men is small improvement on white men killing black men in so far as the victims are concerned and that capitalism may not be responsible for all the ills that flesh is heir to from drug addiction to poor syntax. I don't suggest that Ronald Callender holds all or indeed any of these reprehensible opinions. But Davie thinks that he does."

Davie threw a book at Hugo and said without rancour:

"Shut up! You talk like the *Daily Telegraph*. And you're boring our visitor."

Sophie Tilling asked suddenly:

"Was it Sir Ronald who suggested that you should question us?"

"He said that you were Mark's friends; he saw you at the inquest and funeral."

Hugo laughed:

"For God's sake, is that his idea of friendship?"

Cordelia said:

"But you were there?"

"We went to the inquest—all of us except Isabelle, who, we thought, would have been decorative but unreliable. It was rather dull. There was a great deal of irrelevant medical evidence about the excellent state of Mark's heart, lungs and digestive system. As far as I can see, he would have gone on living for ever if he hadn't put a belt round his neck."

"And the funeral—were you there too?"

"We were, at the Cambridge Crematorium. A very subdued affair. There were only six of us present in addition to the undertaker's men; we three, Ronald Callender, that secretary/housekeeper of his and an old nanny type dressed in black. She cast rather a gloom over the proceedings, I thought. Actually she looked so exactly like an old family retainer that I suspect she was a policewoman in disguise."

"Why should she be? Did she look like one?"

"No, but then you don't look like a private eye."

"You've no idea who she was?"

"No, we weren't introduced; it wasn't a chummy kind of funeral. Now I recall it, not one of us spoke a single word to any of the others. Sir Ronald wore a mask of public grief, the King mourning the Crown Prince."

"And Miss Leaming?"

63

"The Queen Consort; she should have had a black veil over her face."

"I thought that her suffering was real enough," said Sophie.

"You can't tell. No one can. Define suffering. Define real."

Suddenly Davie Stevens spoke, rolling over onto his stomach like a playful dog.

"Miss Leaming looked pretty sick to me. Incidentally, the old lady was called Pilbeam; anyway, that was the name on the wreath."

Sophie laughed:

"That awful cross of roses with the black-edged card? I might have guessed it came from her; but how do you know?"

"I looked, honey. The undertaker's men took the wreath off the coffin and propped it against the wall so I took a quick butchers. The card read 'With sincere sympathy from Nanny Pilbeam'."

Sophie said:

"So you did, I remember now. How beautifully feudal! Poor old nanny, it must have cost her a packet."

"Did Mark ever talk about a Nanny Pilbeam?" Cordelia asked.

They glanced at each other quickly. Isabelle shook her head. Sophie said "not to me."

Hugo Tilling replied:

"He never talked about her, but I think I did see her once before the funeral. She called at college about six weeks ago—on Mark's twenty-first birthday actually, and asked to see him. I was in the porter's Lodge at the time and Robbins asked me if Mark was in college. She went up to his room and they were there together for about an hour. I saw her leaving, but he never mentioned her to me either then or later."

And soon afterwards, thought Cordelia, he gave up university. Could there be a connection? It was only a tenuous lead, but she would have to follow it.

She asked out of a curiosity that seemed both perverse and irrelevant.

"Were there any other flowers?"

It was Sophie who replied:

"A simple bunch of unwired garden flowers on the coffin. No card. Miss Leaming, I suppose. It was hardly Sir Ronald's style."

Cordelia said:

"You were his friends. Please tell me about him."

They looked at each other as if deciding who should speak. Their embarrassment was almost palpable. Sophie Tilling was picking at

small blades of grass and rolling them in her hands. Without look-ing up, she said:

"Mark was a very private person. I'm not sure how far any of us knew him. He was quiet, gentle, self-contained, unambitious. He was intelligent without being clever. He was very kind; he cared about people, but without inflicting them with his concern. He had little self-esteem but it never seemed to worry him. I don't think there is anything else we can say about him."

Suddenly Isabelle spoke in a voice so low that Cordelia could hardly catch it. She said:

"He was sweet."

Hugo said with a sudden angry impatience.

"He was sweet and he is dead. There you have it. We can't tell you any more about Mark Callender than that. We none of us saw him after he chucked college. He didn't consult us before he left, and he didn't consult us before he killed himself. He was, as my sister has told you, a very private person. I suggest that you leave him his privacy."

"Look," said Cordelia, "you went to the inquest, you went to the funeral. If you had stopped seeing him, if you were so unconcerned about him, why did you bother?"

"Sophie went out of affection. Davie went because Sophie did. I went out of curiosity and respect; you mustn't be seduced by my air of casual flippancy into thinking that I haven't a heart."

Cordelia said obstinately:

"Someone visited him at the cottage on the evening he died. Some-one had coffee with him. I intend to find out who that person was."

Was it her fancy that this news surprised them? Sophie Tilling looked as if she were about to ask a question when her brother quickly broke in:

"It wasn't any of us. On the night Mark died we were all in the second row of the dress circle of the Arts Theatre watching Pinter. I don't know that I can prove it. I doubt whether the booking clerk has kept the chart for that particular night, but I booked the seats and she may remember me. If you insist on being tediously meticu-lous, I can probably introduce you to a friend who knew of my in-tention to take a party to the play; to another who saw some at least of us in the bar in the interval; and to another with whom I subse-quently discussed the performance. None of this will prove anything; my friends are an accommodating bunch. It would be simpler for you to accept that I am telling the truth. Why should I lie? We were all four at the Arts Theatre on the night of 26th May."

Davie Stevens said gently:

"Why not tell that arrogant bastard Pa Callender to go to hell and leave his son in peace, then find yourself a nice simple case of larceny?"

"Or murder," said Hugo Tilling.

"Find yourself a nice simple case of murder."

As if in obedience to some secret code, they began getting up, piling their books together, brushing the grass cuttings from their clothes. Cordelia followed them through the courts and out of college. Still in a silent group they made their way to a white Renault parked in the forecourt.

Cordelia came up to them and spoke directly to Isabelle.

"Did you enjoy the Pinter? Weren't you frightened by that dreadful last scene when Wyatt Gillman is gunned down by the natives?"

It was so easy that Cordelia almost despised herself. The immense violet eyes grew puzzled.

"Oh, no! I did not care about it, I was not frightened. I was with Hugo and the others, you see."

Cordelia turned to Hugo Tilling.

"Your friend doesn't seem to know the difference between Pinter and Osborne."

Hugo was settling himself into the driving seat of the car. He twisted round to open the back door for Sophie and Davie. He said calmly:

"My friend, as you choose to call her, is living in Cambridge, inadequately chaperoned I'm happy to say, for the purpose of learning English. So far her progress has been erratic and in some respects disappointing. One can never be certain how much my friend has understood."

The engine purred into life. The car began to move. It was then that Sophie Tilling thrust her head out of the window and said impulsively:

"I don't mind talking about Mark if you think it will help. It won't, but you can come round to my house this afternoon if you like—57 Norwich Street. Don't be late; Davie and I are going on the river. You can come too if you feel like it."

The car accelerated. Cordelia watched it out of sight. Hugo raised his hand in ironic farewell but not one of them turned a head.

Cordelia muttered the address to herself until it was safely written down: 57 Norwich Street. Was that the address where Sophie lodged, a hostel perhaps, or did her family live in Cambridge? Well, she would find out soon enough. When ought she to arrive? Too early would look over eager; too late and they might have set out for the river. Whatever motive had prompted Sophie Tilling to issue that belated invitation, she mustn't lose touch with them now.

They had some guilty knowledge; that had been obvious. Why else had they reacted so strongly to her arrival? They wanted the facts of Mark Callender's death to be left undisturbed. They would try to persuade, cajole, even to shame her into abandoning the case. Would they, she wondered, also threaten? But why? The most likely theory was that they were shielding someone. But again, why? Murder wasn't a matter of climbing late into college, a venial infringement of rules which a friend would automatically condone and conceal. Mark Callender had been their friend; to two of them he might have been more than a friend. Someone whom he knew and trusted had pulled a strap tight round his neck, had watched and listened to his agonized choking, had strung his body on a hook like the carcass of an animal. How could one reconcile that appalling knowledge with Davie Stevens' slightly amused and rueful glance at Sophie, with Hugo's cynical calm, with Sophie's friendly and interested eyes? If they were conspirators, then they were monsters. And Isabelle? If they were shielding anyone, it was most likely to be her. But Isabelle de Lasterie couldn't have murdered Mark. Cordelia remembered those frail sloping shoulders, those ineffective hands almost transparent in the sun, the long nails painted like elegant pink talons. If Isabelle were guilty, she hadn't acted alone. Only a tall and very strong woman could have heaved that inert body onto the chair and up to the hook.

Norwich Street was a one-way thoroughfare and, initially, Cordelia approached it from the wrong direction. It took her some time to find her way back to Hills Road, past the Roman Catholic church and down the fourth turning to the right. The street was terraced with small brick houses, obviously early Victorian. Equally obviously, the road was on its way up. Most of the houses looked well cared for; the paint on the identical front doors was fresh and bright; lined curtains had replaced the draped lace at the single ground-floor windows and the bases of the walls were scarred where a damp course had been installed. Number fifty-seven had a black front door with the house number painted in white behind the glass panel above.

Cordelia was relieved to see that there was space to park the Mini. There was no sign of the Renault among the almost continuous row of old cars and battered bicycles which lined the edge of the pavement.

The front door was wide open. Cordelia pressed the bell and stepped tentatively into a narrow white hall. The interior of the house was immediately familiar to her. From her sixth birthday she had lived for two years in just such a Victorian terraced cottage with Mrs. Gibson on the outskirts of Romford. She recognized the steep and narrow staircase immediately ahead, the door on the right leading to the front parlour, the second door set aslant which led to the back parlour and through it to the kitchen and yard. She knew that there would be cupboards and a curved alcove on each side of the fireplace; she knew where to find the door under the stairs. Memory was so sharp that it imposed on this clean, sun-scented interior the strong odour of unwashed napkins, cabbage and grease which had permeated the Romford house. She could almost hear the children's voices calling her outlandish name across the rookery of the primary school playground across the road, stamping the asphalt with the ubiquitous Wellington boots which they wore in all seasons, flailing their thin jersied arms: "Cor, Cor, Cor!"

The furthest door was ajar and she could glimpse a room painted bright yellow and spilling over with sunlight. Sophie's head appeared.

"Oh, it's you! Come in. Davie has gone to collect some books from college and to buy food for the picnic. Would you like tea now or shall we wait? I'm just finishing the ironing."

"I'd rather wait, thank you."

Cordelia sat down and watched while Sophie wound the flex around the iron and folded the cloth. She glanced around the room. It was welcoming and attractive, furnished in no particular style or period, a cosy hotch-potch of the cheap and the valuable, unpretentious and pleasing. There was a sturdy oak table against the wall; four rather ugly dining chairs; a Windsor chair with a plump yellow cushion; an elegant Victorian sofa covered with brown velvet and set under the window; three good Staffordshire figures on the mantel shelf above the hooded wrought-iron grate. One of the walls was almost covered with a notice board in dark cork which displayed posters, cards, *aides-mémoire*, and pictures cut from magazines. Two, Cordelia saw, were beautifully photographed and attractive nudes.

Outside the yellow-curtained window the small walled garden was a riot of greenery. An immense and multi-flowered hollyhock bur-

geoned against a tatty looking trellis; there were roses planted in Ali Baba jars and a row of pots of bright-red geraniums lined the top of the wall.

Cordelia said:

"I like this house. Is it yours?"

"Yes, I own it. Our grandmother died two years ago and left Hugo and me a small legacy. I used mine for the down payment on this house and got a local authority grant towards the cost of conversion. Hugo spent all of his laying down wine. He was ensuring a happy middle age; I was ensuring a happy present. I suppose that's the difference between us."

She folded the ironing cloth on the end of the table and stowed it away in one of the cupboards. Sitting opposite to Cordelia, she asked abruptly:

"Do you like my brother?"

"Not very much. I thought he was rather rude to me."

"He didn't mean to be."

"I think that's rather worse. Rudeness should always be intentional, otherwise it's insensitivity."

"Hugo isn't at his most agreeable when he's with Isabelle. She has that affect on him."

"Was she in love with Mark Callender?"

"You'll have to ask her, Cordelia, but I shouldn't think so. They hardly knew each other. Mark was my lover, not hers. I thought I'd better get you here to tell you myself since someone's bound to sooner or later if you go around Cambridge ferreting out facts about him. He didn't live here with me, of course. He had rooms in college. But we were lovers for almost the whole of last year. It ended just after Christmas when I met Davie."

"Were you in love?"

"I'm not sure. All sex is a kind of exploitation, isn't it? If you mean, did we explore our own identities through the personality of the other, then I suppose we were in love or thought that we were. Mark needed to believe himself in love. I'm not sure I know what the word means."

Cordelia felt a surge of sympathy. She wasn't sure either. She thought of her own two lovers; Georges whom she had slept with because he was gentle and unhappy and called her Cordelia, a real name, her name, not Delia, Daddy's little fascist; and Carl who was young and angry and whom she had liked so much that it seemed churlish not to show it in the only way which seemed to him impor-

tant. She had never thought of virginity as other than a temporary and inconvenient state, part of the general insecurity and vulnerability of being young. Before Georges and Carl she had been lonely and inexperienced. Afterwards she had been lonely and a little less inexperienced. Neither affair had given her the longed-for assurance in dealing with Daddy or the landladies, neither had inconveniently touched her heart. But for Carl she had felt tenderness. It was just as well that he had left Rome before his lovemaking had become too pleasurable and he too important to her. It was intolerable to think that those strange gymnastics might one day become necessary. Lovemaking, she had decided, was overrated, not painful but surprising. The alienation between thought and action was so complete. She said:

"I suppose I only meant were you fond of each other, and did you like going to bed together?"

"Both of those things."

"Why did it end? Did you quarrel?"

"Nothing so natural or uncivilized. One didn't quarrel with Mark. That was one of the troubles about him. I told him that I didn't want to go on with the affair and he accepted my decision as calmly as if I were just breaking a date for a play at the Arts. He didn't try to argue or dissuade me. And if you're wondering whether the break had anything to do with his death, well you're wrong. I wouldn't rank that high with anyone, particularly not Mark. I was probably fonder of him than he was of me."

"So why did it end?"

"I felt that I was under moral scrutiny. It wasn't true; Mark wasn't a prig. But that's how I felt, or pretended to myself that I felt. I couldn't live up to him and I didn't even want to. There was Gary Webber, for example. I'd better tell you about him; it explains a lot about Mark. He's an autistic child, one of the uncontrollable, violent ones. Mark met him with his parents and their other two children on Jesus Green about a year ago; the children were playing on the swings there. Mark spoke to Gary and the boy responded to him. Children always did. He took to visiting the family and looking after Gary one evening a week so that the Webbers could get out to the pictures. During his last two vacs he stayed in the house and looked after Gary completely while the whole family went off for a holiday. The Webbers couldn't bear the boy to go to hospital; they'd tried it once and he didn't settle. But they were perfectly happy to leave him with Mark. I used to call in some evenings and see them together.

Mark would hold the boy on his lap and rock him backwards and forwards for hours at a time. It was the one way to quieten him. We disagreed about Gary. I thought he would be better dead and I said so. I still think it would be better if he died, better for his parents, better for the rest of the family, better for him. Mark didn't agree. I remember saying:

" 'Oh well, if you think it reasonable that children should suffer so that you can enjoy the emotional kick of relieving them——' After that the conversation became boringly metaphysical. Mark said:

" 'Neither you nor I would be willing to kill Gary. He exists. His family exists. They need help which we can give. It doesn't matter what we feel. Actions are important, feelings aren't.' "

Cordelia said:

"But actions arise out of feelings."

"Oh, Cordelia, don't you start! I've had this particular conversation too many times before. Of course they do!"

They were silent for a moment. Then Cordelia, reluctant to shatter the tenuous confidence and friendship which she sensed was growing between them, made herself ask:

"Why did he kill himself—if he did kill himself?" Sophie's reply was as emphatic as a slammed door.

"He left a note."

"A note perhaps. But, as his father pointed out, not an explanation. It's a lovely passage of prose—at least I think so—but as a justification for suicide it just isn't convincing."

"It convinced the jury."

"It doesn't convince me. Think, Sophie! Surely there are only two reasons for killing oneself. One is either escaping from something or to something. The first is rational. If one is in intolerable pain, despair or mental anguish and there is no reasonable chance of a cure, then it's probably sensible to prefer oblivion. But it isn't sensible to kill oneself in the hope of gaining some better existence or to extend one's sensibilities to include the experience of death. It isn't possible to experience death. I'm not even sure it's possible to experience dying. One can only experience the preparations for death, and even that seems pointless since one can't make use of the experience afterwards. If there's any sort of existence after death we shall all know soon enough. If there isn't, we shan't exist to complain that we've been cheated. People who believe in an after life are perfectly reasonable. They're the only ones who are safe from ultimate disillusionment."

"You've thought it all out, haven't you. I'm not sure that suicides do. The act is probably both impulsive and irrational."

"Was Mark impulsive and irrational?"

"I didn't know Mark."

"But you were lovers! You slept with him!"

Sophie looked at her and cried out in angry pain.

"I didn't know him! I thought I did, but I didn't know the first thing about him!"

They sat without speaking for almost two minutes. Then Cordelia asked:

"You went to dinner at Garforth House didn't you? What was it like?"

"The food and the wine were surprisingly good, but I don't suppose that's what you had in mind. The dinner party wasn't otherwise memorable. Sir Ronald was amiable enough when he noticed I was there. Miss Leaming, when she could tear her obsessive attention from the presiding genius, looked me over like a prospective mother-in-law. Mark was rather silent. I think he'd taken me there to prove something to me, or perhaps to himself; I'm not sure what. He never talked about the evening or asked me what I thought. A month later Hugo and I both went to dinner. It was then I met Davie. He was the guest of one of the research biologists and Ronald Callender was angling to get him. Davie did a vac job there in his final year. If you want the inside dope on Garforth House, you should ask him."

Five minutes later Hugo, Isabelle and Davie arrived. Cordelia had gone upstairs to the bathroom and heard the car stop and the jabber of voices in the hall. Footsteps passed beneath her towards the back parlour. She turned on the hot water. The gas boiler in the kitchen immediately gave forth a roar as if the little house were powered by a dynamo. Cordelia let the tap run, then stepped out of the bathroom, closing the door gently behind her. She stole to the top of the stairs. It was hard luck on Sophie to waste her hot water, she thought guiltily; but worse was the sense of treachery and shabby opportunism as she crept down the first three stairs and listened. The front door had been closed but the door to the back parlour was open. She heard Isabelle's high unemphatic voice:

"But if this man Sir Ronald is paying her to find out about Mark, why cannot I pay her to stop finding out?"

Then Hugo's voice, amused, a little contemptuous:

"Darling Isabelle, when will you learn that not everyone can be bought?"

"She can't, anyway. I like her."

It was Sophie speaking. Her brother replied:

"We all like her. The question is, how do we get rid of her?"

Then for a few minutes there was a murmur of voices, the words undistinguishable, broken by Isabelle.

"It is not, I think, a suitable job for a woman."

There was the sound of a chair scraping against the floor, a shuffle of feet. Cordelia darted guiltily back into the bathroom and turned off the tap. She recalled Bernie's complacent admonition when she had asked whether they needed accept a divorce case.

"You can't do our job, partner, and be a gentleman." She stood watching at the half-open door. Hugo and Isabelle were leaving. She waited until she heard the front door close and the car drive away. Then she went down to the parlour. Sophie and Davie were together, unpacking a large carrier bag of groceries. Sophie smiled and said:

"Isabelle has a party tonight. She has a house quite close to here in Panton Street. Mark's tutor, Edward Horsfall, will probably be there and we thought it might be useful for you to talk to him about Mark. The party's at eight o'clock but you can call for us here. Just now we're packing a picnic; we thought we'd take a punt on the river for an hour or so. Do come if you'd like to. It's really much the pleasantest way of seeing Cambridge."

❖❖❖

Afterwards, Cordelia remembered the river picnic as a series of brief but intensely clear pictures, moments in which sight and sense fused and time seemed momentarily arrested while the sunlit image was impressed on her mind. Sunlight sparkling on the river and gilding the hairs of Davie's chest and forearms; the flesh of his strong upper arms speckled like an egg; Sophie lifting her arm to wipe the sweat from her brow as she rested between thrusts of the punt pole; green-black weeds dragged by the pole from mysterious depths to writhe sinuously below the surface; a bright duck cocking its white tail before disappearing in a flurry of green water. When they had rocked under Silver Street Bridge a friend of Sophie's swam alongside, sleek and snoutnosed like an otter, his black hair laying like blades across his cheeks. He rested his hands on the punt and opened his mouth to be fed chunks of sandwiches by a protesting Sophie. The punts

and canoes scraped and jostled each other in the turbulence of white water racing under the bridge. The air rang with laughing voices and the green banks were peopled with half-naked bodies lying supine with their faces to the sun.

Davie punted until they reached the higher level of the river and Cordelia and Sophie stretched out on the cushions at opposite ends of the punt. Thus distanced it was impossible to carry on a private conversation; Cordelia guessed that this was precisely what Sophie had planned. From time to time, she would call out snatches of information as if to emphasize that the outing was strictly educational.

"That wedding cake is John's—we're just passing under Clare bridge, one of the prettiest, I think. Thomas Grumbald built it in 1639. They say he was only paid three shillings for the design. You know that view, of course; it's a good view of Queen's, though."

Cordelia's courage failed her at the thought of interrupting this desultory tourist's chat with the brutal demand:

"Did you and your brother kill your lover?"

Here, rocking gently on the sunlit river, the question seemed both indecent and absurd. She was in danger of being lulled into a gentle acceptance of defeat; viewing all her suspicions as a neurotic hankering after drama and notoriety, a need to justify her fee to Sir Ronald. She believed Mark Callender had been murdered because she wanted to believe it. She had identified with him, with his solitariness, his self-sufficiency, his alienation from his father, his lonely childhood. She had even—most dangerous presumption of all—come to see herself as his avenger. When Sophie took over the pole, just past the Garden House Hotel, and Davie edged his way along the gently rocking punt and stretched himself out beside her, she knew that she wouldn't be able to mention Mark's name. It was out of no more than a vague, unintrusive curiosity that she found herself asking:

"Is Sir Ronald Callender a good scientist?" Davie took up a short paddle and began lazily to stir the shining water.

"His science is perfectly respectable, as my dear colleagues would say. Rather more than respectable, in fact. At present the lab is working on ways of expanding the use of biological monitors to assess pollution of the sea and estuaries; that means routine surveys of plants and animals which might serve as indicators. And they did some very useful preliminary work last year on the degradation of plastics. R.C. isn't so hot himself, but then you can't expect much original science from the over fifties. But he's a great spotter of talent

74

and he certainly knows how to run a team if you fancy that dedicated, one for all, band of brothers approach. I don't. They even publish their papers as the Callender Research Laboratory, not under individual names. That wouldn't do for me. When I publish, it's strictly for the glory of David Forbes Stevens and, incidentally, for the gratification of Sophie. The Tillings like success."

"Was that why you didn't want to stay on when he offered you a job?"

"That among other reasons. He pays too generously and he asks too much. I don't like being bought and I've a strong objection to dressing up every night in a dinner jacket like a performing monkey in a zoo. I'm a molecular biologist. I'm not looking for the holy grail. Dad and Mum brought me up as a Methodist and I don't see why I should chuck a perfectly good religion which served me very well for twelve years just to put the great scientific principle or Ronald Callender in its place. I distrust these sacerdotal scientists. It's a bloody wonder that little lot at Garforth House aren't genuflecting three times a day in the direction of the Cavendish."

"And what about Lunn? How does he fit in?"

"Oh, that boy's a bloody wonder! Ronald Callender found him in a children's home when he was fifteen—don't ask me how—and trained him to be a lab assistant. You couldn't find a better. There isn't an instrument made which Chris Lunn can't learn to understand and care for. He's developed one or two himself and Callender has had them patented. If anyone in that lab is indispensable it's probably Lunn. Certainly Ronald Callender cares a damn sight more for him than he did for his son. And Lunn, as you might guess, regards R.C. as God almighty, which is very gratifying for them both. It's extraordinary really, all that violence which used to be expressed in street fights and coshing old ladies, harnessed to the service of science. You've got to hand it to Callender. He certainly knows how to pick his slaves."

"And is Miss Leaming a slave?"

"Well, I wouldn't know just what Eliza Leaming is. She's responsible for the business management and, like Lunn, she's probably indispensable. Lunn and she seem to have a love-hate relationship, or, perhaps, a hate-hate relationship. I'm not very clever at detecting these psychological nuances."

"But how on earth does Sir Ronald pay for it all?"

"Well, that's the thousand-dollar question, isn't it? It's rumoured that most of the money came from his wife and that he and Elizabeth

Leaming between them invested it rather cleverly. They certainly needed to. And then he gets a certain amount from contract work. Even so, it's an expensive hobby. While I was there they were saying that the Wolvington Trust were getting interested. If they come up with something big—and I gather it's below their dignity to come up with anything small—then most of Ronald Callender's troubles should be over. Mark's death must have hit him. Mark was due to come into a pretty substantial fortune in four years' time and he told Sophie that he intended to hand most of it over to Dad."

"Why on earth should he do that?"

"God knows. Conscience money, perhaps. Anyway, he obviously thought it was something that Sophie ought to know."

Conscience money for what, Cordelia wondered sleepily. For not loving his father enough? For rejecting his enthusiasms? For being less than the son he had hoped for? And what would happen to Mark's fortune now? Who stood to gain by Mark's death? She supposed that she ought to consult his grandfather's will and find out. But that would mean a trip to London. Was it really worth it?

She stretched back her face to the sun and trailed one hand in the river. A splash of water from the punt pole stung her eyes. She opened them and saw that the punt was gliding close to the bank and under the shade of overhanging trees. Immediately in front of her a torn branch, cleft at the end and thick as a man's body, hung by a thread of bark and turned gently as the punt passed beneath it. She was aware of Davie's voice; he must have been talking for a long time. How odd that she couldn't remember what he'd been saying!

"You don't need reasons for killing yourself; you need reasons for not killing yourself. It was suicide, Cordelia. I should let it go at that."

Cordelia thought that she must have briefly slept, since he seemed to be answering a question she couldn't remember having asked. But now there were other voices, louder and more insistent. Sir Ronald Callender's: "My son is dead. *My* son. If I am in some way responsible, I'd prefer to know. If anyone else is responsible, I want to know that too." Sergeant Maskell's: "How would you use this to hang yourself, Miss Gray?" The feel of the belt, smooth and sinuous, slipping like a live thing through her fingers.

She sat bolt upright, hands clasped around her knees, with such suddenness that the punt rocked violently and Sophie had to clutch at an overhanging branch to keep her balance. Her dark face, intriguingly fore-shortened and patterned with the shadow of leaves,

looked down at Cordelia from what seemed an immense height. Their eyes met. In that moment Cordelia knew how close she had come to giving up the case. She had been suborned by the beauty of the day, by sunshine, indolence, the promise of comradeship, even friendship, into forgetting why she was here. The realization horrified her. Davie had said that Sir Ronald was a good picker. Well, he had picked her. This was her first case and nothing and no one was going to hinder her from solving it.

She said formally:

"It was good of you to let me join you, but I don't want to miss the party tonight. I ought to talk to Mark's tutor and there may be other people there who could tell me something. Isn't it time that we thought about turning back?"

Sophie turned her glance on Davie. He gave an almost imperceptible shrug. Without speaking, Sophie drove the pole hard against the bank. The punt began slowly to turn.

❖❖❖

Isabelle's party was due to begin at eight o'clock but it was nearly nine when Sophie, Davie and Cordelia arrived. They walked to the house which was only five minutes from Norwich Street; Cordelia never discovered the exact address. She liked the look of the house and wondered how much it was costing Isabelle's father in rent. It was a long, white, two-storey villa with tall curved windows and green shutters, set well back from the street, with a semi-basement and a flight of steps to the front door. A similar flight led down from the sitting-room to the long garden.

The sitting-room was already fairly full. Looking at her fellow guests, Cordelia was glad that she had bought the kaftan. Most people seemed to have changed although not necessarily, she thought, into something more attractive. What was aimed at was originality; it was preferable to look spectacular, even bizarre, than to appear nondescript.

The sitting-room was elegantly but unsubstantially furnished and Isabelle had impressed on it her own untidy, impractical and iconoclastic femininity. Cordelia doubted whether the owners had provided the ornate crystal chandelier, far too heavy and large for the room, which hung like a sunburst from the middle of the ceiling, or the many silken cushions and curtains which gave the room's

77

austere proportions something of the ostentatious opulence of a courtesan's boudoir. The pictures, too, must surely be Isabelle's. No house owner letting his property would leave pictures of this quality on the walls. One, hanging above the fireplace, was of a young girl hugging a puppy. Cordelia gazed at it in excited pleasure. Surely she couldn't mistake that individual blue of the girl's dress, that marvellous painting of the cheeks and plump young arms, skin which simultaneously absorbed and reflected light—lovely, tangible flesh. She cried out involuntarily so that people turned to look at her:

"But that's a Renoir!"

Hugo was at her elbow. He laughed.

"Yes; but don't sound so shocked, Cordelia. It's only a small Renoir! Isabelle asked Papa for a picture for her sitting-room. You didn't expect him to provide a print of the Haywain or one of those cheap reproductions of Van Gogh's boring old chair."

"Would Isabelle have known the difference?"

"Oh, yes. Isabelle knows an expensive object when she sees one."

Cordelia wondered whether the bitterness, the hard edge of contempt in his voice, was for Isabelle or for himself. They looked across the room to where she stood, smiling at them. Hugo moved towards her like a man in a dream and took her hand. Cordelia watched. Isabelle had dressed her hair in a high cluster of curls, Grecian style. She was wearing an ankle-length dress of cream matt silk, with a very low square neckline and small intricately tucked sleeves. It was obviously a model and should, Cordelia felt, have looked out of place at an informal party. But it didn't. It merely made every other woman's dress look like an improvization and reduced her own, whose colours had seemed muted and subtle when she bought it, to the status of a gaudy rag.

Cordelia was determined to get Isabelle alone some time during the evening but could see that it wasn't going to be easy. Hugo stuck tenaciously to her side, steering her among her guests with one proprietorial hand on her waist. He seemed to be drinking steadily and Isabelle's glass was always filled. Perhaps as the evening wore on they would get careless and there would be a chance to separate them. In the meantime, Cordelia decided to explore the house, and a more practical matter, to find out before she needed it where the lavatory was. It was the kind of party where guests were left to find out these things for themselves.

She went up to the first floor and making her way down the pas-

sage pushed gently open the door of the far room. The smell of whisky met her immediately; it was overpowering and Cordelia instinctively slipped into the room and closed the door behind her, afraid that it might permeate the house. The room, which was in an indescribable state of disarray, wasn't empty. On the bed and half covered by the counterpane a woman was lying; a woman with bright ginger hair splayed over the pillow and wearing a pink silk dressing-gown. Cordelia walked up to the bed and looked down at her. She was insensible with drink. She lay there emitting puffs of foul, whisky-laden breath which rose like invisible balls of smoke from the half-open mouth. Her lower lip and jaw were tense and creased, giving the face a look of stern censoriousness as if she disapproved strongly of her own condition. Her thin lips were thickly painted, the strong purple stain had seeped into the cracks around the mouth so that the body looked parched in an extremity of cold. Her hands, the gnarled fingers brown with nicotine and laden with rings, lay quietly on the counterpane. Two of the talon-like nails were broken and the brick-red varnish on the others was cracked or peeled away.

The window was obstructed by a heavy dressing-table. Averting her eyes from the mess of crumpled tissues, open bottles of face cream, spilt powder and half drunk cups of what looked like black coffee, Cordelia squeezed behind it and pushed open the window. She gulped in lungfulls of fresh, cleansing air. Below her in the garden pale shapes moved silently over the grass and between the trees like the ghosts of long dead revellers. She left the window open and went back to the bed. There was nothing here that she could do but she placed the cold hands under the counterpane and, taking a second and warmer gown from the hook on the door, tucked it around the woman's body. That, at least, would compensate for the fresh air blowing across the bed.

That done, Cordelia slipped back into the passage, just in time to see Isabelle coming out of the room next door. She shot out an arm and half dragged the girl back into the bedroom. Isabelle gave a little cry, but Cordelia planted her back firmly against the door and said in a low, urgent whisper:

"Tell me what you know about Mark Callender."

The violet eyes slewed from door to window as if desperate for escape.

"I wasn't there when he did it."

"When who did what?"

Isabelle retreated towards the bed as if the inert figure, who was now groaning stertorously, could offer support. Suddenly the woman turned on her side and gave a long snort like an animal in pain. Both girls glanced at her in startled alarm. Cordelia reiterated:

"When who did what?"

"When Mark killed himself; I wasn't there."

The woman on the bed gave a little sigh. Cordelia lowered her voice:

"But you were there some days earlier, weren't you? You called at the house and enquired for him. Miss Markland saw you. Afterwards you sat in the garden and waited until he'd finished work."

Was it Cordelia's imagination that the girl suddenly seemed more relaxed, that she was relieved at the innocuousness of the question?

"I just called to see Mark. They gave me his address at the college Lodge. I went to visit him."

"Why?" The harsh question seemed to puzzle her. She replied simply:

"I wanted to be with him. He was my friend."

"Was he your lover too?" asked Cordelia. This brutal frankness was surely better than asking whether they had slept together, or gone to bed together—stupid euphemisms which Isabelle might not even understand: it was hard to tell from those beautiful but frightened eyes just how much she did understand.

"No, Mark was never my lover. He was working in the garden and I had to wait for him at the cottage. He gave me a chair in the sun and a book until he was free."

"What book?"

"I don't remember, it was very dull. I was dull too until Mark came. Then we had tea with funny mugs that had a blue band, and after tea we went for a walk and then we had supper. Mark made a salad."

"And then?"

"I drove home."

She was perfectly calm now. Cordelia pressed on, aware of the sound of footsteps passing up and down the stairs, of the ring of voices.

"And the time before that? When did you see him before that tea party?"

"It was a few days before Mark left college. We went for a picnic in my car to the seaside. But first we stopped at a town—St. Edmunds town, is it?—and Mark saw a doctor."

"Why? Was he ill?"

"Oh no, he was not ill, and he did not stay long enough for what you call it—an examination. He was in the house a few minutes only. It was a very poor house. I waited for him in the car, but not just outside the house you understand."

"Did he say why he went there?"

"No, but I do not think he got what he wanted. Afterwards he was sad for a little time, but then we went to the sea and he was happy again."

She, too, seemed happy now. She smiled at Cordelia, her sweet, unmeaning smile. Cordelia thought: it's just the cottage that terrifies her. She doesn't mind talking about the living Mark, it's his death she can't bear to think about. And yet, this repugnance wasn't born of personal grief. He had been her friend; he was sweet; she liked him. But she was getting on very well without him.

There was a knock at the door. Cordelia stood aside and Hugo came in. He lifted an eyebrow at Isabelle and, ignoring Cordelia, said:

"It's your party, ducky; coming down?"

"Cordelia wanted to talk to me about Mark."

"No doubt. You told her, I hope, that you spent one day with him motoring to the sea and one afternoon and evening at Summertrees and that you haven't seen him since."

"She told me," said Cordelia. "She was practically word perfect. I think she's safe to be let out on her own now."

He said easily:

"You shouldn't be sarcastic, Cordelia, it doesn't suit you. Sarcasm is all right for some women, but not for women who are beautiful in the way that you are beautiful."

They were passing down the stairs together to meet the hubbub in the hall. The compliment irritated Cordelia. She said:

"I suppose that woman on the bed is Isabelle's chaperone. Is she often drunk?"

"Mademoiselle de Congé? Not often as drunk as that, but I admit that she is seldom absolutely sober."

"Then oughtn't you to do something about it?"

"What should I do? Hand her over to the twentieth-century Inquisition—a psychiatrist like my father? What has she done to us to deserve that? Besides, she is tediously conscientious on the few occasions when she's sober. It happens that her compulsions and my interest coincide."

Cordelia said severely:

"That may be expedient but I don't think it's very responsible and it isn't kind."

He stopped in his tracks and turned towards her, smiling directly into her eyes.

"Oh, Cordelia, you talk like the child of progressive parents who has been reared by a nonconformist nanny and educated at a convent school. I do like you!"

He was still smiling as Cordelia slipped away from them and infiltrated into the party. She reflected that his diagnosis hadn't been so very wrong.

She helped herself to a glass of wine, then moved slowly round the room listening unashamedly to scraps of conversation, hoping to hear Mark's name mentioned. She heard it only once. Two girls and a very fair, rather insipid young man were standing behind her. One of the girls said:

"Sophie Tilling seems to have recovered remarkably quickly from Mark Callender's suicide. She and Davie went to the cremation, did you know? Typical of Sophie to take her current lover to see the previous one incinerated. I suppose it gave her some kind of a kick."

Her companion laughed.

"And little brother takes over Mark's girl. If you can't get beauty, money and brains, settle for the first two. Poor Hugo! He suffers from a sense of inferiority. Not quite handsome enough; not quite clever enough—Sophie's First must have shaken him—not quite rich enough. No wonder he has to rely on sex to give him confidence."

"And, even there, not quite . . ."

"Darling, you should know."

They laughed and moved away. Cordelia felt her face burning. Her hand shook almost spilling her wine. She was surprised to find how much she cared, how much she had come to like Sophie. But that, of course, was part of the plan, that was Tilling strategy. If you can't shame her into giving up the case, suborn her; take her on the river; be nice to her; get her on our side. And it was true, she was on their side, at least against malicious detractors. She comforted herself with the censorious reflection that they were as bitchy as guests at a suburban cocktail party. She had never in her life attended one of those innocuous if boring gatherings for the routine consumption of gossip, gin and canapés but, like her father who had never attended one either, she found no difficulty in believing that they were hot beds of snobbery, spite and sexual innuendo.

A warm body was pressing against her. She turned and saw Davie. He was carrying three bottles of wine. He had obviously heard at least part of the conversation, as the girls had no doubt intended, but he grinned amiably.

"Funny how Hugo's discarded women always hate him so much. It's quite different with Sophie. Her ex-lovers clutter up Norwich Street with their beastly bicycles and broken-down cars. I'm always finding them in the sitting-room drinking my beer and confiding to her the awful trouble they're having with their present girls."

"Do you mind?"

"Not if they don't get any further than the sitting-room. Are you enjoying yourself?"

"Not very much."

"Come and meet a friend of mine. He's been asking who you are."

"No thank you, Davie. I must keep myself free for Mr. Horsfall. I don't want to miss him."

He smiled at her, rather pityingly she thought, and seemed about to speak. But he changed his mind and moved away, clutching his bottles to his chest and shouting a cheerful warning as he edged himself through the throng.

Cordelia worked her way around the room, watching and listening. She was intrigued by the overt sexuality; she had thought that intellectuals breathed too rarefied air to be much interested in the flesh. Obviously this was a misapprehension. Come to think of it, the comrades, who might have been supposed to live in randy promiscuity, had been remarkably staid. She had sometimes felt that their sexual activities were prompted more by duty than instinct, more a weapon of revolution or a gesture against the bourgeois mores they despised than a response to human need. Their basic energies were all devoted to politics. It was not difficult to see where most of the energies of those present were directed.

She needn't have worried about the success of the kaftan. A number of men showed themselves willing or even eager to detach themselves from their partners for the pleasure of talking to her. With one particularly, a decorative and ironically amusing young historian, Cordelia felt that she could have spent an entertaining evening. To enjoy the sole attention of one agreeable man and no attention at all from anyone else was all she ever hoped from a party. She wasn't naturally gregarious and, alienated by the last six years from her own generation, found herself intimidated by the noise,

the underlying ruthlessness and the half-understood conventions of these tribal matings. And she told herself firmly that she wasn't here to enjoy herself at Sir Ronald's expense. None of her prospective partners knew Mark Callender or showed any interest in him, dead or alive. She mustn't get herself tied for the evening to people who had no information to give. When this seemed a danger and the talk became too beguiling, she would murmur her excuses and slip away to the bathroom or into the shadows of the garden where little groups were sitting on the grass smoking pot. Cordelia couldn't be mistaken in that evocative smell. They showed no disposition to chat and here, at least, she could stroll in privacy gaining courage for the next foray, for the next artfully casual question, the next inevitable response.

"Mark Callender? Sorry—we never met. Didn't he go off to sample the simple life and end by hanging himself or something?"

Once she took refuge in Mademoiselle de Congé's room, but she saw that the inert figure had been unceremoniously dumped on a cushion of pillows on the carpet and that the bed was being occupied for quite another purpose.

She wondered when Edward Horsfall would arrive or whether he would arrive at all. And if he did, would Hugo remember or bother to introduce her? She couldn't see either of the Tillings in the hot crush of gesticulating bodies which by now had crammed the sitting-room and spilled into the hall and half-way up the stairs. She was beginning to feel that this would be a wasted evening when Hugo's hand fell on her arm. He said:

"Come and meet Edward Horsfall. Edward, this is Cordelia Gray; she wants to talk about Mark Callender."

Edward Horsfall was another surprise. Cordelia had subconsciously conjured up the picture of an elderly don, a little distrait with the weight of his learning, a benevolent if detached mentor of the young. Horsfall could not have been much over thirty. He was very tall, his hair falling long over one eye, his lean body curved as a melon rind, a comparison reinforced by the pleated yellow shirt front under a jutting bow tie.

Any half acknowledged, half shameful hope which Cordelia may have nourished that he would immediately take to her and be happily ungrudging of his time so long as they were together was quickly dispersed. His eyes were restless, flicking obsessively back to the door. She suspected that he was alone by choice, deliberately keeping himself free from encumbrances until the hoped-for companion ar-

rived. He was so fidgety that it was difficult not to be fretted by his anxiety. She said:

"You don't have to stay with me all the evening you know, I only want some information."

Her voice recalled him to an awareness of her and to some attempt at civility.

"That wouldn't exactly be a penance. I'm sorry. What do you want to know?"

"Anything you can tell me about Mark. You taught him history didn't you? Was he good at it?"

It wasn't a particularly relevant question but one which she felt all teachers might respond to as a start.

"He was more rewarding to teach than some students I'm afflicted with. I don't know why he chose history. He could very well have read one of the sciences. He had a lively curiosity about physical phenomenon. But he decided to read history."

"Do you think that was to disoblige his father?"

"To disoblige Sir Ronald?" He turned and stretched out an arm for a bottle. "What are you drinking? There's one thing about Isabelle de Lasterie's parties, the drink is excellent, presumably because Hugo orders it. There's an admirable absence of beer."

"Doesn't Hugo drink beer then?" asked Cordelia.

"He claims not to. What were we talking about? Oh, yes, disobliging Sir Ronald. Mark said that he chose history because we have no chance of understanding the present without understanding the past. That's the sort of irritating cliché people come out with at interviews, but he may have believed it. Actually, of course, the reverse is true; we interpret the past through our knowledge of the present."

"Was he any good?" asked Cordelia. "I mean, would he have got a First?"

A First, she naively believed, was the ultimate in scholastic achievement, the certificate of pronounced intelligence that the recipient carried unchallenged through life. She wanted to hear that Mark was safe for a First.

"Those are two separate and distinct questions. You seem to be confusing merit with achievement. Impossible to predict his class, hardly a First. Mark was capable of extraordinarily good and original work but he limited his material to the number of his original ideas. The result tended to be rather thin. Examiners like originality but you've got to spew up the accepted facts and orthodox opinions first if only to show that you've learnt them. An exceptional memory and

fast legible handwriting; that's the secret of a First. Where are you, incidentally?" He noticed Cordelia's brief look of incomprehension.

"At what college?"

"None; I work. I'm a private detective."

He took this information in his stride.

"My uncle employed one of those once to find out if my aunt was being screwed by their dentist. She was, but he could have found out more easily by the simple expedient of asking them. His way, he lost the services of a wife and of a dentist simultaneously and paid through the nose for information he could have got for nothing. It made quite a stir in the family at the time. I should have thought that the job was——"

Cordelia finished the sentence for him.

"An unsuitable job for a woman?"

"Not at all. Entirely suitable I should have thought, requiring, I imagine, infinite curiosity, infinite pains and a penchant for interfering with other people." His attention was wandering again. A group near to them were talking and snatches of the conversation came to them.

"——typical of the worst kind of academic writing. Contempt for logic; a generous sprinkling of vogue names; spurious profundity and bloody awful grammar."

The tutor gave the speakers a second's attention, dismissed their academic chat as beneath his notice and condescended to transfer his attention but not his regard back to Cordelia.

"Why are you so interested in Mark Callender?"

"His father has employed me to find out why he died. I was hoping that you might be able to help. I mean, did he ever give you a hint that he might be unhappy, unhappy enough to kill himself? Did he explain why he gave up college?"

"Not to me. I never felt that I got near him. He made a formal goodbye, thanked me for what he chose to describe was my help, and left. I made the usual noises of regret. We shook hands. I was embarrassed, but not Mark. He wasn't I think, a young man susceptible to embarrassment."

There was a small commotion at the door and a group of new arrivals pushed themselves noisily into the throng. Among them was a tall, dark girl in a flame-coloured frock, open almost to the waist. Cordelia felt the tutor stiffen, saw his eyes fixed on the new arrival with an intense, half anxious, half supplicating look, which she had seen before. Her heart sank. She would be lucky now to get any more

information. Desperately trying to recapture his attention, she said:

"I'm not sure that Mark did kill himself. I think it could have been murder."

He spoke inattentively, his eyes on the newcomers.

"Unlikely, surely. By whom? For what reason? He was a negligible personality. He didn't even provoke a vague dislike except possibly from his father. But Ronald Callender couldn't have done it if that's what you're hoping. He was dining in Hall at High Table on the night Mark died. It was a College Feast night. I sat next to him. His son telephoned him."

Cordelia said eagerly, almost tugging at his sleeve.

"At what time?"

"Soon after the meal started, I suppose. Benskin, he's one of the College servants, came in and gave him the message. It must have been between eight and eight-fifteen. Callender disappeared for about ten minutes then returned and got on with his soup. The rest of us still hadn't reached the second course."

"Did he say what Mark wanted? Did he seem disturbed?"

"Neither. We hardly spoke through the meal. Sir Ronald doesn't waste his conversational gifts on non-scientists. Excuse me, will you?"

He was gone, threading his way through the throng towards his prey. Cordelia put down her glass and went in search of Hugo.

"Look," she said, "I want to talk to Benskin, a servant at your college. Would he be there tonight?"

Hugo put down the bottle he was holding.

"He may be. He's one of the few who live in college. But I doubt whether you would winkle him out of his lair on your own. If it's all that urgent, I'd better come with you."

❖❖❖

The college porter ascertained without curiosity that Benskin was in the college and Benskin was summoned. He arrived after a wait of five minutes during which Hugo chatted to the porter and Cordelia walked outside the Lodge to amuse herself reading the college notices. Benskin arrived, unhurrying, imperturbable. He was a silver-haired, formally dressed old man, his face creased and thick skinned as an anaemic blood orange, and would, Cordelia thought, have looked like an advertisement for the ideal butler, were it not for an expression of lugubrious and sly disdain.

Cordelia gave him sight of Sir Ronald's note of authority and plunged straight into her questions. There was nothing to be gained by subtlety and since she had enlisted Hugo's help, she had little hope of shaking him off. She said:

"Sir Ronald has asked me to enquire into the circumstances of his son's death."

"So I see, Miss."

"I am told that Mr. Mark Callender telephoned his father while Sir Ronald was dining at High Table on the night his son died and that you passed the message to Sir Ronald shortly after dinner began?"

"I was under the impression at the time that it was Mr. Callender who was ringing, Miss, but I was mistaken."

"How can you be sure of that, Mr. Benskin?"

"Sir Ronald himself told me, Miss, when I saw him in college some few days after his son's death. I've known Sir Ronald since he was an undergraduate and I made bold to express my condolences. During our brief conversation I made reference to the telephone call of 26th May and Sir Ronald told me that I was mistaken, that it was not Mr. Callender who had called."

"Did he say who it was?"

"Sir Ronald informed me that it was his laboratory assistant, Mr. Chris Lunn."

"Did that surprise you—that you were wrong, I mean?"

"I confess that I was somewhat surprised, Miss, but the mistake was perhaps excusable. My subsequent reference to the incident was fortuitous and in the circumstances regrettable."

"But do you really believe that you mis-heard the name?"

The obstinate old face did not relax.

"Sir Ronald could have been in no doubt about the person who telephoned him."

"Was it usual for Mr. Callender to ring his father while he was dining in College?"

"I had never previously taken a call from him, but then answering the telephone is not part of my normal duties. It is possible that some of the other college servants may be able to help but I hardly think that an enquiry would be productive or that the news that college servants had been questioned would be gratifying to Sir Ronald."

"Any enquiry which can help ascertain the truth is likely to be gratifying to Sir Ronald," said Cordelia. Really, she thought, Benskin's prose style is becoming infectious. She added more naturally:

"Sir Ronald is very anxious to find out everything possible about his son's death. Is there anything that you can tell me, any help that you can give me, Mr. Benskin?"

This was perilously close to an appeal but it met with no response.

"Nothing, Miss. Mr. Callender was a quiet and pleasant young gentleman who seemed, as far as I was able to observe him, to be in good health and spirits up to the time he left us. His death has been very much felt in the college. Is there anything else, Miss?"

He stood patiently waiting to be dismissed and Cordelia let him go. As she and Hugo left college together and walked back into Trumpington Street she said bitterly:

"He doesn't care, does he?"

"Why should he? Benskin's an old phoney but he's been at college for seventy years and he's seen it all before. A thousand ages in his sight are but an evening gone. I've only known Benskin distressed once over the suicide of an undergraduate and that was a Duke's son. Benskin thought that there were some things that the college shouldn't permit to happen."

"But he wasn't mistaken about Mark's call. You could tell that from his whole manner, at least I could. He knows what he heard. He isn't going to admit it, of course, but he knows in his heart he wasn't mistaken."

Hugo said lightly:

"He was being the old college servant, very correct, very proper; that's Benskin all over. 'The young gentlemen aren't what they were when I first came to college.' I should bloody well hope not! They wore side whiskers then and noblemen sported fancy gowns to distinguish them from the plebs. Benskin would bring all that back if he could. He's an anachronism, pottering through the court hand in hand with a statelier past."

"But he isn't deaf. I deliberately spoke in a soft voice and he heard me perfectly. Do you really believe that he was mistaken?"

"Chris Lunn and his son are very similar sounds."

"But Lunn doesn't announce himself that way. All the time I was with Sir Ronald and Miss Leaming they just called him Lunn."

"Look, Cordelia, you can't possibly suspect Ronald Callender of having a hand in his son's death! Be logical. You accept, I suppose, that a rational murderer hopes not to be found out. You admit, no doubt, that Ronald Callender, although a disagreeable bastard, is a rational being. Mark is dead and his body cremated. No one except you has mentioned murder. Then Sir Ronald employs you to stir

things up. Why should he if he's got something to hide? He doesn't even need to divert suspicion; there has been no suspicion, there is no suspicion."

"Of course I don't suspect him of killing his son. He doesn't know how Mark died and he desperately needs to know. That's why he's taken me on. I could tell that at our interview; I couldn't be wrong about that. But I don't understand why he should have lied about the telephone call."

"If he is lying there could be half a dozen innocent explanations. If Mark did ring the college it must have been something pretty urgent, perhaps something which his father didn't particularly want to make public, something which gives a clue to his son's suicide."

"Then why employ me to find out why he killed himself?"

"True, wise Cordelia; I'll try again. Mark asked him for help, perhaps an urgent visit which Dad refused. You can imagine his reaction. 'Don't be ridiculous, Mark, I'm dining at High Table with the Master. Obviously I can't leave the cutlets and claret just because you telephone in this hysterical way and demand to see me. Pull yourself together.' That sort of thing wouldn't sound so good in open court; coroners are notoriously censorious." Hugo's voice took on a deep magisterial tone. " 'It is not for me to add to Sir Ronald's distress, but it is, perhaps, unfortunate that he chose to ignore what was obviously a cry for help. Had he left his meal immediately and gone to his son's side this brilliant young student might have been saved.' Cambridge suicides, so I've noticed, are always brilliant; I'm still waiting to read the report of an inquest where the college authorities testify that the student only just killed himself in time before they kicked him out."

"But Mark died between seven and nine p.m. That telephone call is Sir Ronald's alibi!"

"He wouldn't see it like that. He doesn't need an alibi. If you know you're not involved and the question of foul play never arises, you don't think in terms of alibis. It's only the guilty who do that."

"But how did Mark know where to find his father? In his evidence Sir Ronald said that he hadn't spoken to his son for over three weeks."

"I can see you have a point there. Ask Miss Leaming. Better still, ask Lunn if it was, in fact, he who rang the college. If you're looking for a villain Lunn should suit admirably. I find him absolutely sinister."

"I didn't know that you knew him."

"Oh, he's pretty well known in Cambridge. He drives that horrid little closed van around with ferocious dedication as if he were transporting recalcitrant students to the gas chambers. Everyone knows Lunn. Seldom he smiles and smiles in such a way as if he mocked himself and scorned his spirit that could be moved to smile at anything. I should concentrate on Lunn."

They walked on in silence through the warm scented night while the waters sang in the runnels of Trumpington Street. Lights were shining now in college doorways and in porters' lodges and the far gardens and inter-connecting courts, glimpsed as they passed, looked remote and ethereal as in a dream. Cordelia was suddenly oppressed with loneliness and melancholy. If Bernie were alive they would be discussing the case, cosily ensconced in the furthest corner of some Cambridge pub, insulated by noise and smoke and anonymity from the curiosity of their neighbours; talking low voiced in their own particular jargon. They would be speculating on the personality of a young man who slept under that gentle and intellectual painting, yet who had bought a vulgar magazine of salacious nudes. Or had he? And if not, how had it come to be in the cottage garden? They would be discussing a father who lied about his son's last telephone call; speculating in happy complicity about an uncleaned spade, a row of earth half dug, an unwashed coffee mug, a quotation from Blake meticulously typed. They would be talking about Isabelle who was terrified and Sophie who was surely honest and Hugo who certainly knew something about Mark's death and who was clever but not as clever as he needed to be. For the first time since the case began Cordelia doubted her ability to solve it alone. If only there were someone reliable in whom she could confide, someone who would reinforce her confidence. She thought again of Sophie, but Sophie had been Mark's mistress and was Hugo's sister. They were both involved. She was on her own and that, when she came to think about it, was no different from how essentially it had always been. Ironically, the realization brought her comfort and a return of hope.

At the corner of Panton Street they paused and he said:

"You're coming back to the party?"

"No, thank you, Hugo; I've got work to do."

"Are you staying in Cambridge?"

Cordelia wondered whether the question was prompted by more than polite interest. Suddenly cautious, she said:

"Only for the next day or two. I've found a very dull but cheap bed and breakfast place near the station."

He accepted the lie without comment and they said goodnight. She made her way back to Norwich Street. The little car was still outside number fifty-seven, but the house was dark and quiet as if to emphasize her exclusion and the three windows were as blank as dead rejecting eyes.

❖❖❖

She was tired by the time she got back to the cottage and had parked the Mini on the edge of the copse. The garden gate creaked at her hand. The night was dark and she felt in her bag for her torch and followed its bright pool round the side of the cottage and to the back door. By its light she fitted the key into the lock. She turned it and, dazed with tiredness, stepped into the sitting-room. The torch, still switched on, hung loosely from her hand, making erratic patterns of light on the tiled floor. Then in one involuntary movement it jerked upwards and shone full on the thing that hung from the centre hook of the ceiling. Cordelia gave a cry and clutched at the table. It was the bolster from her bed, the bolster with a cord drawn tight about one end making a grotesque and bulbous head, and the other end stuffed into a pair of Mark's trousers. The legs hung pathetically flat and empty, one lower than the other. As she stared at it in fascinated horror, her heart hammering, a slight breeze wafted in from the open door and it swung slowly round as if twisted by a living hand.

She must have stood there rooted with fear and staring wild-eyed at the bolster for seconds only, yet it seemed minutes before she found the strength to pull out a chair from the table and take the thing down. Even in the moment of repulsion and terror she remembered to look closely at the knot. The cord was attached to the hook by a simple loop and two half-hitches. So, either her secret visitor had chosen not to repeat his former tactics, or he hadn't known how the first knot had been tied. She laid the bolster on the chair and went outside for the gun. In her tiredness she had forgotten it, but now she longed for the reassurance of the hard cold metal in her hand. She stood at the back door and listened. The garden seemed suddenly full of noises, mysterious rustlings, leaves moving in the slight breeze like human sighs, furtive scurryings in the undergrowth, the bat-like squeak of an animal disconcertingly close at hand. The night seemed to be holding its breath as she crept out towards the elder

bush. She waited, listening to her own heart, before she found courage to turn her back and stretch up her hand to feel for the gun. It was still there. She sighed audibly with relief and immediately felt better. The gun wasn't loaded but that hardly seemed to matter. She hurried back to the cottage, her terror assuaged.

It was nearly an hour before she finally went to bed. She lit the lamp and, gun in hand, made a search of the whole cottage. Next she examined the window. It was obvious enough how he had got in. The window had no catch and was easy to push open from outside. Cordelia fetched a roll of Scotch tape from her scene-of-crime kit and, as Bernie had shown her, cut two very narrow strips and pasted them across the base of the pane and the wooden frame. She doubted whether the front windows could be opened but she took no chances and sealed them in the same way. It wouldn't stop an intruder but at least she would know next morning that he had gained access. Finally, having washed in the kitchen, she went upstairs to bed. There was no lock on her door but she wedged it slightly open and balanced a saucepan lid on the top of the frame. If anyone did succeed in getting in, he wouldn't take her by surprise. She loaded the gun and placed it on her bedside table, remembering that she was dealing with a killer. She examined the cord. It was a four-foot length of ordinary strong string, obviously not new and frayed at one end. Her heart sank at the hopelessness of trying to identify it. But she labelled it carefully, as Bernie had taught her, and packed it in her scene-of-crime kit. She did the same with the curled strap and the typed passage of Blake, transferring them from the bottom of her shoulder bag to plastic exhibit envelopes. She was so weary that even this routine chore cost her an effort of will. Then she placed the bolster back on the bed, resisting an impulse to sling it on the floor and sleep without it. But, by then, nothing—neither fear nor discomfort—could have kept her awake. She lay for only a few minutes listening to the ticking of her watch before tiredness overcame her and bore her unresisting down the dark tide of sleep.

Chapter Four

❖❖❖

Cordelia was awakened early next morning by the discordant chattering of the birds and the strong clear light of another fine day. She lay for several minutes stretching herself within her sleeping-bag, savouring the smell of a country morning, that subtle and evocative fusion of earth, sweet wet grass and stronger farmyard smell. She washed in the kitchen as Mark had obviously done, standing in the tin bath from the shed and gasping as she poured saucepans of cold tap water over her naked body. There was something about the simple life which disposed one to these austerities. Cordelia thought it unlikely that, in any circumstances, she would willingly have bathed in cold water in London or so much relished the smell of the paraffin stove superimposed on the appetizing sizzle of frying bacon, or the flavour of her first strong mug of tea.

The cottage was filled with sunlight, a warm friendly sanctum from which she could safely venture out to whatever the day held. In the calm peace of a summer morning the little sitting-room seemed untouched by the tragedy of Mark Callender's death. The hook in the ceiling looked as innocuous as if it had never served its dreadful purpose. The horror of that moment when her torch had first picked out the dark swollen shadow of the bolster moving in the night breeze now had the unreality of a dream. Even the memory of the precautions of the night before were embarrassing viewed in the unambiguous light of day. She felt rather foolish as she unloaded the gun, secreted the ammunition among her underclothes, and hid the pistol in the elder bush, watching carefully to see that she wasn't observed. When the washing-up was done and the one teacloth washed through and hung out to dry, she picked a small posy of pansies, cowslips and meadow-sweet from the far end of the garden and set them on the table in one of the ribbed mugs.

She had decided that her first task must be to try to trace Nanny Pilbeam. Even if the woman had nothing to tell her about Mark's death or his reason for leaving college, she would be able to speak about his childhood and boyhood; she, probably better than anyone, would know what his essential nature had been. She had cared

enough about him to attend the funeral and to send an expensive wreath. She had called on him in college on his 21st birthday. He had probably kept in touch with her, might even have confided in her. He had no mother and Nanny Pilbeam could have been, in some sense, a substitute.

As she drove into Cambridge Cordelia considered tactics. The probability was that Miss Pilbeam lived somewhere in the district. It was unlikely that she actually lived in the city since Hugo Tilling had only seen her once. From his brief account of her, it sounded as if she were old and probably poor. It was unlikely, therefore, that she would travel far to attend the funeral. It was apparent that she hadn't been one of the official mourners from Garforth House, hadn't been invited by Sir Ronald. According to Hugo, none of the party had even spoken to each other. This hardly suggested that Miss Pilbeam was the elderly and valued retainer of tradition, almost one of the family. Sir Ronald's neglect of her on such an occasion intrigued Cordelia. She wondered just what Miss Pilbeam's position in the family had been.

If the old lady lived near Cambridge, she had probably ordered the wreath at one of the city florists. Villages were very unlikely to provide this kind of service. It had been an ostentatious wreath, which suggested that Miss Pilbeam had been prepared to spend lavishly and had probably gone to one of the larger florists. The likelihood was that she had ordered it personally. Elderly ladies, apart from the fact that they were seldom on the telephone, like to attend to these matters direct, having, Cordelia suspected, a well-founded suspicion that only face-to-face confrontation and the meticulous recital of one's precise requirements extracted the best service. If Miss Pilbeam had come in from her village by train or by bus, she had probably selected a shop somewhere near the centre of the city. Cordelia decided to begin her search by enquiring of passers-by if they could recommend the name of a good florist.

She had already learned that Cambridge was not a city for the cruising motorist. She drew up and consulted the folding map at the back of her guide book and decided to leave the Mini on the car park next to Parker's Piece. Her search might take some time and would be best done on foot. She daren't risk a parking fine nor the impounding of the car. She checked her watch. It was still only a few minutes after nine o'clock. She had made a good start to the day.

The first hour was disappointing. The people of whom she enquired were anxious to be helpful but their ideas of what constituted

a reliable florist somewhere near the centre of the city were peculiar. Cordelia was directed to small greengrocers selling a few bunches of cut flowers as a side line, to the supplier of gardening equipment who dealt in plants but not in wreaths, and once to a funeral director. The two florists' shops which at first sight seemed possible had never heard of Miss Pilbeam and had provided no wreaths for the Mark Callender funeral. A little weary with much walking and beginning to feel despondent, Cordelia decided that the whole quest had been unreasonably sanguine. Probably Miss Pilbeam had come in from Bury St. Edmunds or Newmarket and had bought the wreath in her own town.

But the visit to the undertakers was not wasted. In reply to her enquiry, they recommended the name of a firm which provided "a very nice class of wreath, Miss, really very nice indeed." The shop was further from the centre of the city than Cordelia had expected. Even from the pavement it smelt of weddings or funerals, as one's mood dictated, and as she pushed open the door Cordelia was welcomed by a gush of sweet warm air which caught at the throat. There were flowers everywhere. Large green buckets lined the walls holding clumps of lilies, irises and lupins; smaller containers were packed tight with wall flowers and marigolds and stocks; there were frigid bundles of tight budded roses on thornless stems, each flower identical in size and colour and looking as if it had been cultivated in a test tube. Pots of indoor plants, decorated with variegated ribbon, lined the path to the counter like a floral guard of honour.

There was a room at the back of the shop where two assistants were working. Through the open door Cordelia watched them. The younger, a languid blonde with a spotted skin, was assistant executioner, laying out roses and freesias, predestined victims, graded according to type and colour. Her senior, whose status was denoted by a better fitting overall and an air of authority, was twisting off the flower heads, piercing each mutilated bloom with wire and threading them closely on to a huge bed of moss in the shape of a heart. Cordelia averted her eyes from this horror.

A buxom lady in a pink smock appeared behind the counter apparently from nowhere. She was as pungently scented as the shop, but had obviously decided that no ordinary floral perfume could compete and that she had better rely on the exotic. She smelt of curry powder and pine so strongly that the effect was practically anaesthetizing.

Cordelia said her prepared speech:

"I'm from Sir Ronald Callender of Garforth House. I wonder whether you can help us? His son was cremated on 3rd of June and their old nurse very kindly sent a wreath, a cross of red roses. Sir Ronald has lost her address and very much wants to write to thank her. The name is Pilbeam."

"Oh, I don't think we executed any orders of that type for 3rd June."

"If you would be kind enough to just look in the book——"

Suddenly the young blonde looked up from her work and called out:

"It's Goddard."

"I beg your pardon, Shirley?" said the buxom lady repressively.

"The name's Goddard. The card on the wreath said Nanny Pilbeam, but the customer was a Mrs. Goddard. Another lady came to enquire from Sir Ronald Callender and that was the name she gave. I looked it up for her. Mrs. Goddard, Lavender Cottage, Ickleton. One cross, four foot long in red roses. Six pounds. It's there in the book."

"Thank you very much," said Cordelia fervently. She smiled her thanks impartially at the three of them and left quickly in case she got embroiled in an argument about the other enquirer from Garforth House. It must have looked odd, she knew, but the three of them would no doubt enjoy themselves discussing it after she had left. Lavender Cottage, Ickleton. She kept repeating the address to herself until she was at a safe distance from the shop and could pause to write it down.

Her tiredness seemed miraculously to have left her as she sped back to the car park. She consulted her map. Ickleton was a village near the Essex border about ten miles from Cambridge. It wasn't far from Duxford so that she would be retracing her steps. She could be there in less than half an hour.

But it took longer than she had expected to thread her way through the Cambridge traffic and it wasn't until thirty-five minutes later, that she came to Ickleton's fine flint and pebble church with its broach spire, and drove the Mini close to the church gate. It was a temptation to take a brief look inside, but she resisted it. Mrs. Goddard might even now be preparing to catch the Cambridge bus. She went in search of Lavender Cottage.

It wasn't, in fact, a cottage at all but a small semi-detached house of hideous red brick at the end of the High Street. There was only a narrow strip of grass between the front door and the road and

neither smell nor sight of lavender. The iron knocker, in the form of a lion's head, fell heavily, shaking the door. The response came, not from Lavender Cottage, but from the next house. An elderly woman appeared, thin, almost toothless and swathed in an immense apron patterned with roses. She had carpet slippers on her feet, a woollen cap decorated with a bobble on her head and an air of lively interest in the world in general.

"You'll be wanting Mrs. Goddard, I daresay?"

"Yes. Could you tell me where I could find her?"

"She'll be over at the graveyard, I don't doubt. She usually is this time of a fine morning."

"I've just come from the church. I didn't see anyone."

"Bless you, Miss, she's not at the church! They haven't been burying us there for many a year now. Her old man is where they'll be putting her in time, in the cemetery on Hinxton Road. You can't miss it. Just keep straight on."

"I'll have to go back to the church for my car," said Cordelia. It was obvious that she was going to be watched out of sight and it seemed necessary to explain why she was departing in the opposite direction to the one indicated. The old woman smiled and nodded and came out to lean on her gate for a better view of Cordelia's progress down the High Street, nodding her head like a marionette so that the bright bobble danced in the sun.

❖❖❖

The cemetery was easily found. Cordelia parked the Mini on a convenient patch of grass where a signpost pointed the footpath to Duxford and walked the few yards back to the iron gates. There was a small flint chapel of rest with an apse at the east end and beside it an ancient wooden seat green with lichen and spattered with bird lime which gave a view of the whole burial ground. A wide swathe of turf ran straight down the middle and on each side were the graves, variously marked with white marble crosses, grey headstones, small rusted circles of iron heeling over towards the smooth turf and bright splashes of flowers patchworked over the newly dug earth. It was very peaceful. The burial ground was surrounded by trees, their leaves scarcely stirring in the calm, hot air. There was little sound except the chirruping of crickets in the grass and from

time to time the nearby ringing of a railway level-crossing bell and the swooping horn of a diesel train.

There was only one other person in the graveyard, an elderly woman bending over one of the far graves. Cordelia sat quietly on the seat, arms folded in her lap, before making her way silently down the grass path towards her. She knew with certainty that this interview was going to be crucial yet paradoxically she was in no hurry to begin. She came up to the woman and stood, still unnoticed, at the foot of the grave.

She was a small woman dressed in black whose old-fashioned straw hat, its brim wreathed with faded net, was screwed to her hair with an immense black bobbed hat pin. She knelt with her back to Cordelia showing the soles of a pair of mis-shapen shoes from which her thin legs stuck out like sticks. She was weeding the grave; her fingers, darting like a reptile's tongue over the grass, plucked at small, almost undetectable weeds. At her side was a punnet holding a folded newspaper and a gardening trowel. From time to time, she dropped into the punnet her little mush of weeds.

After a couple of minutes, during which Cordelia watched her in silence, she paused satisfied and began smoothing the surface of the grass as if comforting the bones beneath. Cordelia read the inscription carved deep on the headstone. "Sacred to the memory of Charles Albert Goddard beloved husband of Annie who departed this life 27th August 1962, aged 70 years. At rest." At rest; the commonest epitaph of a generation to whom rest must have seemed the ultimate luxury, the supreme benediction.

The woman rested back for a second on her heels and contemplated the grave with satisfaction. It was then that she became aware of Cordelia. She turned a bright much wrinkled face towards her and said without curiosity or resentment at her presence:

"It's a nice stone, isn't it?"

"Yes, it is. I was admiring the lettering."

"Cut deep that is. It cost a mint of money but it was worth it. That'll last, you see. Half the lettering here won't, it's that shallow. It takes the pleasure out of a cemetery. I like to read the grave stones, like to know who people were and when they died and how long the women lived after they buried their men. It sets you wondering how they managed and whether they were lonely. There's no use in a stone if you can't read the lettering. Of course, this stone looks a bit top-heavy at present. That's because I asked them to leave space for

me: 'Also to Annie his wife, departed this life, . . .' and then the
date: That'll even it up nicely. I've left the money to pay for it."

"What text were you thinking of having?" enquired Cordelia.

"Oh, no text! At rest will be good enough for the both of us. We
shan't be asking more of the good Lord than that."

Cordelia said:

"That cross of roses you sent to Mark Callender's funeral was
beautiful."

"Oh, did you see it? You weren't at the funeral were you? Yes, I
was pleased with it. They made a nice job of it, I thought. Poor boy,
he hadn't much else, had he?"

She looked at Cordelia with benign interest:

"So you knew Mr. Mark? Would you be his young lady perhaps?"

"No, not that, but I care about him. It's odd that he never talked
about you, his old nurse."

"But I wasn't his nurse, my dear, or at least, only for a month or
two. He was a baby then, it meant nothing to him. No, I was nurse
to his dear mother."

"But you visited Mark on his twenty-first birthday?"

"So he told you that, did he? I was glad to see him again after all
those years, but I wouldn't have pushed myself on him. It wouldn't
have been right, his father feeling as he did. No, I went to give him
something from his mother, to do something she had asked me to do
when she was dying. Do you know, I hadn't seen Mr. Mark for over
twenty years—odd, really, considering that we didn't live that far
apart—but I knew him at once. He had a great look of his mother
about him, poor boy."

"Could you tell me about it? It's not just curiosity; it's important
for me to know."

Leaning for support on the handle of her basket, Mrs. Goddard
got laboriously to her feet. She picked at a few short blades of grass
adhering to her skirt, felt in her pocket for a pair of grey cotton gloves
and put them on. Together they made their way slowly down the
path.

"Important, is it? I don't know why it should be. It's all in the past
now. She's dead, poor lady, and so is he. All that hope and promise
come to nothing. I haven't spoken to anyone else about it, but then
who would care to know?"

"Perhaps we could sit on this bench and talk together for a time?"

"I don't see why we shouldn't. There's nothing to hurry home for
now. Do you know, my dear, I didn't marry my husband until I was

fifty-three and yet I miss him as if we had been childhood sweethearts. People said I was a fool to take on a man at that age but you see I had known his wife for thirty years, we were at school together, and I knew him. If a man's good to one woman, he'll be good to another. That's what I reckoned and I was right."

They sat side by side on the bench gazing over the green swathe towards the grave. Cordelia said:

"Tell me about Mark's mother."

"She was a Miss Bottley, Evelyn Bottley. I went to her mother as under-nursemaid before she was born. There was only little Harry then. He was killed in the war on his first raid over Germany. His Dad took it very hard; there was never anyone to match Harry, the sun shone out of his eyes. The master never really cared for Miss Evie, it was all the boy with him. Mrs. Bottley died when Evie was born and that may have made a difference. People say that it does, but I've never believed it. I've known fathers who loved a baby even more—poor innocent things, how can they be blamed? If you ask me, it was just an excuse for not taking to the child, that she killed her mother."

"Yes, I know a father who made it an excuse too. But it isn't their fault. We can't make ourselves love someone just because we want to."

"More's the pity, my dear, or the world would be an easier place. But his own child, that's not natural!"

"Did she love him?"

"How could she? You won't get love from a child if you don't give love. But she never had the trick of pleasing him, of humouring him —he was a big man, fierce, loud talking, frightening to a child. He would have done better with a pretty, pert little thing, who wouldn't have been afraid of him."

"What happened to her? How did she meet Sir Ronald Callender?"

"He wasn't Sir Ronald then, my dear. Oh, dear no! He was Ronny Callender the gardener's son. They lived at Harrogate you see. Oh, such a lovely house they had! When I first went into service there they had three gardeners. That was before the war, of course. Mr. Bottley worked in Bradford; he was in the wool trade. Well, you were asking about Ronny Callender. I remember him well, a pugnacious, good-looking lad but one who kept his thoughts to himself. He was clever that one, oh he was clever! He got a scholarship to the grammar school and did very well."

"And Evelyn Bottley fell in love?"

"She may have done, my dear. What there was between them when they were young, who can tell. But then the war came and he went away. She was wild to do something useful and they took her on as a V.A.D., though how she passed the medical I'll never know. And then they met again in London as people did in the war and the next thing we knew they were married."

"And came to live here outside Cambridge?"

"Not until after the war. At first she kept on with her nursing and he was sent overseas. He had what the men call a good war; we'd call it a bad war I daresay, a lot of killing and fighting, imprisonment and escaping. It ought to have made Mr. Bottley proud of him and reconciled to the marriage but it didn't. I think he thought that Ronny had his eye on the money, because there was money to come, no doubt about that. He may have been right, but who's to blame the boy? My mother used to say, 'Don't marry for money, but marry where money is!' There's no harm in looking for money as long as there's kindness as well."

"And do you think there was kindness?"

"There was never unkindness that I could see, and she was mad about him. After the war he went up to Cambridge. He'd always wanted to be a scientist and he got a grant because he was ex-service. She had some money from her father and they bought the house he lives in now so that he could live at home when he was studying. It didn't look the same then, of course. He's done a lot to it since. They were quite poor then and Miss Evie managed with practically no one to help, only me. Mr. Bottley used to come and stay from time to time. She used to dread his visits, poor darling. He was looking for a grandchild, you see, and one didn't come. And then Mr. Callender finished at the university and got a job teaching. He wanted to stay on at college to be a don or something like that, but they wouldn't have him. He used to say it was because he hadn't influence, but I think he may not have been quite clever enough. In Harrogate we thought he was the cleverest boy in the grammar school. But then, Cambridge is full of clever men."

"And then Mark was born?"

"Yes, on the 25th April 1951, nine years after they were married. He was born in Italy. Mr. Bottley was that pleased when she became pregnant that he increased the allowance and they used to spend a lot of holidays in Tuscany. My lady loved Italy, always had, and I think she wanted the child to be born there. Otherwise she wouldn't have gone on holiday in the last month of her pregnancy.

I went to visit her about a month after she came home with the baby and I've never seen a woman so happy. Oh, he was a lovely little boy!"

"But why did you visit her; weren't you living and working there?"

"No, my dear. Not for some months. She wasn't well in the early days of her pregnancy. I could see that she was strained and unhappy and then one day Mr. Callender sent for me and told me that she had taken against me and that I'd have to leave. I wouldn't have believed it, but when I went to her she just put out her hand and said: 'I'm sorry, Nanny, I think it would be better if you went.'

"Pregnant women have strange fancies, I know, and the baby was so important to them both. I thought she might have asked me to come back afterwards and so she did, but not living in. I took a bedsitting room in the village with the postmistress and used to give four mornings a week to my lady and the rest to other ladies in the village. It worked very well, really, but I missed the baby when I wasn't with him. I hadn't seen her often during her pregnancy but once we met in Cambridge. She must have been near the end of her time. She was very heavy, poor dear, dragging herself along. At first she pretended that she hadn't noticed me and then she thought better of it and came across the road. 'We're off to Italy next week, Nanny,' she said. 'Isn't it lovely?' I said: 'If you're not careful, my dear, that baby will be a little Italian,' and she laughed. It seemed as though she couldn't wait to get back to the sun."

"And what happened after she came home?"

"She died after nine months, my dear. She was never strong, as I said, and she caught influenza. I helped look after her and I'd have done more but Mr. Callender took over the nursing himself. He couldn't bear anyone else to be near her. We only had a few minutes together just before she died and it was then that she asked me to give her prayer book to Mark on his twenty-first birthday. I can hear her now: 'Give it to Mark when he's twenty-one, Nanny. Wrap it up carefully and take it to him when he comes of age. You won't forget will you?' I said: 'I'll not forget, my darling, you know that.' Then she said a strange thing. 'If you do, or if you die before then, or if he doesn't understand, it won't really matter. It will mean that God wants it that way.'"

"What do you think she meant?"

"Who's to say, my dear? She was very religious was Miss Evie, too religious for her own good, I sometimes thought. I believe we should accept our own responsibilities, solve our own problems, not leave

it all to God as if He hadn't enough to be thinking about with the world in the state it is. But that's what she said not three hours before she died and that's what I promised. So when Mr. Mark was twenty-one, I found out what college he was at and went to see him."

"What happened?"

"Oh, we had a very happy time together. Do you know, his father had never spoken about his mother. That sometimes happens when a wife dies but I think a son ought to know about his mother. He was full of questions, things that I thought his father would have told him.

"He was glad to get the prayer book. It was a few days later that he came to see me. He asked the name of the doctor who had treated his mother. I told him that it was old Dr. Gladwin. Mr. Callender and she had never had any other doctor. I used to think it a pity sometimes, Miss Evie being so frail. Dr. Gladwin must have been seventy then, and although there were people who wouldn't say a word against him, I never thought much of him myself. Drink, you know, my dear; he was never really reliable. But I expect he's gone to his rest long since, poor man. Anyway, I told Mr. Mark the name and he wrote it down. Then we had tea and a little chat and he left. I never saw him again."

"And no one else knows about the prayer book?"

"No one in the world, my dear. Miss Leaming saw the florist's name on my card and asked them for my address. She came here the day after the funeral to thank me for attending but I could see it was only curiosity. If she and Sir Ronald were so pleased to see me, what was to stop them from coming over and shaking hands? She as good as suggested that I was there without an invitation. An invitation to a funeral! Who ever heard of such a thing?"

"So you told her nothing?" asked Cordelia.

"I've told no one but you, my dear, and I'm not sure why I've told you. But no, I didn't tell her. I never liked her, to tell you the truth. I'm not saying there was anything between her and Sir Ronald, not while Miss Evie was alive anyway. There was never any gossip and she lived in a flat in Cambridge and kept herself to herself, I'll give her that. Mr. Callender met her when he was teaching science at one of the village schools. She was the English mistress. It wasn't until after Miss Evie died that he set up his own laboratory."

"Do you mean that Miss Leaming has a degree in English?"

"Oh, yes, my dear! She wasn't trained as a secretary. Of course

she gave up the teaching when she started working for Mr. Callender."

"So you left Garforth House after Mrs. Callender died? You didn't stay on to care for the baby?"

"I wasn't wanted. Mr. Callender employed one of those new college-trained girls and then, when Mark was still only a baby, he was sent away to school. His father made it plain that he didn't like me to see the child and after all, a father has his rights. I wouldn't have gone on seeing Mr. Mark knowing that his father didn't approve. It would have only put the boy in a false position. But now he's dead and we've all lost him. The coroner said that he killed himself, and he may have been right."

Cordelia said:

"I don't think he killed himself."

"Don't you, my dear? That's kind of you. But he's dead, isn't he, so what does it matter now? I think it's time for me to go home. If you don't mind, I won't ask you to tea, my dear, I'm a little tired today. But you know where to find me, and if ever you want to see me again, you'll always be welcome."

They made their way out of the burial ground together. At the gates, they parted. Mrs. Goddard patted Cordelia on the shoulder with the clumsy affection she might have shown to an animal, then walked off slowly towards the village.

As Cordelia drove round the curve of the road, the level-crossing came into sight. A train had just passed and the barriers were being raised. Three vehicles had been caught at the crossing and the last in line was quickest away, accelerating past the first two cars as they bumped slowly over the rails. Cordelia saw that it was a small black van.

❖❖❖

Later Cordelia remembered little of the journey back to the cottage. She drove fast, concentrating on the road ahead, trying to control her rising excitement by meticulous attention to gears and brakes. She drove the Mini hard against the front hedge, careless of whether it were seen. The cottage looked and smelt just as she had left it. She had almost expected to find it ransacked and the prayer book gone. Sighing with relief, she saw that the white spine was still there among the taller and darker covers. Cordelia opened it. She hardly

knew what she expected to find; an inscription perhaps, or a message, cryptic or plain, a letter folded between the leaves. But the only inscription could have no possible relevance to the case. It was written in a shaky, old-fashioned hand; the steel nib had crawled spider-like over the page. "To Evelyn Mary on the occasion of her confirmation, with love from her Godmother, 5th August 1934."

Cordelia shook the book. No slip of paper fluttered out. She skimmed through the pages. Nothing.

She sat on the bed drooping with disappointment. Had it been unreasonable to imagine that there was something significant in the bequest of the prayer book; had she fabricated a promising edifice of conjecture and mystery on an old woman's confused recollections of a perfectly ordinary and understandable action—a devout and dying mother leaving a prayer book to her son? And even if she hadn't been wrong, why should the message still be there? If Mark had found a note from his mother, placed between the leaves, he might well have destroyed it after reading. And if he hadn't destroyed it, someone else might have done so. The note, if it ever existed, was now probably part of the shifting heap of white ash and charred debris in the cottage grate.

She shook herself out of her despondency. There was still a line of enquiry to pursue; she would try to trace Dr. Gladwin. After a second's thought she put the prayer book in her bag. Looking at her watch, she saw that it was nearly one o'clock. She decided to have a picnic lunch of cheese and fruit in the garden and then set off again for Cambridge to visit the central library and consult a medical directory.

Less than an hour later she found the information she wanted. There was only one Dr. Gladwin still on the register who could have attended Mrs. Callender as an old man of over seventy, twenty years ago. He was Emlyn Thomas Gladwin who had qualified at St. Thomas's Hospital in 1904. She wrote down the address in her note book: 4 Pratts Way, Ixworth Road, Bury St. Edmunds. Edmunds town! The town which Isabelle had said that she and Mark had visited on their way to the sea.

So the day hadn't been wasted after all—she was following in Mark Callender's footsteps. Impatient to consult a map she went over to the atlas section of the library. It was now two-fifteen. If she took the A45 road direct through Newmarket she could be in Bury St. Edmunds in about an hour. Allow an hour for the visit to the doctor

and another for the return journey. She could be home at the cottage before half past five.

She was driving through the gentle unemphatic countryside just outside Newmarket when she noticed the black van following her. It was too far away to see who was driving but she thought it was Lunn and that he was alone. She accelerated, trying to keep the distance between them, but the van drew a little nearer. There was no reason, of course, why Lunn shouldn't be driving to Newmarket on Sir Ronald Callender's business, but the sight of the squat little van perpetually in her driving mirror was disconcerting. Cordelia decided to throw him off. There were few side turns on the road she was travelling and the country was unfamiliar to her. She decided to wait until she reached Newmarket and seize what opportunity offered.

The main through street of the town was a tangle of traffic and every turn seemed to be blocked. It was only at the second set of traffic lights that Cordelia saw her chance. The black van was caught at the intersection about fifty yards behind. As the light turned green, she accelerated quickly and swung round to the left. There was another turn to the left and she took it, then one to the right. She drove on through unfamiliar streets, then after about five minutes, stopped at an intersection and waited. The black van did not appear. It looked as if she had succeeded in shaking him off. She waited for another five minutes, then made her way slowly back to the main road and joined in the flow of eastward traffic. Half an hour later she had passed through Bury St. Edmunds and was driving very slowly down the Ixworth Road, watching for Pratts Way. Fifty yards farther on she came to it, a row of six small stucco houses standing back from a lay-by. She stopped the car outside number four remembering Isabelle, biddable and docile, who had obviously been told to drive further on and wait in the car. Was that because Mark thought the white Renault too conspicuous? Even the arrival of the Mini had provoked interest. There were faces at upper windows and a small group of children had mysteriously appeared, clustered around a neighbouring gate and watching her with wide and expressionless eyes.

Number four was a depressing house; the front garden was unweeded and the fence had gaps where the planks had rotted or had been wrenched apart. The external paint had flaked away to the bare wood and the brown front door had peeled and blistered in the sun. But Cordelia saw that the bottom windows were shining

and that the white net curtains were clean. Mrs. Gladwin was probably a careful housewife, struggling to keep up her standards but too old for the heavy work and too poor to afford help. Cordelia felt benevolently towards her. But the woman who, after some minutes, finally opened to her knock—the bell was out of order—was a disconcerting antidote to her sentimental pity. Compassion died before those hard distrustful eyes, that mouth tight as a trap, the thin arms clasped in a bony barrier across her chest as if to repel human contact. It was difficult to guess her age. Her hair, screwed back into a small tight bun, was still black but her face was deeply lined and the sinews and veins stood out in the thin neck like cords. She was wearing carpet slippers and a gaudy cotton overall. Cordelia said:

"My name is Cordelia Gray. I wondered if I could talk to Dr. Gladwin, if he's in. It's about an old patient."

"He's in, where else would he be? He's in the garden. You'd better go through."

The house smelt horrible, an amalgam of extreme old age, the sour taint of excreta and stale food, with an overlay of strong disinfectant. Cordelia went through to the garden, carefully avoiding looking at the hall or kitchen since curiosity might seem impertinent.

Dr. Gladwin was sitting in a high Windsor chair placed in the sun. Cordelia had never seen a man so old. He seemed to be wearing a woollen track suit, his swollen legs were encased in immense felt slippers and there was a knitted patchwork shawl across his knees. His two hands hung over the arms of the chair as if too heavy for the frail wrists, hands stained and brittle as autumn leaves which trembled with a gentle insistence. The high-domed skull, spiked with a few grey bristles, looked as small and vulnerable as a child's. The eyes were pale yolks swimming in their glutinous blue-veined whites.

Cordelia went to him and called him gently by his name. There was no response. She knelt on the grass at his feet and looked up into his face.

"Dr. Gladwin, I wanted to talk to you about a patient. It was a long time ago. Mrs. Callender. Do you remember Mrs. Callender of Garforth House?"

There was no reply. Cordelia knew that there wouldn't be. Even to ask again seemed an outrage. Mrs. Gladwin was standing beside him as if displaying him to a wondering world.

"Go on, ask him! It's all in his head you know. That's what he

used to tell me. 'I'm not one for records and notes. It's all in my head.'"

Cordelia said:

"What happened to his medical records when he gave up practice? Did any one take them over?"

"That's what I've just told you. There never were any records. And it's no use asking me. I told the boy that too. The doctor was glad enough to marry me when he wanted a nurse, but he didn't discuss his patients. Oh, dear no! He was drinking all the practice profits away, but he could still talk about medical ethics."

The bitterness in her voice was horrible. Cordelia could not meet her eyes. Just then she thought she saw the old man's lips move. She bent down her head and caught the one word. "Cold."

"I think he's trying to say that he's cold. Is there another shawl perhaps that he could have round his shoulders?"

"Cold! In this sun! He's always cold."

"But perhaps another blanket would help. Shall I fetch it for you?"

"You let him be, Miss. If you want to look after him, then look after him. See how you enjoy keeping him clean like a baby, washing his nappies, changing the bed every morning. I'll get him another shawl, but in two minutes he'll be pushing it off. He doesn't know what he wants."

"I'm sorry," said Cordelia helplessly. She wondered whether Mrs. Gladwin was getting all the help available, whether the District Nurse called, whether she had asked her doctor to try to find a hospital bed. But these were useless questions. Even she could recognize the hopeless rejection of help, the despair which no longer had energy even to look for relief. She said:

"I'm sorry; I won't trouble either of you any further."

They walked back together through the house. But there was one question Cordelia had to ask. When they reached the front gate she said:

"You talked about a boy who visited. Was his name Mark?"

"Mark Callender. He was asking about his mother. And then about ten days later we get the other one calling."

"What other one?"

"He was a gentleman all right. Walked in as if he owned the place. He wouldn't give a name but I've seen his face somewhere. He asked to see Dr. Gladwin and I showed him in. We were sitting in the back parlour that day as there was a breeze. He went up to the doctor and said 'Good afternoon, Gladwin' loudly as if talking to

a servant. Then he bent down and looked at him. Eye to eye they were. Then he straightened up, wished me good day and left. Oh, we're getting popular, we are! Any more of you and I'll have to charge for the show."

They stood together at the gate. Cordelia wondered whether to hold out her hand but sensed that Mrs. Gladwin was willing her not to go. Suddenly the woman spoke in a loud and gruff voice, looking straight ahead.

"That friend of yours, the boy who came here. He left his address. He said he wouldn't mind sitting with the doctor on a Sunday if I wanted a break; he said he could get them both a bit of dinner. I have a fancy to see my sister over at Haverhill this Sunday. Tell him he can come if he wants to."

The capitulation was ungracious, the invitation grudging, but Cordelia could guess what it had cost her to give it. She said impulsively:

"I could come on Sunday instead. I've got a car, I could get here sooner."

It would be a day lost to Sir Ronald Callender, but she wouldn't charge him. And even a private eye was surely entitled to a day off on Sundays.

"He won't want a slip of a girl. There's things to do for him that need a man. He took to that boy. I could see that. Tell him he can come."

Cordelia turned to her.

"He would have come, I know he would. But he can't. He's dead."

Mrs. Gladwin did not speak. Cordelia put out a tentative hand and touched her sleeve. There was no response. She whispered:

"I'm sorry. I'll go now." She nearly added: "If there's nothing I can do for you," but stopped herself in time. There was nothing she or anyone could do.

She looked back once as the road bent towards Bury and saw the rigid figure still at the gate.

❖❖❖

Cordelia wasn't sure what made her decide to stop at Bury and walk for ten minutes in the Abbey gardens. But she felt she couldn't face the drive back to Cambridge without calming her spirits and the glimpse of grass and flowers through the great Norman doorway was

irresistible. She parked the Mini on Angel Hill, then walked through the gardens to the river bank. There she sat for five minutes in the sun. She remembered that there was money spent on petrol to be recorded in her notebook and felt for it in her bag. Her hand brought out the white prayer book. She sat quietly thinking. Suppose she had been Mrs. Callender and had wanted to leave a message, a message which Mark would find and other searchers might miss. Where would she place it? The answer now seemed childishly simple. Surely somewhere on the page with the collect, gospel and epistle for St. Mark's Day. He had been born on April 25th. He had been named after the Saint. Quickly she found the place. In the bright sunlight reflected from the water she saw what a quick rustle through the pages had missed. There against Cranmer's gentle petition for grace to withstand the blasts of false doctrine was a small pattern of hieroglyphics so faint that the mark on the paper was little more than a smudge. She saw that it was a group of letters and figures.

E M C
A A
14.1.52

The first three letters, of course, were his mother's initials. The date must be that on which she wrote the message. Hadn't Mrs. Goddard said that Mrs. Callender had died when her son was about nine months old? But the double A? Cordelia's mind chased after motoring associations before she remembered the card in Mark's wallet. Surely these two letters under an initial could only show one thing, the blood group. Mark had been B. His mother was AA. There was only one reason why she should have wanted him to have that information. The next step was to discover Sir Ronald Callender's group.

She almost cried out with triumph as she ran through the gardens and turned the Mini again towards Cambridge. She hadn't thought out the implications of this discovery, or even whether her arguments were valid. But at least she had something to do, at least she had a lead. She drove fast, desperate to get to the city before the post office closed. There, she seemed to remember, it was possible to get a copy of the Executive Council's list of local doctors. It was handed over. And now for a telephone. She knew only one house in Cambridge where there was a chance of being left in peace to telephone for up to an hour. She drove to 57 Norwich Street.

Sophie and Davie were at home playing chess in the sitting-room, fair head and dark almost touching over the board. They showed no surprise at Cordelia's plea to use the telephone for a series of calls.

"I'll pay, of course. I'll make a note of how many."

"You'll want the room to yourself, I expect?" said Sophie. "We'll finish the game in the garden, Davie."

Blessedly incurious they carried the chess board with care through the kitchen and set it up on the garden table. Cordelia drew a chair to the table and settled down with her list. It was formidably long. There was no clue about where to begin but perhaps those doctors with group practices and addresses near the centre of the city would be the best bet. She would start with them, ticking off their names after each call. She remembered another reported pearl of the Superintendent's wisdom: "Detection requires a patient persistence which amounts to obstinacy." She thought of him as she dialled the first number. What an intolerably demanding and irritating boss he must have been! But he was almost certainly old now—forty-five at least. He had probably eased up a bit by now.

But an hour's obstinacy was unfruitful. Her calls were invariably answered; one advantage of ringing a doctor's surgery was that the telephone was at least manned. But the replies, given politely, curtly or in tones of harassed haste by a variety of respondents from the doctors themselves to obliging daily women prepared to convey a message, were the same. Sir Ronald Callender was not a patient of this practice. Cordelia repeated her formula. "I'm so sorry to have troubled you. I must have misheard the name."

But after nearly seventy minutes of patient dialling she struck lucky. The doctor's wife answered.

"I'm afraid you've got the wrong practice. Dr. Venables looks after Sir Ronald Callender's household."

This was luck indeed! Dr. Venables wasn't on her preliminary list and she wouldn't have reached the V's for at least another hour. She ran her finger quickly down the names and dialled for the last time.

It was Dr. Venables' nurse who answered. Cordelia spoke her prepared piece:

"I'm ringing for Miss Leaming from Garforth House. I'm sorry to trouble you but could you please remind us of Sir Ronald Callender's blood group? He wants to know it before the Helsinki Conference next month."

"Just a minute, please." There was a brief wait; the sound of footsteps returning.

"Sir Ronald is Group A. I should make a careful note of it if I were you. His son had to ring a month or so ago with the same enquiry."

"Thank you! Thank you! I'll be careful to make a note." Cordelia decided to take a risk.

"I'm new here, assisting Miss Leaming, and she did tell me to note it down last time but stupidly I forgot. If she should happen to call, please don't tell her that I had to trouble you again."

The voice laughed, indulgent to the inefficiency of the young. After all, it wasn't likely to inconvenience her much.

"Don't worry—, I shan't tell her. I'm glad she's got herself some help at last. Everyone's well, I hope?"

"Oh, yes! Everyone's fine."

Cordelia put down the receiver. She looked out of the window and saw that Sophie and Davie were just finishing their game and were putting the pieces back in the box. She had just finished in time. She knew the answer to her query but she still had to verify it. The information was too important to leave to her own vague recollection of the Mendelian rules of inheritance gleaned from the chapter on blood and identity in Bernie's book on forensic medicine. Davie would know, of course. The quickest way would be to ask him now. But she couldn't ask Davie. It would mean going back to the public library, and she would have to hurry if she were to be there before it closed.

But she got there just in time. The librarian, who by now had got used to seeing her, was as helpful as ever. The necessary reference book was quickly produced. Cordelia verified what she had already known. A man and wife both of whose bloods were A could not produce a B group child.

❖❖❖

Cordelia was very tired by the time she got back to the cottage. So much had happened during one day; so much had been discovered. It seemed impossible that less than twelve hours previously she had started out on her search for Nanny Pilbeam with only a vague hope that the woman, if she could be found, might provide a clue to Mark Callender's personality, might tell her something about his formative

years. She was exhilarated by the success of the day, restless with excitement, but too mentally exhausted to tease out the tangle of conjecture which lay knotted at the back of her mind. At present the facts were disordered; there was no clear pattern, no theory which would at once explain the mystery of Mark's birth, Isabelle's terror, Hugo and Sophie's secret knowledge, Miss Markland's obsessive interest in the cottage, Sergeant Maskell's almost reluctant suspicions, the oddities and unexplained inconsistencies which surrounded Mark's death.

She busied herself about the cottage with the energy of mental overtiredness. She washed the kitchen floor, laid a fire on top of the heap of ash in case the next evening should be chilly, weeded the back flower patch, then made herself a mushroom omelette and ate it sitting, as he must have done, at the simple table. Last of all, she fetched the gun from its hiding place and set it on the table beside the bed. She locked the back door carefully and drew the curtains across the window, checking once more that the seals were intact. But she didn't balance a saucepan on the top of her door. Tonight that particular precaution seemed childish and unnecessary. She lit her bedside candle then went to the window to choose a book. The night was balmy and windless; the flame of the candle burned steadily in the still air. Outside, darkness had not yet fallen but the garden was very quiet, the peace broken only by the distant crescendo of a car on the main road or the cry of a night bird. And then, seen dimly through the gloaming, she glimpsed a figure at the gate. It was Miss Markland. The woman hesitated, hand on the latch, as if wondering whether to enter the garden. Cordelia slipped to one side, back pressed against the wall. The shadowy figure was so still that it seemed as if she sensed a watching presence and had frozen like an animal surprised. Then, after two minutes, she moved away and was lost among the trees of the orchard. Cordelia relaxed, took a copy of *The Warden* from Mark's row of books, and wriggled into her sleeping-bag. Half an hour later, she blew out the candle and stretched her body comfortably for the slow acquiescent descent into sleep.

She stirred in the early hours and was instantly awake, eyes wide open in the half darkness. Time lay suspended; the still air was expectant as if the day had been taken by surprise. She could hear the ticking of her wrist watch on the bedside table and could see beside it the crooked, comforting outline of the pistol, the black cylinder of her torch. She lay and listened to the night. One lived so seldom

in these still hours, the time most often slept or dreamt away, that one came to them tentative and unpractised like a creature newly born. She wasn't aware of fear, only of an all-embracing peace, a gentle lassitude. Her breathing filled the quiet room, and the still, uncontaminated air seemed to be breathing in unity with her.

Suddenly, she realized what had woken her. Visitors were coming to the cottage. She must subconsciously in some brief phase of uneasy sleep have recognized the sound of a car. Now there was the whine of the gate, the rustle of feet, furtive as an animal in undergrowth, a faint, broken murmur of voices. She wriggled out of her sleeping-bag and stole to the window. Mark hadn't attempted to clean the glass of the front windows; perhaps he hadn't had time, perhaps he welcomed their occluding dirt. Cordelia rubbed her fingers with desperate haste against the gritty accretion of years. But, at last, she felt the cold smooth glass. It squeaked with the friction of her fingers, high and thin like an animal's squeal so that she thought the noise must betray her. She peered through the narrow strip of clear pane into the garden below.

The Renault was almost hidden by the high hedge but she could see the front of the bonnet gleaming by the gate and the two pools of light from the side lamps shining like twin moons on the lane. Isabelle was wearing something long and clinging; her pale figure trembled like a wave against the dark of the hedge. Hugo was only a black shadow at her side. But then he turned and Cordelia saw the flash of a white shirt-front. They were both in evening dress. They came together quietly up the path and conferred briefly at the front door, then moved towards the corner of the cottage.

Snatching up her torch, Cordelia rushed on silent, naked feet down the stairs and threw herself across the sitting-room to unlock the back door. The key turned easily and silently. Hardly daring to breathe she retreated back into the shadows at the foot of the stairs. She was just in time. The door opened, letting in a shaft of paler light. She heard Hugo's voice:

"Just a minute, I'll strike a match."

The match flared, illuminating in a gentle, momentary light the two grave anticipatory faces, Isabelle's immense and terrified eyes. Then it went out. She heard Hugo's muttered curse followed by the scratch of the second match striking against the box. This time he held it high. It shone on the table, on the mute accusing hook; on the silent watcher at the foot of the stairs. Hugo gasped; his hand

jerked and the match went out. Immediately, Isabelle began to scream.

Hugo's voice was sharp.

"What the hell——"

Cordelia switched on her torch and came forward.

"It's only me; Cordelia."

But Isabelle was beyond hearing. The screams rang out with such piercing intensity that Cordelia half feared that the Marklands must hear. The sound was inhuman, the shriek of animal terror. It was cut short by the swing of Hugo's arm; the sound of a slap; a gasp. It was succeeded by a second of absolute silence, then Isabelle collapsed against Hugo sobbing quietly.

He turned harshly on Cordelia:

"What the hell did you do that for?"

"Do what?"

"You terrified her, lurking there. What are you doing here anyway?"

"I could ask you that."

"We came to collect the Antonello which Isabelle lent to Mark when she came to supper with him, and to cure her of a certain morbid obsession with this place. We've been to the Pitt Club Ball. It seemed a good idea to call here on our way home. Obviously, it was a bloody stupid idea. Is there any drink in the cottage?"

"Only beer."

"Oh God, Cordelia, there would be! She needs something stronger."

"There isn't anything stronger, but I'll make coffee. You set a light to the fire. It's laid."

She stood the torch upright on the table and lit the table lamp, turning the wick low, then helped Isabelle into one of the fireside chairs.

The girl was trembling. Cordelia fetched one of Mark's heavy sweaters and placed it round her shoulders. The kindling began to flame under Hugo's careful hands. Cordelia went into the kitchen to make coffee, laying her torch on its side at the edge of the window sill so that it shone on the oil stove. She lit the stronger of the two burners and took from the shelf a brown earthenware jug, the two blue-rimmed mugs and a cup for herself. A second and chipped cup held the sugar. It took only a couple of minutes to boil half a kettle of water and to pour it over the coffee grains. She could hear Hugo's voice from the sitting-room, low, urgent, consolatory, inter-

posed with Isabelle's monosyllabic replies. Without waiting for the coffee to brew she placed it on the only tray, a bent tin one patterned with a chipped picture of Edinburgh castle, and carried it into the sitting-room, setting it down in the hearth. The faggots spluttered and blazed, shooting out a falling shower of bright sparks which patterned Isabelle's dress with stars. Then a stouter brand caught flame and the fire glowed with a stronger, more mellow, heart.

As she bent forward to stir the coffee Cordelia saw a small beetle scurrying in desperate haste along the ridges of one of the small logs. She picked up a twig from the kindling still in the hearth and held it out as a way of escape. But it confused the beetle still more. It turned in panic and raced back towards the flame, then doubled in its tracks and fell finally into a split in the wood. Cordelia pictured its fall into black burning darkness and wondered whether it briefly comprehended its dreadful end. Putting a match to a fire was such a trivial act to cause such agony, such terror.

She handed Isabelle and Hugo their mugs and took her own. The comforting smell of fresh coffee mingled with the resinous tang of the burning wood. The fire threw long shadows over the tiled floor and the oil lamp cast its gentle glow over their faces. Surely, thought Cordelia, no murder suspects could have been interrogated in a cosier setting. Even Isabelle had lost her fears. Whether it was the reassurance of Hugo's arm across her shoulders, the stimulus of the coffee or the homely warmth and crackle of the fire, she seemed almost at ease.

Cordelia said to Hugo:

"You said that Isabelle was morbidly obsessed by this place. Why should she be?"

"Isabelle's very sensitive; she isn't tough like you."

Cordelia privately thought that all beautiful women were tough—how else could they survive?—and that Isabelle's fibres could compare well for resilience with her own. But nothing would be gained by challenging Hugo's illusions. Beauty was fragile, transitory, vulnerable. Isabelle's sensitivities must be protected. The toughies could look after themselves. She said:

"According to you, she's only been here once before. I know that Mark Callender died in this room, but you hardly expect me to believe that she's grieving over Mark. There's something that both of you know and it would be better if you told me now. If you don't I shall have to report to Sir Ronald Callender that Isabelle, your sister and you are somehow concerned in his son's death and it will

be up to him to decide whether to call in the police. I can't see Isabelle standing up to even the mildest police questioning, can you?"

Even to Cordelia it sounded a stilted, sententious little speech, an unsubstantiated accusation backed up by an empty threat. She half expected Hugo to counter it with amused contempt. But he looked at her for a minute as if assessing more than the reality of the danger. Then he said quietly:

"Can't you accept my word that Mark died by his own hand and that if you do call in the police it will cause unhappiness and distress to his father, to his friends and be absolutely no help to anyone?"

"No, Hugo, I can't."

"Then if we do tell you what we know, will you promise that it won't go any further?"

"How can I, any more than I can promise to believe you?"

Suddenly Isabelle cried:

"Oh, tell her, Hugo! What does it matter?"

Cordelia said:

"I think that you must. I don't think you've any choice."

"So it seems. All right." He put his coffee mug down in the hearth and looked into the fire.

"I told you that we went—Sophie, Isabelle, Davie and I—to the Arts Theatre on the night Mark died but that, as you've probably guessed, was only three-quarters true. They had only three seats left when I booked so we allocated them to the three people mostly likely to enjoy the play. Isabelle goes to the theatre to be seen rather than to see and is bored by any show with a cast of less than fifty, so she was the one left out. Thus neglected by her current lover, she very reasonably decided to seek consolation with the next."

Isabelle said with a secret, anticipatory smile:

"Mark was not my lover, Hugo."

She spoke without rancour or resentment. It was a matter of putting the record straight.

"I know. Mark was a romantic. He never took a girl to bed—or anywhere else that I could see—until he judged that there was an adequate depth of inter-personal communication, or whatever jargon he used, between them. Actually, that's unfair. It's my father who uses bloody awful meaningless phrases like that. But Mark agreed with the general idea. I doubt whether he could enjoy sex until he'd convinced himself that he and the girl were in love. It was a necessary preliminary—like undressing. I gather that with Isabelle the

118

relationship hadn't reached the necessary depths, hadn't achieved the essential emotional rapport. It was only a matter of time, of course. Where Isabelle was concerned, Mark was as capable of self-deception as the rest of us."

The high, slightly hesitant voice was edged with jealousy.

Isabelle said, slowly and patiently, like a mother explaining to a wilfully obtuse child:

"Mark never made love to me, Hugo."

"That's what I'm saying. Poor Mark! He exchanged the substance for the shadow and now he has neither."

"But what happened that night?"

Cordelia spoke to Isabelle, but it was Hugo who replied.

"Isabelle drove here and arrived shortly after half past seven. The curtains were drawn across the back window, the front one is impenetrable anyway, but the door was open. She came in. Mark was already dead. His body was hanging by the strap from that hook. But he didn't look as he did when Miss Markland found him next morning."

He turned to Isabelle:

"You tell her." She hesitated. Hugo bent forward and kissed her lightly on the lips.

"Go on, tell. There are some unpleasantnesses which all Papa's money can't entirely shield from you and this, darling, is one."

❖❖❖

Isabelle turned her head and looked intently into the four corners of the room as if satisfying herself that the three of them were really alone. The irises of her remarkable eyes were purple in the firelight. She leaned towards Cordelia with something of the confiding relish of a village gossip about to relate the latest scandal. Cordelia saw that her panic had left her. Isabelle's agonies were elemental, violent but short lived, easily comforted. She would have kept her secret while Hugo instructed her to keep it, but she was glad of his order of release. Probably her instinct told her that the story, once told, would lose the sting of terror. She said:

"I thought I would call to see Mark and, perhaps, that we would have supper together. Mademoiselle de Congé was not well and Hugo and Sophie were at the theatre and I was bored. I came to the back door because Mark had told me that the front door would

not open. I thought that I might see him in the garden, but he was not there, only the garden fork in the ground and his shoes at the door. So I pushed open the door. I did not knock because I thought that I would be a surprise for Mark."

She hesitated and looked down into the mug of coffee, twisting it between her hands.

"And then?" prompted Cordelia.

"And then I saw him. He was hanging there by the belt from that hook in the ceiling and I knew he was dead. Cordelia, it was horrible! He was dressed like a woman in a black bra and black lace panties. Nothing else. And his face! He had painted his lips, all over his lips Cordelia, like a clown! It was terrible but it was funny too. I wanted to laugh and scream at the same time. He didn't look like Mark. He didn't look like a human being at all. And on the table there were three pictures. Not nice pictures Cordelia. Pictures of naked women."

Her wide eyes stared into Cordelia's, dismayed, uncomprehending. Hugo said:

"Don't look like that, Cordelia. It was horrible for Isabelle at the time and disagreeable to think about now. But it isn't so very uncommon. It does happen. It's probably one of the more innocuous of sexual deviations. He wasn't involving anyone but himself. And he didn't mean to kill himself; that was just bad luck. I imagine that the buckle of the belt slipped and he never had a chance." Cordelia said:

"I don't believe it."

"I thought you might not. But it's true, Cordelia. Why not come with us now and ring Sophie? She'll confirm it."

"I don't need confirmation of Isabelle's story. I already have that. I mean I still don't believe that Mark killed himself."

As soon as she spoke she knew that it had been a mistake. She shouldn't have revealed her suspicions. But it was too late now and there were questions she had to ask. She saw Hugo's face, his quick impatient frown at her obtuseness, her obstinacy. And then she detected a subtle change of mood; was it irritation, fear, disappointment? She spoke directly to Isabelle.

"You said that the door was open. Did you notice the key?"

"It was in this side of the door. I saw it when I went out."

"What about the curtains?"

"They were like now, across the window."

"And where was the lipstick?"

"What lipstick, Cordelia?"

"The one used to paint Mark's lips. It wasn't in the pockets of his jeans or the police would have found it, so where was it? Did you see it on the table?"

"There was nothing on the table except the pictures."

"What colour was the lipstick?"

"Purple. An old lady's colour. No one would choose such a colour I think."

"And the underclothes, could you describe them?"

"Oh, yes! They were from M & S. I recognized them."

"You mean that you recognized those particular ones, that they were yours?"

"Oh, no Cordelia! They were not mine. I never wear black underclothes. I only like white next to my skin. But they were the kind I usually buy. I always get my underclothes from M & S."

Cordelia reflected that Isabelle was hardly one of the store's best customers, but that no other witness would have been as reliable when it came to details, particularly of clothes. Even in that moment of absolute terror and revulsion, Isabelle had noticed the type of underclothes. And if she said that she hadn't seen the lipstick, then it was because the lipstick hadn't been there to see.

Cordelia went on inexorably:

"Did you touch anything, Mark's body perhaps, to see if he was dead?"

Isabelle was shocked. The facts of life she could take in her stride, but not the facts of death.

"I couldn't touch Mark! I touched nothing. And I knew that he was dead."

Hugo said: "A respectable, sensible, law-abiding citizen would have found the nearest telephone and rung the police. Luckily Isabelle is none of these things. Her instinct was to come to me. She waited until the play ended, and then met us outside the theatre. When we came out she was pacing up and down the pavement on the other side of the road. Davie, Sophie and I came back here with her in the Renault. We only stopped briefly at Norwich Street to collect Davie's camera and flash."

"Why?"

"That was my idea. Obviously, we had no intention of letting the fuzz and Ronald Callender know how Mark had died. Our idea was to fake a suicide. We planned to dress him in his own clothes, clean his face and then leave him for someone else to find. We hadn't it in mind to fake a suicide note; that was a refinement somewhat out-

side our powers. We collected the camera so that we could photograph him as he was. We didn't know what particular law we were breaking in faking a suicide, but there must have been one. You can't do the simplest service for your friends these days without it being liable to misconstruction by the fuzz. If there were trouble we wanted some evidence of the truth. We were all fond of Mark in our different ways, but not fond enough to risk a murder charge. However, our good intentions were frustrated. Someone else had got here first."

"Tell me about it."

"There's nothing to tell. We told the two girls to wait in the car, Isabelle because she had already seen enough and Sophie because Isabelle was too frightened to be left alone. Besides, it seemed only fair to Mark to keep Sophie out of it, to prevent her from seeing him. Don't you find it odd, Cordelia, this concern one has for the susceptibilities of the dead?"

Thinking of her father and Bernie, Cordelia said:

"Perhaps it's only when people are dead that we can safely show how much we cared about them. We know that it's too late then for them to do anything about it."

"Cynical but true. Anyway, there was nothing for us to do here. We found Mark's body and this room as Miss Markland described them at the inquest. The door was open, the curtains drawn across. Mark was naked except for his blue jeans. There were no magazine pictures on the table and no lipstick on his face. But there was a suicide note in the typewriter and a mound of ash in the grate. It looked as if the visitor had made a thorough job of it. We didn't linger. Someone else—perhaps someone from the house—might have turned up at any minute. Admittedly, it was very late by then but it seemed an evening for people to pop in. Mark must have had more visitors that night than during his whole time at the cottage; first Isabelle; then the unknown samaritan; then us."

Cordelia thought that there had been someone before Isabelle. Mark's murderer had been there first. She asked suddenly:

"Someone played a stupid trick on me last night. When I got back here from the party there was a bolster slung from that hook. Did you do that?"

If his surprise were not genuine, then Hugo was a better actor than Cordelia thought possible.

"Of course I didn't! I thought you were living in Cambridge not here. And why on earth should I?"

"To warn me off."

"But that would be crazy! It wouldn't warn you off, would it? It might scare some women, but not you. We wanted to convince you that there was nothing to investigate about Mark's death. That sort of trick would only convince you that there was. Someone else was trying to scare you. The most likely person is the one who came here after us."

"I know. Someone took a risk for Mark. He—or she—won't want me ferreting around. But he would have got rid of me more sensibly by telling me the truth."

"How could he know whether to trust you? What will you do now, Cordelia? Go back to town?"

He was trying to keep his voice casual but she thought she detected the underlying anxiety. She replied.

"I expect so. I'll have to see Sir Ronald first."

"What will you tell him?"

"I'll think of something. Don't worry."

Dawn was staining the eastern sky and the first chorus of birds was noisily contradicting the new day before Hugo and Isabelle left. They took the Antonello with them. Cordelia saw it taken down with a pang of regret as if something of Mark were leaving the cottage. Isabelle examined the picture closely with a grave professional eye before tucking it under her arm. Cordelia thought that she was probably generous enough with her possessions, both people and pictures, provided they were on loan only, to be returned promptly on demand and in the same condition as when she parted with them. Cordelia watched from the front gate as the Renault, with Hugo driving, moved out of the shadow of the hedge. She lifted her hand in a formal gesture of farewell like a weary hostess speeding her final guests, then turned back to the cottage.

The sitting-room seemed empty and cold without them. The fire was dying and she hastily pushed in the few remaining sticks from the hearth and blew on them to kindle the flame. She moved restlessly about the little room. She was too lively to go back to bed, but her short and disturbed night had left her edgy with tiredness. But her mind was tormented by something more fundamental than lack of sleep. For the first time she knew that she was afraid. Evil existed—it hadn't needed a convent education to convince her of that reality—and it had been present in this room. Something here had been stronger than wickedness, ruthlessness, cruelty or expedience. Evil. She had no doubt that Mark had been murdered, but with

what diabolical cleverness it had been done! If Isabelle told her story, who now would ever believe that he hadn't died accidentally, but by his own hand? Cordelia had no need to refer to her book on forensic medicine to know how it would appear to the police. As Hugo had said, these cases weren't so very uncommon. He, as a psychiatrist's son, would have heard or read of them. Who else would know? Probably any reasonably sophisticated person. But it couldn't have been Hugo. Hugo had an alibi. Her mind revolted at the thought that Davie or Sophie could have participated in such a horror. But how typical that they should have collected the camera. Even their compassion had been overlaid with self concern. Would Hugo and Davie have stood here, under Mark's grotesque body, calmly discussing distance and exposure before taking the photograph which would, if necessary, exonerate them at his expense?

She went into the kitchen to make tea, glad to be free of the malignant fascination of that hook in the ceiling. Previously it had hardly worried her, now it was as obtrusive as a fetish. It seemed to have grown since the previous night, to be growing still as it drew her eyes compulsively upwards. And the sitting-room itself had surely shrunk; no longer a sanctum but a claustrophobic cell, tawdry and shameful as an execution shed. Even the bright morning air was redolent with evil.

Waiting for the kettle to boil she made herself contemplate the day's activities. It was still too early to theorize; her mind was too preoccupied with horror to deal rationally with its new knowledge. Isabelle's story had complicated, not illumined the case. But there were still relevant facts to be discovered. She would go on with the programme she had already planned. Today she would go to London to examine Mark's grandfather's will.

But there were still two hours to get through before it was time to start out. She had decided to travel to London by train and to leave the car at Cambridge station since this would be both quicker and easier. It was irritating to have to spend a day in town when the heart of the mystery so obviously lay in Cambridgeshire, but for once she wasn't sorry at the prospect of leaving the cottage. Shocked and restless, she wandered aimlessly from room to room and prowled around the garden, fretting to be away. Finally in desperation she took hold of the garden fork and completed the digging of Mark's unfinished row. She wasn't sure that this was wise; Mark's interrupted work was part of the evidence for his murder. But other people, including Sergeant Maskell, had seen it and could testify if

necessary, and the sight of the partly-completed job, of the fork still askew in the soil, was unbearably irritating. When the row was completed she felt calmer and she dug on without pausing for another hour before carefully cleaning the fork and placing it with the other tools in the garden shed.

At last it was time to go. The seven o'clock weather forecast had prophesied thundery storms in the south-east so she put on her suit, the heaviest protection she had brought with her. She hadn't worn it since Bernie's death and she discovered that the waist band was uncomfortably loose. She had lost some weight. After a moment's thought, she took Mark's belt from the scene-of-crime kit and wound it twice round her waist. She felt no repugnance as the leather tightened against her. It was impossible to believe that anything he had ever touched or owned could frighten or distress her. The strength and heaviness of the leather so close to her skin was even obscurely comforting and reassuring, as if the belt were a talisman.

Chapter Five

❖❖❖

The storm broke just as Cordelia alighted from the number 11 bus
outside Somerset House. There was a jagged flash of lightning and,
almost instantaneously, the thunder crashed like a barrage round her
ears and she raced across the inner courtyard between the ranks of
parked cars through a wall of water while the rain spouted around
her ankles as if the paving stones were being raked with bullets. She
pushed open the door and stood draining pools of water on the mat
and laughing aloud with relief. One or two of the people present
glanced up from their perusal of wills and smiled at her, while a
motherly looking woman behind the counter tut-tutted her concern.
Cordelia shook her jacket over the mat then hung it on the back of
one of the chairs and tried ineffectually to dry her hair with her
handkerchief before approaching the counter.

The motherly woman was helpful. Consulted by Cordelia on the
correct procedure, she indicated the shelves of heavy, bound volumes in the middle of the hall and explained that the wills were
indexed under the surname of the testator and the year in which
the document was lodged with Somerset House. It was for Cordelia
to trace the catalogue number and bring the volume to the desk. The
original will would then be sent for and she could consult it for a
fee of 20 pence.

Not knowing when George Bottley had died, Cordelia was in
some perplexity where to begin her search. But she deduced that the
will must have been made after the birth, or at least the conception,
of Mark, since he had been left a fortune by his grandfather. But
Mr. Bottley had also left money to his daughter and this part of his
fortune had come on her death to her husband. The strong probability was that he had died before her, since otherwise he would
surely have made a new will. Cordelia decided to begin her search
with the year of Mark's birth, 1951.

Her deductions proved correct. George Albert Bottley of Stonegate
Lodge, Harrogate, had died on 26th July 1951, exactly three months
and one day after the birth of his grandson and only three weeks
after making his will. Cordelia wondered whether his death had

been sudden and unexpected or whether this was the will of a dying man. She saw that he had left an estate of nearly three quarters of a million pounds. How had he made this, she wondered? Surely not all from wool. She heaved the heavy book across to the counter, the clerk wrote the details on a white form and pointed out the way to the cashier's office. Within a surprisingly few minutes of paying what seemed to her a modest fee, Cordelia was seated under the light at one of the desks near the window with the will in her hands.

She hadn't liked what she had heard about George Bottley from Nanny Pilbeam and she didn't like him any better after reading his will. She had feared that the document might be long, complicated and difficult to understand; it was surprisingly short, simple and intelligible. Mr. Bottley directed that all his possessions should be sold, "since I wish to prevent the usual unseemly wrangling over bric-à-brac". He left modest sums to servants in his employ at the time of death but there was no mention, Cordelia noticed, of his gardener. He bequeathed half of the residue of his fortune to his daughter, absolutely, "now that she has demonstrated that she has at least one of the normal attributes of a woman." The remaining half he left to his beloved grandson Mark Callender on attaining his twenty-fifth birthday, "by which date, if he hasn't learned the value of money, he will at least be of an age to avoid exploitation." The income from the capital was left to six Bottley relations, some of them, apparently, only distant kinsmen. The will created a residual trust; as each beneficiary died his share would be distributed among the survivors. The testator was confident that this arrangement would promote in the beneficiaries a lively interest in each others' health and survival while encouraging them to achieve the distinction of longevity, no other distinction being within their reach. If Mark died before his twenty-fifth birthday the family trust would continue until all the beneficiaries were dead and the capital would then be distributed among a formidable list of charities chosen, as far as Cordelia could see, because they were well known and successful rather than because they represented any personal concern or sympathy on the part of the testator. It was as if he had asked his lawyers for a list of the more reliable charities, having no real interest in what happened to his fortune if his own issue were not alive to inherit it.

It was a strange will. Mr. Bottley had left nothing to his son-in-law yet had apparently been unworried by the possibility that his daughter, whom he knew not to be strong, might die and leave her fortune to her husband. In some respects it was a gambler's will and

Cordelia wondered again how George Bottley had made his fortune. But, despite the cynical unkindness of its comments, the will was neither unfair nor ungenerous. Unlike some very rich men he hadn't attempted to control his great fortune from beyond the grave, obsessively determined that not one penny should ever get into unfavoured hands. His daughter and his grandson had both been left their fortunes absolutely. It was impossible to like Mr. Bottley but difficult not to respect him. And the implications of his will were very clear. No one stood to gain by Mark's death except a long list of highly respectable charities.

Cordelia made a note of the main clauses of the will, more because of Bernie's insistence on meticulous documentation than from any fear of forgetting them; slipped the receipt for 20p into the expenses page of her notebook; added the cost of her cheap day return ticket from Cambridge and her bus fare, and returned the will to the counter. The storm had been as short as it was violent. The hot sun was already drying the windows and the puddles lay bright on the rain-washed courtyard. Cordelia decided that she ought to charge Sir Ronald for half a day only and spend the rest of her time in London at the office. There might be post to collect. There might even be another case awaiting her.

But the decision was a mistake. The office seemed even more sordid than when she had left it and the air smelt sour in contrast to the rain-washed streets outside. There was a thick film of dust over the furniture and the bloodstain on the rug had deepened into a brick-brown which looked even more sinister than the original bright red. There was nothing in the letterbox but a final demand from the electricity board and a bill from the stationer. Bernie had paid dearly—or rather, had not paid—for the despised writing paper.

Cordelia wrote a cheque for the electricity bill, dusted the furniture, made one last and unsuccessful attempt to clean the rug. Then she locked the office and set off to walk to Trafalgar Square. She would seek consolation in the National Gallery.

❖❖❖

She caught the eighteen-sixteen train from Liverpool Street and it was nearly eight o'clock before she arrived back at the cottage. She parked the Mini in its usual place in the shelter of the copse and made her way round the side of the cottage. She hesitated for a mo-

ment wondering whether to collect the gun from its hiding place, but decided that this could wait until later. She was hungry and the first priority was to get a meal. She had carefully locked the back door and had stuck a thin strip of Scotch tape across the window sill before leaving that morning. If there were any more secret visitors she wanted to be warned. But the tape was still intact. She felt in her shoulder bag for the key and, bending down, fitted it into the lock. She wasn't expecting trouble outside the cottage and the attack took her completely by surprise. There was the half-second of pre-knowledge before the blanket fell but that was too late. There was a cord around her neck pulling the mask of hot stifling wool taut against her mouth and nostrils. She gasped for breath and tasted the dry strong-smelling fibres on her tongue. Then a sharp pain exploded in her chest and she remembered nothing.

The movement of liberation was a miracle and a horror. The blanket was whipped off. She never saw her assailant. There was a second of sweet reviving air, a glimpse, so brief that it was barely comprehended, of blinding sky seen through greenness and then she felt herself falling, falling in helpless astonishment into cold darkness. The fall was a confusion of old nightmares, unbelievable seconds of childhood terrors recalled. Then her body hit the water. Ice-cold hands dragged her into a vortex of horror. Instinctively, she had closed her mouth at the moment of impact and she struggled to the surface through what seemed an eternity of cold encompassing blackness. She shook her head and, through her stinging eyes, she looked up. The black tunnel that stretched above her ended in a moon of blue light. Even as she looked, the well lid was dragged slowly back like the shutter of a camera. The moon became a half moon; then a crescent. At last there was nothing but eight thin slits of light.

Desperately she trod water, reaching tentatively for the bottom. There was no bottom. Frantically moving hands and feet, willing herself not to panic, she felt around the walls of the well for a possible foothold. There was none. The funnel of bricks, smooth, sweating with moisture, stretched around and above her like a circular tomb. As she gazed upwards they writhed, expanded, swayed and reeled like the belly of a monstrous snake.

And then she felt a saving anger. She wouldn't let herself drown, wouldn't die in this horrible place, alone and terrified. The well was deep but small, the diameter barely three feet. If she kept her head

and took time, she could brace her legs and shoulders against the bricks and work her way upwards.

She hadn't bruised or stunned herself against the walls as she fell. Miraculously she was uninjured. The fall had been clean. She was alive and capable of thought. She had always been a survivor. She would survive.

She floated on her back, bracing her shoulders against the cold walls, spreading her arms and digging her elbows into the interstices of the bricks to get a better grip. Shuffling off her shoes, she planted both feet against the opposite wall. Just beneath the surface of the water, she could feel that one of the bricks was slightly unaligned. She curved her toes around it. It gave her a precarious but welcome foothold for the start of the climb. By means of it, she could lift her body out of the water and could relieve for a moment the strain on the muscles of her back and thighs.

Then slowly she began to climb, first shifting her feet, one after the other in tiny sliding steps, then humping up her body inch by painful inch. She kept her eyes fixed on the opposite curve of the wall, willing herself not to look down, nor up, counting progress by the width of each brick. Time passed. She couldn't see Bernie's watch, although its ticking seemed unnaturally loud, a regular obtrusive metronome to the thumping of her heart and the fierce gasping of her breath. The pain in her legs was intense and her shirt was sticking to her back with a warm, almost comforting effusion, which she knew must be blood. She willed herself not to think of the water beneath her or of the thin, but widening clefts of light above. If she were to survive, all her energy must be harnessed for the next painful inch.

Once, her legs slipped and she slithered back several yards before her feet, scrabbling ineffectually against the slimy walls, at last found a purchase. The fall had grazed her injured back and left her whimpering with self-pity and disappointment. She scourged her mind into courage and began climbing again. Once she was gripped by cramp and lay stretched as if on a rack until the agony passed and her fixed muscles could move. From time to time her feet found another small foothold and she was able to stretch her legs and rest. The temptation to stay in comparative safety and ease was almost irresistible and she had to will herself to start again on the slow torturous climb.

It seemed that she had been climbing for hours, moving in a parody of a difficult labour towards some desperate birth. Darkness was

falling. The light from the well top was wider now but less strong. She told herself that the climb wasn't really difficult. It was only the darkness and loneliness which made it seem so. If this were a fabricated obstacle race, an exercise in the school gymnasium, surely she could have done it easily enough. She filled her mind with the comforting images of rib stools and vaulting horses, of the fifth form shouting their encouragement. Sister Perpetua was there. But why wasn't she looking at Cordelia? Why had she turned away? Cordelia called her and the figure turned slowly and smiled at her. But it wasn't Sister after all. It was Miss Leaming, the lean pale face sardonic under the white veil.

And now when she knew that, unaided, she could get no further, Cordelia saw salvation. A few feet above her was the bottom rung of a short wooden ladder fixed to the last few feet of the well. At first she thought that it was an illusion, a phantasm born of exhaustion and despair. She shut her eyes for a few minutes; her lips moved. Then she opened her eyes again. The ladder was still there, seen dimly but comfortingly solid in the fading light. She lifted impotent hands towards it knowing, even as she did so, that it was out of reach. It could save her life and she knew that she hadn't the strength to reach it.

It was then, without conscious thought or scheming, that she remembered the belt. Her hand dropped to her waist feeling for the heavy brass buckle. She undid it and drew the long snake of leather from her body. Carefully she threw the buckled end towards the bottom rung of the ladder. The first three times the metal struck the wood with a sharp crack but didn't fall over the rung; the fourth time it did. She pushed the other end of the belt gently upwards and the buckle dropped towards her until she could stretch out her hand and grasp it. She fastened it to the other end to form a strong loop. Then she pulled, at first very gently and then harder until most of her weight was on the strap. The relief was indescribable. She braced herself against the brickwork, gathering strength for the final triumphant effort. Then it happened. The rung, rotted at its joints, broke loose with a harsh tearing sound and spun past her into darkness, just missing her head. It seemed minutes rather than seconds before the distant splash reverberated round the wall.

She unbuckled the belt and tried again. The next rung was a foot higher and the throw more difficult. Even this small effort was exhausting in her present state and she made herself take time. Every unsuccessful throw made the next more difficult. She didn't count

the number of attempts, but at last the buckle fell over the rung and dropped towards her. When it snaked within reach she found that she could only just buckle the strap. The next rung would be too high. If this one broke, it would be the end.

But the rung held. She had no clear memory of the last half hour of the climb but at last she reached the ladder and strapped herself firmly to the uprights. For the first time she was physically safe. As long as the ladder held she needn't fear falling. She let herself relax into brief unconsciousness. But then the wheels of the mind which had been spinning blissfully free, took hold again and she began to think. She knew that she had no hope of moving the heavy wooden cover unaided. She stretched out both hands and pushed against it but it didn't shift, and the high concave dome made it impossible for her to brace her shoulders against the wood. She would have to rely on outside help and that wouldn't come till daylight. It might not come even then, but she pushed the thought away. Sooner or later Miss Markland would come to the cottage. Sooner or later someone would come. She could hope to hold on, thus strapped, for several days. Even if she lost consciousness there was a chance that she would be rescued alive. Miss Markland knew that she was at the cottage; her things were still there. Miss Markland would come.

She gave thought to how she could attract attention. There was room to push something between the boards of wood if only she had something sufficiently stiff to push. The edge of the buckle was possible provided she strapped herself more tightly. But that must wait until the morning. There was nothing she could do now. She would relax and sleep and await rescue.

And then the final horror burst upon her. There would be no rescue. Someone would be coming to the well, coming on quiet and stealthy feet under the cover of darkness. But it would be her murderer. He had to return; it was part of his plan. The attack, which at the time had seemed so astonishingly, so brutally stupid, hadn't been stupid at all. It was intended to look like an accident. He would come back that night and remove the well cover again. Then, some time next day or within the next few days, Miss Markland would blunder through the garden and discover what had happened. No one would ever be able to prove that Cordelia's death wasn't an accident. She recalled the words of Sergeant Maskell: "It isn't what you suspect; it's what you can prove." But this time would there even be suspicion? Here was a young, impulsive, over-curious young woman living at the cottage without the owner's authority. She had

obviously decided to explore the well. She had smashed the padlock, drawn back the lid with the coil of rope which the killer would leave ready to be found, and tempted by the ladder, had let herself down those few steps until the final rung broke beneath her. Her prints and no one else's would be found on the ladder, if they took the trouble to look. The cottage was utterly deserted; the chance that her murderer would be seen returning was remote. There was nothing she could do but wait until she heard his footsteps, his heavy breathing, and the lid was drawn slowly back to reveal his face.

After the first intensity of terror, Cordelia waited for death without hope and without further struggle. There was even a kind of peace in resignation. Strapped like a victim to the uprights of the ladder she drifted mercifully into brief oblivion and prayed that it might be so when her killer returned, that she might not be conscious at the moment of the final blow. She had no longer any interest in seeing her murderer's face. She wouldn't humiliate herself by pleading for her life, wouldn't beg for mercy from a man who had strung up Mark. She knew that there would be no mercy.

But she was conscious when the well lid began slowly to move. The light came in above her bowed head. The gap widened. And then she heard a voice, a woman's voice, low, urgent and sharp with terror.

"Cordelia!"

She looked up.

Kneeling at the rim of the well, her pale face immense and seeming to float disembodied in space like the phantasm of a nightmare, was Miss Markland. And the eyes which stared into Cordelia's face were as wild with terror as her own.

Ten minutes later Cordelia was lying slumped in the fireside chair. Her whole body ached and she was powerless to control her violent shivering. Her thin shirt was stuck to her wounded back and every shift of movement was pain. Miss Markland had put a light to the kindling and was now making coffee. Cordelia could hear her moving to and fro in the little kitchen and could smell the stove as it was turned high and, soon, the evocative aroma of coffee. These familiar sights and sounds would normally have been reassuring and comforting, but now she was desperate to be alone. The killer would still return. He had to return, and when he did, she wanted to be there to meet him. Miss Markland brought in the two mugs and pressed one into Cordelia's shivering hands. She stumped upstairs and came down with one of Mark's jumpers which she wound round the

girl's neck. Her terror had left her, but she was as agitated as a young girl sharing her first half-shameful adventure. Her eyes were wild, her whole body trembled with excitement. She sat down directly in front of Cordelia and fixed her with her sharp inquisitive eyes.

"How did it happen? You must tell me."

Cordelia had not forgotten how to think.

"I don't know. I can't remember anything that happened before I hit the water. I must have decided to explore the well and lost my balance."

"But the well lid! The lid was in place!"

"I know. Someone must have replaced it."

"But why? Who would have come this way?"

"I don't know. But someone must have seen it. Someone must have dragged it back."

She said more gently:

"You saved my life. How did you notice what had happened?"

"I came to the cottage to see if you were still here. I came earlier today but there was no sign of you. There was a coil of rope—the one that you used, I expect—left in the path and I stumbled over it. Then I noticed that the well lid wasn't quite in place and that the padlock had been smashed."

"You saved my life," said Cordelia again, "but please go now. Please go. I'm all right, really I am."

"But you aren't fit to be left alone! And that man—the one who replaced the lid—he might return. I don't like to think of strangers snooping around the cottage and you here alone."

"I'm perfectly safe. Besides, I have a gun. I only want to be left in peace to rest. Please don't worry about me!"

Cordelia could detect the note of desperation, almost of hysteria, in her own voice.

But Miss Markland seemed not to hear. Suddenly she was on her knees in front of Cordelia and pouring out a spate of high, excited chatter. Without thought and without compassion, she was confiding to the girl her terrible story, a story of her son, the four-year-old child of herself and her lover, who had broken his way through the cottage hedge and fallen into the well to his death. Cordelia tried to shake herself free from the wild eyes. It was surely all a fantasy. The woman must be mad. And if it were true, it was horrible and unthinkable and she could not bear to hear it. Sometime later she would remember it, remember every word, and think of the child, of his last terror, his desperate cry for his mother, the cold suffocating

water dragging him to his death. She would live his agony in night-mares as she would re-live her own. But not now. Through the spate of words, the self-accusations, the terror recalled, Cordelia recognized the note of liberation. What to her had been horror, to Miss Markland had been release. A life for a life. Suddenly Cordelia could bear it no longer. She said violently:

"I'm sorry! I'm sorry! You've saved my life and I'm grateful. But I can't bear to listen. I don't want you here. For God's sake go!"

All her life she would remember the woman's hurt face, her silent withdrawal. Cordelia didn't hear her go, didn't remember the soft closing of the door. All she knew was that she was alone. The shaking was over now although she still felt very cold. She went upstairs and pulled on her slacks then unwound Mark's jumper from her neck and put it on. It would cover the blood stains on her shirt and the warmth was immediately comforting. She was moving very quickly. She felt for the ammunition, took her torch and let herself out of the back door of the cottage. The gun was where she had left it, in the fold of the tree. She loaded it and felt its familiar shape and heaviness in her hand. Then she stood back among the bushes and waited.

❖❖❖

It was too dark to see the dial of her wrist watch but Cordelia reckoned that she must have waited there immobile in the shadows for nearly half an hour before her ears caught the sound for which she was waiting. A car was approaching down the lane. Cordelia held her breath. The sound of the engine reached a brief crescendo and then faded away. The car had driven on without stopping. It was unusual for a car to pass down the lane after dark and she wondered who it could be. Again she waited, moving deeper into the shelter of the elder bush so that she could rest her back against the bark. She had been clutching the gun so tightly that her right wrist ached and she moved the pistol to her other hand and rotated the wrist slowly, stretching the cramped fingers.

Again she waited. The slow minutes passed. The silence was broken only by the furtive scuffling of some small night prowler in the grass and the sudden wild hoot of an owl. And then once more she heard the sound of an engine. This time the noise was faint and it came no closer. Someone had stopped a car further up the road.

She took the gun in her right hand, cradling the muzzle with her left. Her heart was pounding so loudly that she felt its wild hammering must betray her. She imagined rather than heard the thin whine of the front gate but the sound of feet moving round the cottage was unmistakable and clear. And now he was in sight, a stocky, broad-shouldered figure, black against the light. He moved towards her and she could see her shoulder bag hanging from his left shoulder. The discovery disconcerted her. She had completely forgotten the bag. But now she had realized why he had seized it. He had wanted to search it for evidence, but it was important that, finally, it should be discovered with her body in the well.

He came forward gently on tip-toe, his long simian arms held stiffly away from his body like a caricature of a film cowboy ready for the draw. When he got to the rim of the well he waited and the moon struck the white of his eyes as he gazed slowly round. Then he bent down and felt in the grass for the coil of rope. Cordelia had lain it where Miss Markland had found it, but something about it, some slight difference perhaps in the way it was coiled, seemed to strike him. He rose uncertainly and stood for a moment with the rope dangling from his hand. Cordelia tried to control her breathing. It seemed impossible that he should not hear, smell or see her, that he should be so like a predator yet without the beast's instinct for the enemy in the dark. He moved forward. Now he was at the well. He bent and threaded one end of the rope through the iron hoop.

Cordelia moved with one step out of the darkness. She held the gun firmly and straight as Bernie had shown her. This time the target was very close. She knew that she wouldn't fire but, in that moment, she knew too what it was that could make a man kill. She said loudly:

"Good evening, Mr. Lunn."

She never knew whether he saw the gun. But for one unforgettable second, as the clouded moon sailed into the open sky, she saw his face clearly; saw the hate, the despair, the agony and the rictus of terror. He gave one hoarse cry, threw down the shoulder bag and the rope and rushed through the garden in a blind panic. She gave chase, hardly knowing why, or what she hoped to achieve, determined only that he shouldn't get back to Garforth House before her. And still she didn't fire the gun.

But he had an advantage. As she threw herself through the gate she saw that he had parked the van some fifty yards up the road and left the engine running. She chased after him but could see that it

was hopeless. Her only hope of catching up with him was to get the Mini. She tore down the lane feeling in her shoulder bag as she ran. The prayer book and her notebook were both gone but her fingers found the car keys. She unlocked the Mini, threw herself in and reversed it violently onto the road. The rear lights of the van were about a hundred yards ahead of her. She didn't know what speed it could do, but doubted whether it could out-pace the Mini. She trod on the accelerator and gave pursuit. She turned left out of the lane on to the subsidiary road and now she could see the van still ahead. He was driving fast and was holding the distance. Now the road turned and for a few seconds he was out of sight. He must be getting very close now to the junction with the Cambridge road.

She heard the crash just before she herself reached the junction, an instantaneous explosion of sound which shook the hedges and made the little car tremble. Cordelia's hands tightened momentarily on the wheel and the Mini jerked to a stop. She ran forward round the corner and saw before her the gleaming, headlamp lit surface of the main Cambridge road. It was peopled with running shapes. The transporter, still upright, was an immense oblong mass blocking the sky line, a barricade slewed across the road. The van had crumpled under its front wheels like a child's toy. There was a smell of petrol, a woman's harsh scream, the squeal of braking tyres. Cordelia walked slowly up to the transporter. The driver was still in his seat, gazing rigidly ahead, his face a mask of dedicated concentration. People were shouting at him, stretching out their arms. He didn't move. Someone—a man in a heavy leather coat and goggles—said:

"It's shock. We'd better drag him clear."

Three figures moved between Cordelia and the driver. Shoulders heaved in unison. There was a grunt of effort. The driver was lifted out, rigid as a manikin, his knees bent, his clenched hands held out as if still grasping the immense wheel. The shoulders bent over him in secret conclave.

There were other figures standing round the crushed van. Cordelia joined the ring of anonymous faces. Cigarette ends glowed and faded like signals, casting a momentary glow on the shaking hands, the wide, horrified eyes. She asked:

"Is he dead?" The man in goggles replied laconically:

"What do you think?"

There was a girl's voice, tentative, breathless.

"Has anyone called the ambulance?"

"Yeah. Yeah. That chap in the Cortina's gone off to 'phone."

The group stood irresolute. The girl and the young man to whom she was clinging began to back away. Another car stopped. A tall figure was pushing his way through the crowd. Cordelia heard a high, authoritative voice.

"I'm a doctor. Has anyone called the ambulance?"

"Yes, sir."

The reply was deferential. They stood aside to let the expert through. He turned to Cordelia, perhaps because she was nearest.

"If you didn't witness the accident, young woman, you'd better get on your way. And stand back, the rest of you. There's nothing that you can do. And put out those cigarettes!"

Cordelia walked slowly back to the Mini, placing each foot carefully before the other like a convalescent trying her first painful steps. She drove carefully round the accident, bumping the Mini on the grass verge. There was the wail of approaching sirens. As she turned off the main road, her driving mirror glowed suddenly red and she heard a whoosh of sound followed by a low, concerted groan which was broken by a woman's high, single scream. There was a wall of flame across the road. The doctor's warning had been too late. The van was on fire. There was no hope now for Lunn; but then, there never had been.

Cordelia knew that she was driving erratically. Passing cars hooted at her and flashed their lights and one motorist slowed down and shouted angrily. She saw a gate and drew in off the road and switched off the engine. The silence was absolute. Her hands were moist and shaking. She wiped them on her handkerchief and laid them in her lap feeling that they were separate from the rest of her body. She was hardly aware of a car passing and then slowing to a halt. A face appeared at the window. The voice was slurred and nervous but horribly ingratiating. She could smell the drink on his breath.

"Anything wrong, Miss?"

"Nothing. I've just stopped for a rest."

"No point in resting alone—a pretty girl like you."

His hand was on the door handle. Cordelia felt in her shoulder bag and drew out the gun. She pushed it into his face.

"It's loaded. Go away at once or I'll shoot."

The menace in her voice struck cold even to her own ears. The pale, moist face disintegrated with surprise, the jaw fell. He backed away.

"Sorry, Miss, I'm sure. My mistake. No offence."

Cordelia waited until his car was out of sight. Then she turned on the engine. But she knew that she couldn't go on. She turned off the engine again. Waves of tiredness flowed over her, an irresistible tide, gentle as a blessing, which neither her exhausted mind nor body had the will to resist. Her head fell forward and Cordelia slept.

Chapter Six

❖❖❖

Cordelia slept soundly but briefly. She didn't know what woke her, whether the blinding light of a passing car sweeping across her closed eyes or her own subconscious knowledge that rest must be rationed to a brief half hour, the minimum necessary to enable her to do what had to be done before she could give herself over to sleep. She eased her body upright, feeling the stab of pain in her strained muscles and the half-pleasurable itch of dried blood on her back. The night air was heavy and odorous with the heat and scents of the day; even the road winding ahead looked tacky in the glare of her headlights. But Cordelia's chilled and aching body was still grateful for the warmth of Mark's jersey. For the first time since she had pulled it over her head she saw that it was dark green. How odd that she hadn't noticed its colour before!

She drove the rest of the journey like a novice, sitting bolt upright, eyes rigidly ahead, hands and feet tense on the controls. And here at last were the gates of Garforth House. They loomed in her headlights far taller and more ornamental than she remembered them, and they were closed. She ran from the Mini praying that they wouldn't be locked. But the iron latch, although heavy, rose to her desperate hands. The gates swung soundlessly back.

There were no other cars in the drive and she parked the Mini some little way from the house. The windows were dark and the only light, gentle and inviting, shone through the open front door. Cordelia took the pistol in her hand and, without ringing, stepped into the hall. She was more exhausted in body than when she had first come to Garforth House, but tonight she saw it with a new intensity, her nerves sensitive to every detail. The hall was empty, the air expectant. It seemed as if the house had waited for her. The same smell met her of roses and lavender, but tonight she saw that the lavender came from a huge Chinese bowl set on a side table. She recalled the insistent ticking of a clock, but now she noticed for the first time the delicate carving of the clock case, the intricate scrolls and whirls on the face. She stood in the middle of the hall, swaying slightly, the pistol held lightly in her drooping right

hand, and looked down. The carpet was a formal geometrical design in rich olive greens, pale blues and crimson, each pattern shaped like the shadow of a kneeling man. It seemed to draw her to her knees. Was it perhaps an eastern prayer mat?

She was aware of Miss Leaming coming quietly down the stairs towards her, her long red dressing-gown sweeping round her ankles. The pistol was taken suddenly but firmly from Cordelia's unresisting hand. She knew that it had gone because her hand felt suddenly lighter. It made no difference. She could never defend herself with it, never kill a man. She had learnt that about herself when Lunn had run from her in terror. Miss Leaming said:

"There is no one here you need defend yourself against, Miss Gray."

Cordelia said:

"I've come to report to Sir Ronald. Where is he?"

"Where he was the last time you came here, in his study."

As before, he was sitting at his desk. He had been dictating and the machine was at his right hand. When he saw Cordelia, he switched it off, then walked to the wall and pulled the plug from the socket. He walked back to the desk and they sat down opposite each other. He folded his hands in the pool of light from the desk lamp and looked up at Cordelia. She almost cried out with shock. His face reminded her of faces seen grotesquely reflected in grubby train windows at night—cavernous, the bones stripped of flesh, eyes set in fathomless sockets—faces resurrected from the dead.

When he spoke his voice was low, reminiscent.

"Half an hour ago I learned that Chris Lunn was dead. He was the best lab assistant I ever had. I took him out of an orphanage fifteen years ago. He never knew his parents. He was an ugly, difficult boy, already on probation. School had done nothing for him. But Lunn was one of the best natural scientists I've ever known. If he'd had the education, he'd have been as good as I am."

"Then why didn't you give him his chance, why didn't you educate him?"

"Because he was more useful to me as a lab assistant. I said that he could have been as good as I am. That isn't quite good enough. I can find plenty of scientists as good. I couldn't have found another lab assistant to equal Lunn. He had a marvellous hand with instruments."

He looked up at Cordelia, but without curiosity, apparently without interest.

"You've come to report, of course. It's very late, Miss Gray, and, as you see, I'm tired. Can't it wait until tomorrow?"

Cordelia thought that this was as close to an appeal as he could ever bring himself. She said:

"No, I'm tired too. But I want to finish the case tonight, now." He picked up an ebony paper-knife from the desk and, without looking at Cordelia, balanced it on his forefinger.

"Then tell me, why did my son kill himself? I take it that you do have news for me? You would hardly have burst in here at this hour without something to report."

"Your son didn't kill himself. He was murdered. He was murdered by someone he knew well, someone he didn't hesitate to let into the cottage, someone who came prepared. He was strangled or suffocated, then slung up on that hook by his own belt. Last of all, his murderer painted his lips, dressed him in a woman's underclothes and spread out pictures of nudes on the table in front of him. It was meant to look like accidental death during sexual experiment; such cases aren't so very uncommon."

There was half a minute of silence. Then he said with perfect calmness:

"And who was responsible, Miss Gray?"

"You were. You killed your son."

"For what reason?" He might have been an examiner, putting his inexorable questions.

"Because he discovered that your wife wasn't his mother, that the money left to her and to him by his grandfather had come by fraud. Because he had no intention of benefiting by it a moment longer, nor of accepting his legacy in four years' time. You were afraid that he might make this knowledge public. And what about the Wolvington Trust? If the truth came out, that would be the end of their promised grant. The future of your laboratory was at stake. You couldn't take the risk."

"And who undressed him again, typed out that suicide note, washed the lipstick from his face?"

"I think I know, but I shan't tell you. That's really what you employed me to discover, isn't it? That's what you couldn't bear not to know. But you killed Mark. You even prepared an alibi just in case it was needed. You got Lunn to ring you at college and announce himself as your son. He was the one person you could rely on absolutely. I don't suppose you told him the truth. He was only your lab assistant. He didn't require explanations, he did what you told him.

And even if he did guess the truth, he was safe, wasn't he? You prepared an alibi which you dared not use, because you didn't know
when Mark's body was first discovered. If someone had found him
and faked that suicide before you had claimed to have spoken to
him on the telephone, your alibi would have been broken, and a
broken alibi is damning. So you made a chance to talk to Benskin
and put matters right. You told him the truth; that it was Lunn who
had rung you. You could rely on Lunn to back up your story. But it
wouldn't really matter, would it, even if he did talk? No one would
believe him."

"No, any more than they will believe you. You've been determined
to earn your fee, Miss Gray. Your explanation is ingenious; there is
even a certain plausibility about some of the details. But you know,
and I know, that no police officer in the world would take it seriously.
It's unfortunate for you that you couldn't question Lunn. But Lunn,
as I said, is dead. He burnt to death in a road accident."

"I know, I saw. He tried to kill me tonight. Did you know that?
And earlier, he tried to scare me into dropping the case. Was that
because he had begun to suspect the truth?"

"If he did try to kill you, he exceeded his instructions. I merely
asked him to keep an eye on you. I had contracted for your sole and
whole-time services, if you remember; I wanted to be sure I was getting value. I am getting value of a kind. But you mustn't indulge
your imagination outside this room. Neither the police nor the courts
are sympathetic to slander nor to hysterical nonsense. And what proof
have you? None. My wife was cremated. There is nothing alive or
dead on this earth to prove that Mark was not her son."

Cordelia said:

"You visited Dr. Gladwin to satisfy yourself that he was too senile
to give evidence against you. You needn't have worried. He never
did suspect, did he? You chose him as your wife's doctor because he
was old and incompetent. But I did have one small piece of evidence.
Lunn was bringing it to you."

"Then you should have looked after it better. Nothing of Lunn
except his bones has survived that crash."

"There are still the female clothes, the black pants and the bra.
Someone might remember who bought them, particularly if that person was a man."

"Men do buy underclothes for their women. But if I were planning such a murder, I don't think buying the accessories would worry
me. Would any harassed shop girl at the cash desk of a popular mul-

tiple store remember a particular purchase, a purchase paid for with cash, one of a number of innocuous items, all presented together at the busiest time of the day? The man might even have worn a simple disguise. I doubt whether she would even notice his face. Would you really expect her to remember, weeks afterwards, to identify one of thousands of customers and identify him with sufficient certainty to satisfy a jury? And if she did, what would it prove unless you have the clothes in question? Be sure of one thing, Miss Gray, if I needed to kill I should do it efficiently. I should not be found out. If the police ever learn how my son was found, as they well may do since, apparently, someone other than yourself knows it, they will only believe with greater certainty that he killed himself. Mark's death was necessary and, unlike most deaths, it served a purpose. Human beings have an irresistible urge towards self-sacrifice. They die for any reason or none at all, for meaningless abstractions like patriotism, justice, peace; for other men's ideals, for other men's power, for a few feet of earth. You, no doubt, would give your life to save a child or if you were convinced that the sacrifice would find a cure for cancer."

"I might. I like to think that I would. But I should want the decision to be mine, not yours."

"Of course. That would provide you with the necessary emotional satisfaction. But it wouldn't alter the fact of your dying nor the result of your death. And don't say that what I'm doing here isn't worth one single human life. Spare me that hypocrisy. You don't know and you're incapable of understanding the value of what I'm doing here. What difference will Mark's death make to you? You'd never heard of him until you came to Garforth House."

Cordelia said:

"It will make a difference to Gary Webber."

"Am I expected to lose everything I've worked for here because Gary Webber wants someone to play squash or discuss history with?"

Suddenly he looked Cordelia full in the face. He said sharply: "What is the matter? Are you ill?"

"No I'm not ill. I knew that I must be right. I knew that what I had reasoned was true. But I can't believe it. I can't believe that a human being could be so evil."

"If you are capable of imagining it, then I'm capable of doing it. Haven't you yet discovered that about human beings, Miss Gray? It's the key to what you would call the wickedness of man."

Suddenly Cordelia could no longer bear this cynical antiphony. She cried out in passionate protest.

"But what is the use of making the world more beautiful if the people who live in it can't love one another?"

She had stung him at last into anger.

"Love! The most overused word in the language. Has it any meaning except the particular sentimental connotation which you choose to give it? What do you mean by love? That human beings must learn to live together with a decent concern for each other's welfare? The law enforces that. The greatest good of the greatest number. Beside that fundamental declaration of common sense all other philosophies are metaphysical abstractions. Or do you define love in the Christian sense, caritas? Read history, Miss Gray. See to what horrors, to what violence, hatred and repression the religion of love has led mankind. But perhaps you prefer a more feminine, more individual definition; love as a passionate commitment to another's personality. Intense personal commitment always ends in jealousy and enslavement. Love is more destructive than hate. If you must dedicate your life to something, dedicate it to an idea."

"I meant love, as a parent loves a child."

"The worse for them both, perhaps. But if he doesn't love, there is no power on earth which can stimulate or compel him to. And where there is no love, there can be none of the obligations of love."

"You could have let him live! The money wasn't important to him. He would have understood your needs and kept silent."

"Would he? How could he—or I—have explained his rejection of a great fortune in four years' time? People at the mercy of what they call their conscience are never safe. My son was a self-righteous prig. How could I put myself and my work in his hands?"

"You are in mine, Sir Ronald."

"You are mistaken. I am in no one's hands. Unfortunately for you that tape recorder is not working. We have no witnesses. You will repeat nothing that has been said in this room to anyone outside. If you do I shall have to ruin you. I shall make you unemployable, Miss Gray. And first of all I shall bankrupt that pathetic business of yours. From what Miss Leaming told me it shouldn't be difficult. Slander can be a highly expensive indulgence. Remember that if you are ever tempted to talk. Remember this too. You will harm yourself; you will harm Mark's memory; you will not harm me."

Cordelia never knew how long the tall figure in the red dressing-gown had been watching and listening in the shadow of the door. She never knew how much Miss Leaming had heard or at what moment she had stolen quietly away. But now she was aware of the red shadow moving soundlessly over the carpet, eyes on the figure behind the desk, the gun held closely against her breast. Cordelia watched in fascinated horror, not breathing. She knew exactly what was going to happen. It must have taken less than three seconds but they passed as slowly as minutes. Surely there had been time to cry out, time to warn, time to leap forward and wrench the gun from that steady hand? Surely there had been time for him to cry out? But he made no sound. He half rose, incredulous, and gazed at the muzzle in blind disbelief. Then he turned his head towards Cordelia as if in supplication. She would never forget that last look. It was beyond terror, beyond hope. It held nothing but the blank acceptance of defeat.

It was an execution, neat, unhurried, ritually precise. The bullet went in behind the right ear. The body leapt into the air, shoulders humped, softened before Cordelia's eyes as if the bones were melting into wax, and lay discarded at last over the desk. A thing; like Bernie; like her father.

Miss Leaming said:

"He killed my son."

"Your son?"

"Of course. Mark was my son. His son and mine. I thought you might have guessed."

She stood with the gun in her hand gazing with expressionless eyes through the open window to the lawn. There was no sound. Nothing moved. Miss Leaming said:

"He was right when he said that no one could touch him. There was no proof."

Cordelia cried out appalled:

"Then how could you kill him? How could you be so sure?"

Without releasing her hold on the pistol, Miss Leaming put her hand into the pocket of her dressing-gown. The hand moved over the desk top. A small gilt cylinder rolled over the polished wood towards Cordelia, then rocked into stillness. Miss Leaming said:

"The lipstick was mine. I found it a minute ago in the pocket of his dress suit. He hadn't worn that suit since he last dined in Hall on Feast night. He was always a magpie. He put small objects instinctively into his pocket."

Cordelia had never doubted Sir Ronald's guilt but now every nerve was desperate for reassurance.

"But it could have been planted there! Lunn could have put it there to incriminate him."

"Lunn didn't kill Mark. He was in bed with me at the time Mark died. He only left my side for five minutes and that was to make a telephone call shortly after eight o'clock."

"You were in love with Lunn!"

"Don't look at me like that! I only loved one man in my life and he's the one I've just killed. Talk about things you understand. Love had nothing to with what Lunn and I needed from each other."

There was a moment's silence. Then Cordelia said:

"Is there anyone in the house?"

"No. The servants are in London. No one is working late at the lab tonight."

And Lunn was dead. Miss Leaming said with weary resignation:

"Hadn't you better phone the police?"

"Do you want me to?"

"What does it matter?"

"Prison matters. Losing your freedom matters. And do you really want the truth to come out in open court? Do you want everyone to know how your son died and who killed him? Is that what Mark himself would want?"

"No. Mark never believed in punishment. Tell me what I have to do."

"We've got to work quickly and plan carefully. We have to trust each other and we have to be intelligent."

"We are intelligent. What must we do?"

Cordelia took out her handkerchief and dropping it over the gun, took the weapon from Miss Leaming and placed it on the desk. She grasped the woman's thin wrist and pushed her protesting hand against Sir Ronald's palm, pulling against the instinctive recoil, forcing the stiff but living fingers against the soft unresisting hand of the dead.

"There may be firing residue. I don't really know much about that, but the police may test for it. Now wash your hands and get me a pair of thin gloves. Quickly."

She went without a word. Left alone, Cordelia looked down at the dead scientist. He had fallen with his chin against the desk top and his arms swinging loosely at his sides, an awkward, uncomfortable-looking pose which gave him the appearance of peer-

ing malevolently over his desk. Cordelia could not look at his eyes, but she was conscious of feeling nothing, not hatred, or anger, or pity. Between her eyes and the sprawled figure swung an elongated shape, head hideously crooked, toes pathetically pointed. She walked over to the open window and looked out over the garden with the casual curiosity of a guest kept waiting in a strange room. The air was warm and very still. The scent of roses came in waves through the open window, alternately sickening sweet and then as elusive as a half-caught memory.

This curious hiatus of peace and timelessness must have lasted less than half a minute. Then Cordelia began to plan. She thought about the Clandon case. Memory pictured herself and Bernie, sitting astride a fallen log in Epping Forest and eating their picnic lunch. It brought back the yeasty smell of fresh rolls, butter and tangy cheese, the heavy fungoid smell of summer woods. He had rested the pistol on the bark between them and had mumbled at her through the bread and cheese. "How would you shoot yourself behind the right ear? Go on, Cordelia—show."

Cordelia had taken the pistol in her right hand, index finger lightly resting on the trigger, and with some difficulty had strained back her arm to place the muzzle of the gun against the base of the skull. "Like that?" "You wouldn't, you know. Not if you were used to a gun. That's the little mistake Mrs. Clandon made and it nearly hanged her. She shot her husband behind the right ear with his service revolver and then tried to fake a suicide. But she pressed the wrong finger on the trigger. If he'd really shot himself behind the right ear he'd have pressed the trigger with his thumb and held the revolver with his palm round the back of the butt. I remember that case well. It was the first murder I worked on with the Super— Inspector Dalgliesh, as he was then. Mrs. Clandon confessed in the end." "What happened to her, Bernie?" "Life. She'd probably have got away with manslaughter if she hadn't tried to fake a suicide. The jury didn't much like what they heard about Major Clandon's little habits."

But Miss Leaming couldn't get away with manslaughter; not unless she told the whole story of Mark's death.

She was back in the room now. She handed Cordelia a pair of thin cotton gloves. Cordelia said:

"I think you'd better wait outside. What you don't see you won't have the trouble of forgetting. What were you doing when you met me in the hall?"

"I was getting myself a nightcap, a whisky."

"Then you would have met me again coming out of the study as you took it up to your room. Get it now and leave the glass on the side table in the hall. That's the kind of detail the police are trained to notice."

Alone again, Cordelia took up the gun. It was astonishing how repulsive she found this inert weight of metal now. How odd that she should ever have seen it as a harmless toy! She rubbed it thoroughly with her handkerchief erasing Miss Leaming's prints. Then she handled it. It was her gun. They would expect to find some of her prints on the butt together with those of the dead man. She placed it again on the desk top and drew on the gloves. This was the more difficult part. She handled the pistol gingerly and took it over to the inert right hand. She pressed his thumb firmly against the trigger, then wound the cold, unresisting hand round the back of the butt. Then she released his fingers and let the gun fall. It struck the carpet with a dull thud. She peeled off the gloves and went out to Miss Leaming in the hall, closing the study door quietly behind her.

"Here, you'd better put these back where you found them. We mustn't leave them lying around for the police to find."

She was gone only a few seconds. When she returned, Cordelia said:

"Now we must act the rest just as it would have happened. You meet me as I come out of the room. I have been with Sir Ronald about two minutes. You put down your glass of whisky on the hall table and walk with me to the front door. You say—what would you say?"

"Has he paid you?"

"No, I'm to come in the morning for my money. I'm sorry it wasn't a success. I've told Sir Ronald that I don't want to go on with the case."

"That's your concern, Miss Gray. It was a foolish business in the first place."

They were walking out of the front door now. Suddenly Miss Leaming turned to Cordelia and said urgently and in her normal voice:

"There's one thing you had better know. It was I who found Mark first and faked the suicide. He'd rung me earlier in the day and asked me to call. I couldn't get away until after nine because of Lunn. I didn't want him to be suspicious."

"But didn't it occur to you when you found Mark that there might

be something odd about the death? The door was unlocked although the curtains were drawn. The lipstick was missing."

"I suspected nothing until tonight when I stood there in the shadows and heard you talking. We're all sexually sophisticated these days. I believed what I saw. It was all horror but I knew what I had to do. I worked quickly, terrified that someone would come. I cleaned his face with my handkerchief dampened with water from the kitchen sink. It seemed that the lipstick would never come off. I undressed him and pulled on his jeans which had been thrown over the back of a chair. I didn't wait to put on his shoes, that didn't seem important. Typing the note was the worst part. I knew that he would have his Blake with him somewhere in the cottage and that the passage I chose might be more convincing than an ordinary suicide note. The clattering of the typewriter keys sounded unnaturally loud in the quietness; I was terrified that someone would hear. He had been keeping a kind of journal. There wasn't time to read it but I burnt the typescript in the sitting-room grate. Last of all, I bundled up the clothes and the pictures and brought them back here to be burnt in the lab incinerator."

"You dropped one of the pictures in the garden. And you didn't quite succeed in cleaning the lipstick from his face."

"So that's how you guessed?"

Cordelia didn't reply immediately. Whatever happened she must keep Isabelle de Lasterie out of the case.

"I wasn't sure if it was you who had been there first but I thought it must have been. There were four things. You didn't want me to investigate Mark's death; you read English at Cambridge and could have known where to find that Blake quotation; you are an experienced typist and I didn't think that the note had been typed by an amateur despite the late attempt to make it look like Mark's work; when I was first at Garforth House and asked about the suicide note you spoke the whole of the Blake quotation; the typed version was ten words short. I first noticed that when I visited the police station and was shown the note. It pointed direct to you. That was the strongest evidence I had."

They had reached the car now and paused together. Cordelia said:

"We mustn't waste any more time before ringing the police. Someone may have heard the shot."

"It's not likely. We're some distance from the village. Do we hear it now?"

"Yes. We hear it now." There was a second's pause then Cordelia said:

"What was that? It sounded like a shot."

"It couldn't have been. It was probably a car back-firing."

Miss Leaming spoke like a bad actress, the words were stilted, unconvincing. But she spoke them; she would remember them.

"But there isn't a car passing. And it came from the house."

They glanced at each other, then ran back together through the open door into the hall. Miss Leaming paused for a moment and looked Cordelia in the face before she opened the study door. Cordelia came in behind her. Miss Leaming said:

"He's been shot! I'd better phone the police."

Cordelia said:

"You wouldn't say that! Don't ever think like that! You'd go up to the body first and then you'd say:

" 'He's shot himself. I'd better phone the police.' "

Miss Leaming looked unemotionally at her lover's body, then glanced round the room. Forgetting her role, she asked:

"What have you done in here? What about finger prints?"

"Never mind. I've looked after that. All you have to remember is that you didn't know I had a gun when I first came to Garforth House; you didn't know Sir Ronald took it from me. You haven't seen that gun until this moment. When I arrived tonight you showed me into the study and met me again when I came out two minutes later. We walked together to the car and spoke as we have just spoken. We heard the shot. We did what we have just done. Forget everything else that has happened. When they question you, don't embroider, don't invent, don't be afraid to say you can't remember. And now—ring the Cambridge police."

❖❖❖

Three minutes later they were standing together at the open door waiting for the police to arrive. Miss Leaming said:

"We mustn't talk together once they're here. And, afterwards, we mustn't meet or show any particular interest in each other. They'll know that this can't be murder unless we two are in it together. And why should we conspire together when we've only met once before, when we don't even like each other?"

She was right, thought Cordelia. They didn't even like each other.

She didn't really care if Elizabeth Leaming went to prison; she did care if Mark's mother went to prison. She cared, too, that the truth of his death should never be known. The strength of that determination struck her as irrational. It could make no difference to him now and he wasn't a boy who had cared over much what people thought of him. But Ronald Callender had desecrated his body after death; had planned to make him an object, at worst of contempt, at best of pity. She had set her face against Ronald Callender. She hadn't wanted him to die; wouldn't have been capable herself of pressing the trigger. But he was dead and she couldn't feel regret, nor could she be an instrument of retribution for his murderer. It was expedient, no more than that, that Miss Leaming shouldn't be punished. Gazing out into the summer night and waiting for the sound of the police cars, Cordelia accepted once and for all the enormity and the justification of what she had done and was still planning to do. She was never afterwards to feel the least tinge of regret or of remorse.

Miss Leaming said:

"There are things you probably want to ask me, things I suppose you've a right to know. We can meet in King's College Chapel after Evensong on the first Sunday after the inquest. I'll go through the screen into the chancel, you stay in the nave. It will seem natural enough for us to meet by chance there, that is if we are both still free."

Cordelia was interested to see that Miss Leaming was taking charge again. She said:

"We shall be. If we keep our heads this can't go wrong."

There was a moment's silence. Miss Leaming said:

"They're taking their time. Surely they should be here by now?"

"They won't be much longer."

Miss Leaming suddenly laughed and said with revealing bitterness:

"What is there to be frightened of? We shall be dealing only with men."

So they waited quietly together. They heard the approaching cars before the headlamps swept over the drive, illuminating every pebble, picking out the small plants at the edge of the beds, bathing the blue haze of the wisteria with light, dazzling the watchers' eyes. Then the lights were dimmed as the cars rocked gently to a stop in front of the house. Dark shapes emerged and came unhurriedly but resolutely forward. The hall was suddenly filled with large, calm men, some in plain clothes. Cordelia effaced herself against the wall and

it was Miss Leaming who stepped forward, spoke to them in a low voice and led them into the study.

Two uniformed men were left in the hall. They stood talking together, taking no notice of Cordelia. Their colleagues were taking their time. They must have used the telephone in the study because more cars and men began to arrive. First the police surgeon, identified by his bag even if he hadn't been greeted with:

"Good evening Doc. In here please."

How often he must have heard that phrase! He glanced with brief curiosity at Cordelia as he trotted through the hall, a fat, dishevelled little man, his face crumpled and petulant as a child when forcibly woken from sleep. Next came a civilian photographer carrying his camera, tripod and box of equipment; a fingerprint expert; two other civilians whom Cordelia, instructed in procedure by Bernie, guessed were scenes-of-crime officers. So they were treating this as a suspicious death. And why not? It was suspicious.

The head of the household lay dead, but the house itself seemed to have come alive. The police talked, not in whispers, but in confident normal voices unsubdued by death. They were professionals doing their job, working easily to the prescribed routine. They had been initiated into the mysteries of violent death; its victims held no awe for them. They had seen too many bodies: bodies scraped off motorways; loaded piecemeal into ambulances; dragged by hook and net from the depths of rivers; dug putrefying from the clogging earth. Like doctors, they were kind and condescendingly gentle to the uninstructed, keeping inviolate their awful knowledge. This body, while it breathed, had been more important than others. It wasn't important now, but it could still make trouble for them. They would be that much more meticulous, that much more tactful. But it was still only a case.

Cordelia sat alone and waited. She was suddenly overcome with tiredness. She longed for nothing but to put down her head on the hall table and sleep. She was hardly aware of Miss Leaming passing through the hall on her way to the drawing room, of the tall officer talking to her as they passed. Neither took any notice of the small figure in its immense woollen jersey, sitting against the wall. Cordelia willed herself to stay awake. She knew what she had to say; it was all clear enough in her mind. If only they would come to question her and let her sleep.

It wasn't until the photographer and the print man had finished their work that one of the senior officers came out to her. She was

never afterwards able to recall his face but she remembered his voice, a careful, unemphatic voice from which every tinge of emotion had been excluded. He held out the gun towards her. It was resting on his open palm, protected by a handkerchief from the contamination of his hand.

"Do you recognize this weapon, Miss Gray?"

Cordelia thought it odd that he should use the word weapon. Why not just say gun?

"I think so. I think it must be mine."

"You aren't sure?"

"It must be mine, unless Sir Ronald owned one of the same make. He took it from me when I first came here four days ago. He promised to let me have it back when I called tomorrow morning for my pay."

"So this is only the second time you've been in this house?"

"Yes."

"Have you ever met Sir Ronald Callender or Miss Leaming before?"

"No. Not until Sir Ronald sent for me to undertake this case."

He went away. Cordelia rested her head back against the wall and took short snatches of sleep. Another officer came. This time he had a uniformed man with him, taking notes. There were more questions. Cordelia told her prepared story. They wrote it down without comment and went away.

She must have dozed. She awoke to find a tall, uniformed officer standing over her. He said:

"Miss Leaming is making tea in the kitchen, Miss. Perhaps you would like to give her a hand. It's something to do, isn't it?"

Cordelia thought; they're going to take away the body. She said: "I don't know where the kitchen is."

She saw his eyes flicker.

"Oh, don't you, Miss? You're a stranger here, are you? Well, it's this way."

The kitchen was at the back of the house. It smelt of spice, oil and tomato sauce, bringing back memories of meals in Italy with her father. Miss Leaming was taking down cups from a vast dresser. An electric kettle was already hissing steam. The police officer stayed. So they weren't to be left alone. Cordelia said:

"Can I help?" Miss Leaming did not look at her.

"There are some biscuits in that tin. You can put them out on a tray. The milk is in the fridge."

Cordelia moved like an automaton. The milk bottle was an icy

column in her hands, the biscuit tin lid resisted her tired fingers and she broke a nail prising it off. She noticed the details of the kitchen—a wall calendar of St. Theresa of Avila, the saint's face unnaturally elongated and pale so that she looked like a hallowed Miss Leaming; a china donkey with two panniers of artificial flowers, its melancholy head crowned with a miniature straw hat; an immense blue bowl of brown eggs.

There were two trays. The police constable took the larger from Miss Leaming and led the way into the hall. Cordelia followed with the second tray, holding it high against her chest like a child, permitted as a privilege to help mother. Police officers gathered round. She took a cup herself and returned to her usual chair.

And now there was the sound of yet another car. A middle-aged woman came in with a uniformed chauffeur at her shoulder. Through the fog of her tiredness, Cordelia heard a high, didactic voice.

"My dear Eliza, this is appalling! You must come back to the Lodge tonight. No, I insist. Is the Chief Constable here?"

"No, Marjorie, but these officers have been very kind."

"Leave them the key. They'll lock up the house when they've finished. You can't possibly stay here alone tonight."

There were introductions, hurried consultations with the detectives in which the newcomer's voice was dominant. Miss Leaming went upstairs with her visitor and reappeared five minutes later with a small case, her coat over her arm. They went off together, escorted to the car by the chauffeur and one of the detectives. None of the little party glanced at Cordelia.

Five minutes later the Inspector came up to Cordelia, key in hand.

"We shall lock up the house tonight, Miss Gray. It's time you were getting home. Are you thinking of staying at the cottage?"

"Just for the next few days, if Major Markland will let me."

"You look very tired. One of my men will drive you in your own car. I should like a written statement from you tomorrow. Can you come to the station as soon as possible after breakfast? You know where it is?"

"Yes, I know."

One of the police panda cars drove off first and the Mini followed. The police driver drove fast, lurching the little car around the corners. Cordelia's head lolled against the back of the seat and, from time to time, was thrown against the driver's arm. He was wearing

shirt sleeves and she was vaguely conscious of the comfort of the warm flesh through the cotton. The car window was open and she was aware of hot night air rushing against her face, of the scudding clouds, of the first unbelievable colours of day staining the eastern sky. The route seemed strange to her and time itself disjointed; she wondered why the car had suddenly stopped and it took a minute for her to recognize the tall hedge bending over the lane like a menacing shadow, the ramshackle gate. She was home. The driver said:

"Is this the place, Miss?"

"Yes, this is it. But I usually leave the Mini further down the lane on the right. There's a copse there where you can drive it off the road."

"Right, Miss."

He got out of the car to consult the other driver. They moved on slowly for the last few yards of the journey. And now, at last, the police car had driven away and she was alone at the gate. It was an effort to push it open against the weight of the weeds and she lurched round the cottage to the back door like a drunken creature. It took some little time to fit the key into the lock, but that was the last problem. There was no longer a gun to hide; there was no longer need to check the tape sealing the windows. Lunn was dead and she was alive. Every night that she had slept at the cottage Cordelia had come home tired, but never before had she been as tired as this. She made her way upstairs as if sleepwalking and, too exhausted even to zip herself into her sleeping-bag, crept underneath it and knew nothing more.

And at last—it seemed to Cordelia after months, not days, of waiting —there was another inquest. It was as unhurried, as unostentatiously formal, as Bernie's had been, but there was a difference. Here, instead of a handful of pathetic casuals who had sneaked into the warmth of the back benches to hear Bernie's obsequies, were grave-faced colleagues and friends, muted voices, the whispered preliminaries of lawyers and police, an indefinable sense of occasion. Cordelia guessed that the grey-haired man escorting Miss Leaming must be her lawyer. She watched him at work, affable but not deferential to the senior police, quietly solicitous for his client, exuding a

confidence that they were all engaged in a necessary if tedious formality, a ritual as unworrying as Sunday Matins.

Miss Leaming looked very pale. She was wearing the grey suit she had worn when Cordelia first met her but with a small black hat, black gloves and a black chiffon scarf knotted at her throat. The two women did not look at each other. Cordelia found a seat at the end of a bench and sat there, unrepresented and alone. One or two of the younger policemen smiled at her with a reassuring but pitying kindness.

Miss Leaming gave her evidence first in a low, composed voice. She affirmed instead of taking the oath, a decision which caused a brief spasm of distress to pass over her lawyer's face. But she gave him no further cause for concern. She testified that Sir Ronald had been depressed at his son's death and, she thought, had blamed himself for not knowing that something was worrying Mark. He had told her that he intended to call in a private detective, and it had been she who had originally interviewed Miss Gray and had brought her back to Garforth House. Miss Leaming said that she had opposed the suggestion; she had seen no useful purpose in it, and thought that this futile and fruitless enquiry would only remind Sir Ronald of the tragedy. She had not known that Miss Gray possessed a gun nor that Sir Ronald had taken it from her. She had not been present during the whole of their preliminary interview. Sir Ronald had escorted Miss Gray to view his son's room while she, Miss Leaming, had gone in search of a photograph of Mr. Callender for which Miss Gray had asked.

The coroner asked her gently about the night of Sir Ronald's death.

Miss Leaming said that Miss Gray had arrived to give her first report shortly after half past ten. She herself had been passing through the front hall when the girl appeared. Miss Leaming had pointed out that it was late, but Miss Gray had said that she had wanted to abandon the case and get back to town. She had showed Miss Gray into the study where Sir Ronald was working. They had been together, she thought, for less than two minutes. Miss Gray had then come out of the study and she had walked with her to her car; they had only talked briefly. Miss Gray said that Sir Ronald had asked her to call back in the morning for her pay. She had made no mention of a gun.

Sir Ronald had, only half an hour before that, received a telephone call from the police to say that his laboratory assistant, Christopher

Lunn, had been killed in a road accident. She had not told Miss Gray the news about Lunn before her interview with Sir Ronald; it hadn't occurred to her to do so. The girl had gone almost immediately into the study to see Sir Ronald. Miss Leaming said that they were standing together at the car talking when they heard the shot. At first she had thought it was a car backfiring but then she had realized that it had come from the house. They had both rushed into the study and found Sir Ronald lying slumped over his desk. The gun had dropped from his hand to the floor.

No, Sir Ronald had never given her any idea that he contemplated suicide. She thought that he was very distressed about the death of Mr. Lunn but it was difficult to tell. Sir Ronald was not a man to show emotion. He had been working very hard recently and had not seemed himself since the death of his son. But Miss Leaming had never for a moment thought that Sir Ronald was a man who would put an end to his life.

She was followed by the police witnesses, deferential, professional, but managing to give an impression that none of this was new to them; they had seen it all before and would see it again.

They were followed by the doctors, including the pathologist, who testified in what the court obviously thought was unnecessary detail to the effect of firing a jacketed hollow-cavity bullet of ninety grains into the human brain. The coroner asked:

"You have heard the police evidence that there was the print of Sir Ronald Callender's thumb on the trigger of the gun and a palm mark smudged around the butt. What would you deduce from that?"

The pathologist looked slightly surprised at being asked to deduce anything but said that it was apparent that Sir Ronald had held the gun with his thumb on the trigger when pointing it against his head. The pathologist thought that it was probably the most comfortable way in which to hold the weapon, indeed the only comfortable way, having regard to the position of the wound of entry.

Lastly, Cordelia was called to the witness box and took the oath. She had given some thought to the propriety of this and had wondered whether to follow Miss Leaming's example. There were moments, usually on a sunny Easter morning, when she wished that she could with sincerity call herself a Christian; but for the rest of the year she knew herself to be what she was—incurably agnostic but prone to unpredictable relapses into faith. This seemed to her, however, a moment when religious scrupulosity was an indulgence

which she couldn't afford. The lies she was about to tell would not be the more heinous because they were tinged with blasphemy.

The coroner let her tell her story without interruption. She sensed that the court was puzzled by her but not unsympathetic. For once, the carefully modulated middle-class accent, which in her six years at the convent she had unconsciously acquired, and which in other people often irritated her as much as her own voice had irritated her father, was proving an advantage. She wore her suit and had bought a black chiffon scarf to cover her head. She remembered that she must call the coroner "sir".

After she had briefly confirmed Miss Leaming's story of how she had been called to the case, the coroner said:

"And now, Miss Gray, will you explain to the court what happened on the night Sir Ronald Callender died?"

"I had decided, sir, that I didn't want to go on with the case. I hadn't discovered anything useful and I didn't think there was anything to discover. I had been living in the cottage where Mark Callender had spent the last weeks of his life and I had come to think that what I was doing was wrong, that I was taking money for prying into his private life. I decided on impulse to tell Sir Ronald that I wanted to finish the case. I drove to Garforth House. I got there at about ten-thirty. I knew it was late but I was anxious to go back to London the next morning. I saw Miss Leaming as she was crossing the hall and she showed me straight into the study."

"Will you please describe to the court how you found Sir Ronald."

"He seemed to be tired and distracted. I tried to explain why I wanted to give up the case but I'm not sure that he heard me. He said I was to come back next morning for my money and I said that I only proposed to charge expenses, but that I would like to have my gun. He just waved a hand in dismissal and said, 'tomorrow morning, Miss Gray. Tomorrow morning.'"

"And then you left him?"

"Yes, sir. Miss Leaming accompanied me back to the car and I was just about to drive away when we heard the shot."

"You didn't see the gun in Sir Ronald's possession while you were in the study with him?"

"No, sir."

"He didn't talk to you about Mr. Lunn's death or give you any idea that he was contemplating suicide?"

"No, sir."

The coroner doodled on the pad before him. Without looking at Cordelia, he said:

"And now, Miss Gray, will you please explain to the court how Sir Ronald came to have your gun."

This was the difficult part, but Cordelia had rehearsed it. The Cambridge police had been very thorough. They had asked the same questions over and over again. She knew exactly how Sir Ronald had come to have the gun. She remembered a piece of Dalgliesh dogma, reported by Bernie, which had seemed to her at the time more appropriate advice for a criminal than a detective. "Never tell an unnecessary lie; the truth has great authority. The cleverest murderers have been caught, not because they told the one essential lie, but because they continued to lie about unimportant detail when the truth could have done them no harm."

She said:

"My partner, Mr. Pryde, owned the gun and was very proud of it. When he killed himself I knew that he meant me to have it. That was why he cut his wrists instead of shooting himself, which would have been quicker and easier."

The coroner looked up sharply.

"And were you there when he killed himself?"

"No, sir. But I found the body."

There was a murmur of sympathy from the court; she could feel their concern.

"Did you know that the gun wasn't licenced?"

"No, sir, but I think I suspected that it might not have been. I brought it with me on this case because I didn't want to leave it in the office and because I found it a comfort. I meant to check up on the licence as soon as I got back. I didn't expect ever to use the gun. I didn't really think of it as a lethal weapon. It's just that this was my first case and Bernie had left it to me and I felt happier having it with me."

"I see," said the coroner.

Cordelia thought that he probably did see and so did the court. They were having no difficulty in believing her because she was telling the somewhat improbable truth. Now that she was about to lie, they would go on believing her.

"And now will you please tell the court how Sir Ronald came to take the gun from you?"

"It was on my first visit to Garforth House when Sir Ronald was showing me his son's bedroom. He knew that I was the sole owner

160

of the Agency, and he asked me if it wasn't a difficult and rather frightening job for a woman. I said that I wasn't frightened but that I had Bernie's gun. When he found that I had it with me in my bag he made me hand it over to him. He said that he didn't propose to engage someone who might be a danger to other people or herself. He said that he wouldn't take the responsibility. He took the gun and the ammunition."

"And what did he do with the gun?"

Cordelia had thought this one out carefully. Obviously he hadn't carried it downstairs in his hand or Miss Leaming would have seen it. She would have liked to have said that he put it into a drawer in Mark's room but she couldn't remember whether the bedside table had had any drawers. She said:

"He took it out of the room with him; he didn't tell me where. He was only away for a moment and then we went downstairs together."

"And you didn't set eyes on the gun again until you saw it on the floor close to Sir Ronald's hand when you and Miss Leaming found his body?"

"No, sir."

Cordelia was the last witness. The verdict was quickly given, one that the court obviously felt would have been agreeable to Sir Ronald's scrupulously exact and scientific brain. It was that the deceased had taken his own life but that there was no evidence as to the state of his mind. The coroner delivered at length the obligatory warning about the danger of guns. Guns, the court were informed, could kill people. He managed to convey that unlicenced guns were particularly prone to this danger. He pronounced no strictures on Cordelia personally although it was apparent that this restraint cost him an effort. He rose and the court rose with him.

After the coroner had left the bench the court broke up into little whispering groups. Miss Leaming was quickly surrounded. Cordelia saw her shaking hands, receiving condolences, listening with grave assenting face to the first tentative proposals for a memorial service. Cordelia wondered how she could ever have feared that Miss Leaming would be suspected. She herself stood a little apart, delinquent. She knew that the police would charge her with illegal possession of the gun. They could do no less. True, she would be lightly punished, if punished at all. But for the rest of her life she would be the girl whose carelessness and naïveté had lost England one of her foremost scientists.

As Hugo had said, all Cambridge suicides were brilliant. But about this one there could be little doubt. Sir Ronald's death would probably raise him to the status of genius.

Almost unnoticed, she came alone out of the courtroom on to Market Hill. Hugo must have been waiting; now he fell into step with her.

"How did it go? I must say death seems to follow you around, doesn't it?"

"It went all right. I seem to follow death."

"I suppose he did shoot himself?"

"Yes. He shot himself."

"And with your gun?"

"As you will know if you were in court. I didn't see you."

"I wasn't there, I had a tutorial, but the news did get around. I shouldn't let it worry you. Ronald Callender wasn't as important as some people in Cambridge may choose to believe."

"You know nothing about him. He was a human being and he's dead. That fact is always important."

"It isn't, you know, Cordelia. Death is the least important thing about us. Comfort yourself with Joseph Hall. 'Death borders upon our birth and our cradle stands in the grave.' And he did choose his own weapon, his own time. He'd had enough of himself. Plenty of people had had enough of him."

They walked together down St. Edward's Passage towards King's Parade. Cordelia wasn't sure where they were making for. Her need at present was just to walk, but she didn't find her companion disagreeable.

She asked:

"Where's Isabelle?"

"Isabelle is home in Lyons. Papa turned up unexpectedly yesterday and found that mademoiselle wasn't exactly earning her wages. Papa decided that dear Isabelle was getting less—or it may have been more—out of her Cambridge education than he had expected. I don't think you need worry about her. Isabelle is safe enough now. Even if the police decide that it's worthwhile going to France to question her—and why on earth should they?—it won't help them. Papa will surround her with a barrage of lawyers. He's not in a mood to stand any nonsense from Englishmen at present."

"And what about you? If anyone asks you how Mark died, you'll never tell them the truth?"

"What do you think? Sophie, Davie and I are safe enough. I'm reliable when it comes to essentials."

For a moment Cordelia wished that he were reliable in less essential matters. She asked:

"Are you sorry about Isabelle leaving?"

"I am rather. Beauty is intellectually confusing; it sabotages common sense. I could never quite accept that Isabelle was what she is: a generous, indolent, over-affectionate and stupid young woman. I thought that any woman as beautiful as she must have an instinct about life, access to some secret wisdom which is beyond cleverness. Every time she opened that delicious mouth I was expecting her to illumine life. I think I could have spent all my life just looking at her and waiting for the oracle. And all she could talk about was clothes."

"Poor Hugo."

"Never poor Hugo. I'm not unhappy. The secret of contentment is never to allow yourself to want anything which reason tells you you haven't a chance of getting."

Cordelia thought that he was young, well-off, clever, even if not clever enough, handsome; there wasn't much that he would have to forgo on that or any other criteria.

She heard him speaking:

"Why not stay in Cambridge for a week or so and let me show you the city? Sophie would let you have her spare room."

"No thank you, Hugo. I have to get back to town."

There was nothing in town for her, but with Hugo there would be nothing in Cambridge for her either. There was only one reason for staying in this city. She would remain at the cottage until Sunday and her meeting with Miss Leaming. After that, as far as she was concerned, the case of Mark Callender would be finished for good.

❖❖❖

Sunday afternoon Evensong was over and the congregation, who had listened in respectful silence to the singing of responses, psalms and anthem by one of the finest choirs in the world, rose and joined with joyous abandon in the final hymn. Cordelia rose and sang with them. She had seated herself at the end of the row close to the richly carved screen. From here she could see into the chancel. The robes

of the choristers gleamed scarlet and white; the candles flickered in patterned rows and high circles of golden light; two tall and slender candles stood each side of the softly illuminated Reubens above the high altar, seen dimly as a distant smudge of crimson, blue and gold. The blessing was pronounced, the final amen impecabbly sung and the choir began to file decorously out of the chancel. The south door was opened and sunlight flooded into the chapel. The members of the college who had attended divine service strolled out after the Provost and Fellows in casual disarray, their regulation surplices dingy and limp over a cheerful incongruity of corduroy and tweed. The great organ snuffled and groaned like an animal gathering breath, before giving forth its magnificent voice in a Bach fugue. Cordelia sat quietly in her chair, listening and waiting. Now the congregation was moving down the main aisle—small groups in bright summer cottons whispering discreetly, serious young men in sober Sunday black, tourists clutching their illustrated guides and half-embarrassed by their obtrusive cameras, a group of nuns with calm and cheerful faces.

Miss Leaming was one of the last, a tall figure in a grey linen dress and white gloves, her head bare, a white cardigan slung carelessly around her shoulders against the chill of the chapel. She was obviously alone and unwatched and her careful pretence of surprise at recognizing Cordelia was probably an unnecessary precaution. They passed out of the chapel together.

The gravel path outside the doorway was thronged with people. A little party of Japanese, festooned with cameras and accessories, added their high staccato jabber to the muted Sunday afternoon chat. From here the silver stream of the Cam was invisible but the truncated bodies of punters glided against the far bank like puppets in a show, raising their arms above the pole and turning to thrust it backwards as if participating in some ritual dance. The great lawn lay unshadowed in the sun, a quintessence of greenness staining the scented air. A frail and elderly Don in gown and mortarboard was limping across the grass; the sleeves of his gown caught a stray breeze and billowed out so that he looked like a winged and monstrous crow struggling to rise. Miss Leaming said, as if Cordelia had asked for an explanation:

"He's a Fellow. The sacred turf is, therefore, uncontaminated by his feet."

They walked in silence by Gibbs Building. Cordelia wondered

when Miss Leaming would speak. When she did, her first question was unexpected.

"Do you think you'll make a success of it?"

Sensing Cordelia's surprise, she added impatiently:

"The Detective Agency. Do you think you'll be able to cope?"

"I shall have to try. It's the only job I know."

She had no intention of justifying to Miss Leaming her affection and loyalty to Bernie; she would have had some difficulty in explaining it to herself.

"Your overheads are too high."

It was a pronouncement made with all the authority of a verdict.

"Do you mean the office and the Mini?" asked Cordelia.

"Yes. In your job I don't see how one person in the field can bring in sufficient income to cover expenses. You can't be sitting in the office taking orders and typing letters and be out solving cases at the same time. On the other hand, I don't suppose you can afford help."

"Not yet. I've been thinking that I might rent a telephone answering service. That will take care of the orders although, of course, clients much prefer to come to the office and discuss their case. If I can only make enough in expenses just to live, then any fees can cover the overheads."

"If there are any fees."

There seemed nothing to say to this and they walked on in silence for a few seconds. Then Miss Leaming said:

"There'll be the expenses from this case anyway. That at least should help towards your fine for illegal possession of the gun. I've put the matter in the hands of my solicitors. You should be getting a cheque fairly soon."

"I don't want to take any money for this case."

"I can understand that. As you pointed out to Ronald, it falls under your fair deal clause. Strictly speaking you aren't entitled to any. All the same, I think it would look less suspicious if you took your expenses. Would thirty pounds strike you as reasonable?"

"Perfectly, thank you."

They had reached the corner of the lawn and had turned to walk towards King's Bridge. Miss Leaming said:

"I shall have to be grateful to you for the rest of my life. That for me is an unaccustomed humility and I'm not sure that I like it."

"Then don't feel it. I was thinking of Mark, not of you."

"I thought you might have acted in the service of justice or some such abstraction."

"I wasn't thinking about any abstraction. I was thinking about a person."

They had reached the bridge now and leaned over it side by side to look down into the bright water. The paths leading up to the bridge were, for a few minutes, empty of people. Miss Leaming said:

"Pregnancy isn't difficult to fake, you know. It only needs a loose corset and judicious stuffing. It's humiliating for the woman, of course, almost indecent if she happens to be barren. But it isn't difficult, particularly if she isn't closely watched. Evelyn wasn't. She had always been a shy, self-contained woman. People expected her to be excessively modest about her pregnancy. Garforth House wasn't filled with friends and relations swopping horror stories about the ante-natal clinic and patting her stomach. We had to get rid of that tedious fool Nanny Pilbeam, of course. Ronald regarded her departure as one of the subsidiary benefits of the pseudo pregnancy. He was tired of being spoken to as if he were still Ronnie Callender, the bright grammar school boy from Harrogate."

Cordelia said:

"Mrs. Goddard told me that Mark had a great look of his mother."

"She would. She was sentimental as well as stupid."

Cordelia did not speak. After a few moments silence Miss Leaming went on:

"I discovered that I was carrying Ronald's child at about the same time as a London specialist confirmed what the three of us already guessed, that Evelyn was most unlikely to conceive. I wanted to have the baby; Ronald desperately wanted a son; Evelyn's father was obsessional about his need for a grandson and was willing to part with half a million to prove it. It was all so easy. I resigned from my teaching job and went off to the safe anonymity of London and Evelyn told her father she was pregnant at last. Neither Ronald nor I had any conscience about defrauding George Bottley. He was an arrogant, brutal, self-satisfied fool who couldn't imagine how the world would continue without his issue to supervise it. He even subsidized his own deceit. The cheques for Evelyn began to arrive, each with a note imploring her to look after her health, to consult the best London doctors, to rest, to take a holiday in the sun. She had always loved Italy, and Italy became part of the plan. The three of us would meet in London every two months and fly together to Pisa. Ronald would rent a small villa outside Florence and, once there, I became Mrs. Callender and Evelyn became me. We had only daily servants and there was no need for them to look at our passports.

They got used to our visits and so did the local doctor who was called in to supervise my health. The locals thought it flattering that the English lady should be so fond of Italy that she came back month after month, so close to her confinement."

Cordelia asked:

"But how could she do it, how could she bear to be there with you in the house, watching you with her husband, knowing that you were going to have his child?"

"She did it because she loved Ronald and couldn't bear to lose him. She hadn't been much success as a woman. If she lost her husband, what else was there for her? She couldn't have gone back to her father. Besides, we had a bribe for her. She was to have the child. If she refused, then Ronald would leave her and seek a divorce to marry me."

"I would rather have left him and gone off to scrub doorsteps."

"Not everyone has a talent for scrubbing doorsteps and not everyone has your capacity for moral indignation. Evelyn was religious. She was, therefore, practised in self-deception. She convinced herself that what we were doing was best for the child."

"And her father? Didn't he ever suspect?"

"He despised her for her piety. He always had. Psychologically he could hardly indulge that dislike and at the same time think her capable of deceit. Besides, he desperately needed that grandchild. It wouldn't have entered his mind that the child might not be hers. And he had a doctor's report. After our third visit to Italy we told Doctor Sartori that Mrs. Callender's father was concerned about her care. At our request he wrote a reassuring medical report on the progress of the pregnancy. We went to Florence together a fortnight before the baby was due and stayed there until Mark arrived. Luckily he was a day or two before time. We'd had the foresight to put back the expected date of delivery so that it genuinely looked as if Evelyn had been caught unexpectedly by a premature birth. Dr. Sartori did what was necessary with perfect competence and the three of us came home with the baby and a birth certificate in the right name."

Cordelia said:

"And nine months later Mrs. Callender was dead."

"He didn't kill her, if that's what you're thinking. He wasn't really the monster that you imagine, at least, not then. But in a sense we did both destroy her. She should have had a specialist, certainly a better doctor than that incompetent fool Gladwin. But the three of

us were desperately afraid that an efficient doctor would know that she hadn't borne a child. She was as worried as we were. She insisted that no other doctor be consulted. She had grown to love the baby, you see. So she died and was cremated and we thought we were safe for ever."

"She left Mark a note before she died, nothing but a scribbled hieroglyphic in her prayer book. She left him her blood group."

"We knew that the blood groups were a danger. Ronald took blood from the three of us and made the necessary tests. But after she was dead even that worry ended."

There was a long silence. Cordelia could see a little group of tourists moving down the path towards the bridge. Miss Leaming said:

"The irony of it is that Ronald never really loved him. Mark's grandfather adored him; there was no difficulty there. He left half his fortune to Evelyn and it came automatically to her husband. Mark was to get the other half on his twenty-fifth birthday. But Ronald never cared for his son. He found that he couldn't love him, and I wasn't allowed to. I watched him grow up and go to school. But I wasn't allowed to love him. I used to knit him endless jerseys. It was almost an obsession. The patterns got more intricate and the wool thicker as he grew older. Poor Mark, he must have thought that I was mad, this strange, discontented woman whom his father couldn't do without but wouldn't marry."

"There are one or two of the jerseys at the cottage. What would you like me to do with his things?"

"Take them away and give them to anyone who needs them. Unless you think I ought to unpick the wool and knit it up into something new? Would that be a suitable gesture, do you think, symbolic of wasted effort, pathos, futility?"

"I'll find a use for them. And his books?"

"Get rid of them too. I can't go again to the cottage. Get rid of everything if you will."

The little group of tourists was very close now but they seemed engrossed in their own chatter. Miss Leaming took an envelope out of her pocket and handed it to Cordelia.

"I've written out a brief confession. There's nothing in it about Mark, nothing about how he died or what you discovered. It's just a brief statement that I shot Ronald Callender immediately after you had left Garforth House and coerced you into supporting my story. You'd better put it somewhere safe. One day you may need it."

Cordelia saw that the envelope was addressed to herself. She didn't open it. She said:

"It's too late now. If you regret what we did, you should have spoken earlier. The case is closed now."

"I've no regrets. I'm glad that we acted as we did. But the case may not be over yet."

"But it is over! The inquest has given its verdict."

"Ronald had a number of very powerful friends. They have influence and, periodically, they like to exercise it if only to prove that they still have it."

"But they can't get this case reopened! It practically takes an act of parliament to change a coroner's verdict."

"I don't say that they'll try to do that. But they may ask questions. They may have what they describe as a quiet word in the right ear. And the right ears are usually available. That's how they work. That's the sort of people they are."

Cordelia said suddenly:

"Have you a light?"

Without question or protest Miss Leaming opened her handbag and handed over an elegant silver tube. Cordelia didn't smoke and was unused to lighters. It took three clicks before the wick burst into flame. Then she leaned over the parapet of the bridge and set fire to the corner of the envelope.

The incandescent flame was invisible in the stronger light of the sun. All Cordelia could see was a narrow band of wavering purple light as the flame bit into the paper and the charred edges widened and grew. The pungent smell of burning was wafted away on the breeze. As soon as the flame tinged her fingers, Cordelia dropped the envelope, still burning, and watched it twist and turn as it floated down small and frail as a snowflake to be lost at last in the Cam. She said:

"Your lover shot himself. That is all that either of us need to remember now or ever."

❖❖❖

They didn't speak again about Ronald Callender's death, but walked silently along the elm-lined path towards the Backs. At one point Miss Leaming glanced at Cordelia and said in a tone of angry petulance:

"You look surprisingly well!"

Cordelia supposed that this brief outburst was the resentment of the middle-aged at the resilience of the young which could so quickly recover from physical disaster. It had only taken one night of long and deep sleep to return her to the state which Bernie, with irritating coyness, used to describe as bright eyed and bushy tailed. Even without the benison of a hot bath the broken skin on her shoulders and back had healed cleanly. Physically, the events of the last fortnight had left her unscathed. She wasn't so sure about Miss Leaming. The sleek platinum hair was still swathed and shaped immaculately to the bones of the head; she still carried her clothes with cool distinction as if it were important to appear the competent and unharassed helpmate of a famous man. But the pale skin was now tinged with grey; her eyes were deeply shadowed, and the incipient lines at the side of the mouth and across the forehead had deepened so that the face, for the first time, looked old and strained.

They passed through King's Gate and turned to the right. Cordelia had found a place and had parked the Mini within a few yards of the gate; Miss Leaming's Rover was further down Queen's Road. She shook hands firmly but briefly with Cordelia and said goodbye as unemotionally as if they were Cambridge acquaintances, parting with unusual formality after an unexpected meeting at Evensong. She didn't smile. Cordelia watched the tall, angular figure striding down the path under the trees towards John's Gate. She didn't look back. Cordelia wondered when, if ever, they would see each other again. It was difficult to believe that they had met only on four occasions. They had nothing in common except their sex, although Cordelia had realized during the days following Ronald Callender's murder the strength of that female allegiance. As Miss Leaming herself had said, they didn't even like each other. Yet each held the other's safety in her hands. There were moments when their secret almost horrified Cordelia by its immensity. But these were few and would get fewer. Time would inevitably diminish its importance. Life would go on. Neither of them would ever forget completely while the brain cells still lived, but she could believe that a day might come when they would glimpse each other across a theatre or restaurant or be borne unprotestingly past on an underground escalator and would wonder whether what they both recalled in the shock of recognition had really once happened. Already, only four days after the inquest, Ronald Callender's murder was beginning to take its place in the landscape of the past.

There was no longer anything to keep her at the cottage. She spent an hour obsessionally cleaning and tidying rooms which no one would enter, probably for weeks. She watered the mug of cowslips on the sitting-room table. In another three days they would be dead and no one would notice, but she couldn't bear to throw out the still living flowers. She went out to the shed and contemplated the bottle of sour milk and the beef stew. Her first impulse was to take both and empty them down the lavatory. But they were part of the evidence. She wouldn't need that evidence again, but ought it to be completely destroyed? She recalled Bernie's reiterated admonition: "Never destroy the evidence." The Super had been full of cautionary tales to emphasize the importance of that maxim. In the end she decided to photograph the exhibits, setting them up on the kitchen table and paying great attention to exposure and light. It seemed a fruitless, somewhat ridiculous, exercise and she was glad when the job was done and the unsavoury contents of bottle and pan could be disposed of. Afterwards she carefully washed them both and left them in the kitchen.

Last of all she packed her bag and stowed her gear in the Mini together with Mark's jerseys and books. Folding the thick wool, she thought of Dr. Gladwin sitting in his back garden, his shrunken veins indifferent to the sun. He would find the jerseys useful, but she couldn't take them to him. That kind of gesture might have been accepted from Mark, but not from her.

She locked the door and left the key under a stone. She couldn't face Miss Markland again and had no wish to hand it back to any other member of the family. She would wait until she got to London, then send a brief note to Miss Markland thanking her for her kindness and explaining where the key could be found. She walked for the last time round the garden. She wasn't sure what impulse led her to the well but she came up to it with a shock of surprise. The soil around the rim had been cleared and dug and had been planted with a circle of pansies, daisies and small clumps of alyssum and lobelia, each plant looking well established in its hollow ring of watered earth. It was a bright oasis of colour among the encroaching weeds. The effect was pretty but ridiculous and disquietingly odd. Thus strangely celebrated, the well itself looked obscene, a wooden breast topped by a monstrous nipple. How could she have seen the well cover as a harmless and slightly elegant folly?

Cordelia was torn between pity and revulsion. This must be the work of Miss Markland. The well, which for years had been to her

an object of horror, remorse and reluctant fascination, was now to be tended as a shrine. It was ludicrous and pitiable and Cordelia wished that she hadn't seen it. She was suddenly terrified of meeting Miss Markland, of seeing the incipient madness in her eyes. She almost ran out of the garden, pulled the gate shut against the weight of the weeds and drove finally away from the cottage without a backward glance. The case of Mark Callender was finished.

Chapter Seven

❖❖❖

Next morning she went to the Kingly Street office promptly at nine o'clock. The unnaturally hot weather had broken at last and, when she opened the window, a keen breeze shifted the layers of dust on desk and filing cabinet. There was only one letter. This was in a long stiff envelope and was headed with the name and address of Ronald Callender's solicitors. It was very brief.

"Dear Madam, I enclose a cheque for £30.00 being expenses due to you in respect of the investigation which you carried out at the request of the late Sir Ronald Callender into the death of his son Mark Callender. If you agree this sum, I would be grateful if you would sign and return the attached receipt."

Well, as Miss Leaming had said, it would at least pay part of her fine. She had sufficient money to keep the Agency going for another month. If there were no further case by that time, there was always Miss Feakins and another temporary job. Cordelia thought of the Feakins Secretarial Agency without enthusiasm. Miss Feakins operated, and that was the appropriate word, from a small office as squalid as Cordelia's own, but which had had a desperate gaiety imposed upon it in the form of multi-coloured walls, paper flowers in a variety of urn-like containers, china ornaments and a poster. The poster had always fascinated Cordelia. A curvaceous blonde, clad in brief hot pants and laughing hysterically, was leapfrogging over her typewriter, a feat she managed to perform with a maximum of exposure while clutching a fistful of five pound notes in each hand. The caption read:

"Be a Girl Friday and join the fun people. All the best Crusoes are on our books."

Beneath this poster Miss Feakins, emaciated, indefatigably cheerful and tinseled like a Christmas tree, interviewed a dispirited trail of the old, the ugly and the virtually unemployable. Her milch cows seldom escaped into permanent employment. Miss Feakins would warn against the unspecified dangers of accepting a permanent job much as Victorian mothers warned against sex. But Cordelia liked

her. Miss Feakins would welcome her back, her defection to Bernie forgiven, and there would be another of those furtive telephone conversations with the fortunate Crusoe made with one bright eye on Cordelia, a brothel madam recommending her latest recruit to one of her fussier customers. "Most superior girl—well educated—you'll like her—and a worker!" The emphasis of amazed wonder on the last word was justified. Few of Miss Feakins' temporaries, beguiled by advertisements, seriously expected to have to work. There were other and more efficient agencies but only one Miss Feakins. Bound by pity and an eccentric loyalty, Cordelia had little hope of escaping that glittering eye. A series of temporary jobs with Miss Feakins' Crusoes might, indeed, be all that was left to her. Didn't a conviction for illegal possession of a weapon under Section I of the Firearms Act 1968 count as a criminal record, barring one for life from socially responsible and safe jobs in the civil service and local government?

She settled down at the typewriter, with the yellow telephone directory to hand, to finish sending out the circular letter to the last twenty solicitors on the list. The letter itself embarrassed and depressed her. It had been concocted by Bernie after a dozen preliminary drafts and, at the time, it hadn't seemed too unreasonable. But his death and the Callender case had altered everything. The pompous phrases about a comprehensive professional service, immediate attendance in any part of the country, discreet and experienced operators and moderate fees, struck her as ridiculously, even dangerously, pretentious. Wasn't there something about false representation in the Trades Description Act? But the promise of moderate fees and absolute discretion was valid enough. It was a pity, she thought drily, that she couldn't get a reference from Miss Leaming. Alibis arranged; inquests attended; murders efficiently concealed; perjury at our own special rates.

The raucous burr of the telephone startled her. The office was so quiet and still that she had taken it for granted that no one would call. She stared at the instrument for several seconds, wide-eyed and suddenly afraid, before stretching out her hand.

The voice was calm and assured, polite but in no way deferential. It uttered no threat, yet to Cordelia, every word was explicit with menace.

"Miss Cordelia Gray? This is New Scotland Yard. We wondered whether you would be back at your office yet. Could you please make

it convenient to call here sometime later today? Chief Superintendent Dalgliesh would like to see you."

❖❖❖

It was ten days later that Cordelia was called for the third time to New Scotland Yard. The bastion of concrete and glass off Victoria Street was, by now, fairly familiar to her although she still entered it with a sense of temporarily discarding part of her identity, like leaving shoes outside a mosque.

Superintendent Dalgliesh had imposed little of his own personality on his room. The books in the regulation bookcase were obviously textbooks on law, copies of regulations and Acts of Parliament, dictionaries and books of reference. The only picture was a large water colour of the old Norman Shaw building on the Embankment painted from the river, an agreeable study in greys and soft ochres lit by the bright golden wings of the R.A.F. Memorial. On this visit, as on previous occasions, there was a bowl of roses on his desk, garden roses with sturdy stems and thorns curved like strong beaks, not the etiolated scentless blooms of a West End florist.

Bernie had never described him; had only fathered on him his own obsessive, unheroic, rough-hewn philosophy. Cordelia, bored by his very name, had asked no questions. But the Superintendent she had pictured was very different from the tall, austere figure who had risen to shake her hand when she first came into this room and the dichotomy between her private imaginings and the reality had been disconcerting. Irrationally, she had felt a twinge of irritation against Bernie for so putting her at a disadvantage. He was old of course, over forty at least, but not as old as she had expected. He was dark, very tall and loose-limbed where she had expected him to be fair, thick set and stocky. He was serious and spoke to her as if she were a responsible adult, not avuncular and condescending. His face was sensitive without being weak and she liked his hands and his voice and the way she could see the structure of his bones under the skin. He sounded gentle and kind, which was cunning since she knew that he was dangerous and cruel, and she had to keep reminding herself of how he had treated Bernie. At some moments during the interrogation she had actually wondered whether he could be Adam Dalgliesh the poet.

They had never been alone together. On each of her visits a police-

woman, introduced as Sergeant Mannering, had been present, seated at the side of the desk with her notebook. Cordelia felt that she knew Sergeant Mannering well having met her at school in the person of the head girl, Teresa Campion-Hook. The two girls could have been sisters. No acne had ever marked their shiningly clean skins; their fair hair curled at precisely the regulation length above their uniformed collars; their voices were calm, authoritarian, determinedly cheerful but never strident; they exuded an ineffable confidence in the justice and logic of the universe and the rightness of their own place in it. Sergeant Mannering had smiled briefly at Cordelia as she came in. The look was open, not overtly friendly since too generous a smile might prejudice the case, but not censorious either. It was a look which disposed Cordelia to imprudence; she disliked looking a fool before that competent gaze.

She had at least had time before her first visit to decide on tactics. There was little advantage and much danger in concealing facts which an intelligent man could easily discover for himself. She would disclose, if asked, that she had discussed Mark Callender with the Tillings and his tutor; that she had traced and interviewed Mrs. Goddard; that she had visited Dr. Gladwin. She decided to say nothing about the attempt on her life or about her visit to Somerset House. She knew which facts it would be vital to conceal: Ronald Callender's murder; the clue in the prayer book; the actual way in which Mark had died. She told herself firmly that she mustn't be drawn into discussing the case, mustn't talk about herself, her life, her present job, her ambitions. She remembered what Bernie had told her. "In this country, if people won't talk, there's nothing you can do to make them, more's the pity. Luckily for the police most people just can't keep their mouths shut. The intelligent ones are the worst. They just have to show how clever they are, and once you've got them discussing the case, even discussing it generally, then you've got them." Cordelia reminded herself of the advice she had given to Elizabeth Leaming: "Don't embroider, don't invent, don't be afraid to say you can't remember."

Dalgliesh was speaking:

"Have you thought of consulting a solicitor, Miss Gray?"

"I haven't got a solicitor."

"The Law Society can give you the names of some very reliable and helpful ones. I should think about it seriously if I were you."

"But I should have to pay him, shouldn't I? Why should I need a solicitor when I'm telling the truth?"

"It's when people start telling the truth that they most often feel the need of a solicitor."

"But I've always told the truth. Why should I lie?" The rhetorical question was a mistake. He answered it seriously as if she had really wanted to know.

"Well, it could be to protect yourself—which I don't think likely—or to protect someone else. The motive for that could be love, fear, or a sense of justice. I don't think you've known any of the people in this case long enough to care for them deeply so that rules out love, and I don't think you would be very easy to frighten. So we're left with justice. A very dangerous concept, Miss Gray."

She had been closely questioned before. The Cambridge police had been very thorough. But this was the first time she had been questioned by someone who knew; knew that she was lying; knew that Mark Callender hadn't killed himself; knew, she felt desperately, all there was to know. She had to force herself to an acceptance of reality. He couldn't possibly be sure. He hadn't any legal proof and he never would have. There was no one alive to tell him the truth except Elizabeth Leaming and herself. And she wasn't going to tell. Dalgliesh could beat against her will with his implacable logic, his curious kindness, his courtesy, his patience. But she wouldn't talk, and in England there was no way in which he could make her.

When she didn't reply, he said cheerfully:

"Well, let's see how far we've got. As a result of your enquiries you suspected that Mark Callender might have been murdered. You haven't admitted that to me but you made your suspicions plain when you visited Sergeant Maskell of the Cambridge police. You subsequently traced his mother's old nurse and learned from her something of his early life, of the Callender marriage, of Mrs. Callender's death. Following that visit you went to see Dr. Gladwin, the general practitioner who had looked after Mrs. Callender before she died. By a simple ruse you ascertained the blood group of Ronald Callender. There would only be point in that if you suspected that Mark wasn't the child of his parents' marriage. You then did what I would have done in your place, visited Somerset House to examine Mr. George Bottley's will. That was sensible. If you suspect murder, always consider who stands to gain by it."

So he had found out about Somerset House and the call to Dr. Venables. Well, it was to be expected. He had credited her with his own brand of intelligence. She had behaved as he would have behaved.

She still didn't speak. He said:

"You didn't tell me about your fall down the well. Miss Markland did."

"That was an accident. I don't remember anything about it, but I must have decided to explore the well and overbalanced. I was always rather intrigued by it."

"I don't think it was an accident, Miss Gray. You couldn't have pulled the lid free without a rope. Miss Markland tripped over a rope, but it was coiled neatly and half-hidden in the undergrowth. Would you have even troubled to detach it from the hook if you'd only been exploring?"

"I don't know. I can't remember anything that happened before I fell. My first memory is hitting the water. And I don't see what this has to do with Sir Ronald Callender's death."

"It might have a great deal to do with it. If someone tried to kill you, and I think that they did, that person could have come from Garforth House."

"Why?"

"Because the attempt on your life was probably connected with your investigation into Mark Callender's death. You had become a danger to someone. Killing is a serious business. The professionals don't like it unless it's absolutely essential and even the amateurs are less happy-go-lucky about murder than you might expect. You must have become a very dangerous woman to someone. Someone replaced that well lid, Miss Gray; you didn't fall through solid wood."

Cordelia still said nothing. There was a silence, then he spoke again:

"Miss Markland told me that after your rescue from the well she was reluctant to leave you alone. But you insisted that she should go. You told her that you weren't afraid to be alone in the cottage because you had a gun."

Cordelia was surprised how much this small betrayal hurt. Yet, how could she blame Miss Markland? The Superintendent would have known just how to handle her, probably persuaded her that frankness was in Cordelia's own interest. Well, she could at least betray in her turn. And this explanation, at least, would have the authority of truth.

"I wanted to get rid of her. She told me some dreadful story about her illegitimate child falling down the well to his death. I'd only just been rescued myself. I didn't want to hear it, I couldn't bear it just then. I told her a lie about the gun just to make her go. I didn't ask

her to confide in me, it wasn't fair. It was only a way of asking for help and I hadn't any to give."

"And didn't you want to get rid of her for another reason? Didn't you know that your assailant would have to return that night; that the well cover would have to be dragged clear again if your death were to look like an accident?"

"If I'd really thought that I was in any danger I should have begged her to take me with her to Summertrees House. I wouldn't have waited alone in the cottage without my gun."

"No, Miss Gray, I believe that. You wouldn't have waited there alone in the cottage that night without your gun."

For the first time Cordelia was desperately afraid. This wasn't a game. It never had been, although at Cambridge the police interrogation had held some of the unreality of a formal contest in which the result was both foreseeable and unworrying since one of the opponents didn't even know he was playing. It was real enough now. If she were tricked, persuaded, coerced into telling him the truth, she would go to prison. She was an accessory after the fact. How many years did one get for helping to conceal murder? She had read somewhere that Holloway smelt. They would take away her clothes. She would be shut up in a claustrophobic cell. There was remission for good conduct but how could one be good in prison? Perhaps they would send her to an open prison. Open. It was a contradiction in terms. And how would she live afterwards? How would she get a job? What real personal freedom could there ever be for those whom society labelled delinquent?

She was terrified for Miss Leaming. Where was she now? She had never dared ask Dalgliesh, and Miss Leaming's name had hardly been mentioned. Was she even now in some other room of New Scotland Yard being similarly questioned? How reliable would she be under pressure? Were they planning to confront the two conspirators with each other? Would the door suddenly open and Miss Leaming be brought in, apologetic, remorseful, truculent? Wasn't that the usual ploy, to interview conspirators separately until the weaker broke down? And who would prove the weaker?

She heard the Superintendent's voice. She thought he sounded rather sorry for her.

"We have some confirmation that the pistol was in your possession that night. A motorist tells us that he saw a parked car on the road about three miles from Garforth House and when he stopped to en-

quire if he could help he was threatened by a young woman with a gun."

Cordelia remembered that moment, the sweetness and silence of the summer night suddenly overlaid by his hot, alcoholic breath.

"He must have been drinking. I suppose the police stopped him for a breath test later that night and now he's decided to come up with this story. I don't know what he expects to gain by it but it isn't true. I wasn't carrying a gun. Sir Ronald took the pistol from me on my first night at Garforth House."

"The Metropolitan Police stopped him just over the force border. I think he may persist in his story. He was very definite. Of course, he hadn't identified you yet but he was able to describe the car. His story is that he thought you were having trouble with it and stopped to help. You misunderstood his motives and threatened him with a gun."

"I understood his motives perfectly. But I didn't threaten him with a gun."

"What did you say, Miss Gray?"

"Leave me alone or I'll kill you."

"Without the gun, surely that was an empty threat?"

"It would always have been an empty threat. But it made him go."

"What exactly did happen?"

"I had a spanner in the front pocket of the car and when he shoved his face in at the window I grasped that and threatened him with it. But no one in his right senses could have mistaken a spanner for a gun!"

But he hadn't been in his right senses. The only person who had seen the gun in her possession that night was a motorist who hadn't been sober. This, she knew, was a small victory. She had resisted the momentary temptation to change her story. Bernie had been right. She recalled his advice; the Superintendent's advice; this time she could almost hear it spoken in his deep, slightly husky voice: "If you're tempted to crime, stick to your original statement. There's nothing that impresses the jury more than consistency. I've seen the most unlikely defence succeed simply because the accused stuck to his story. After all, it's only someone else's word against yours; with a competent counsel that's half-way to a reasonable doubt."

The Superintendent was speaking again. Cordelia wished that she could concentrate more clearly on what he was saying. She hadn't been sleeping very soundly for the past ten days—perhaps that had something to do with this perpetual tiredness.

"I think that Chris Lunn paid you a visit on the night he died. There's no other reason that I could discover why he should have been on that road. One of the witnesses to the accident said that he came out in the little van from that side road as if all the devils in hell were following him. Someone was following him—you, Miss Gray."

"We've had this conversation before. I was on my way to see Sir Ronald."

"At that hour? And in such a hurry?"

"I wanted to see him urgently to tell him that I'd decided to drop the case. I couldn't wait."

"But you did wait, didn't you? You went to sleep in the car on the side of the road. That's why it was nearly an hour after you'd been seen at the accident before you arrived at Garforth House."

"I had to stop. I was tired and I knew it wasn't safe to drive on."

"But you knew too, that it was safe to sleep. You knew that the person you had most to fear from was dead."

Cordelia didn't reply. A silence fell on the room but it seemed to her a companionable not an accusing silence. She wished that she wasn't so tired. Most of all, she wished that she had someone to talk to about Ronald Callender's murder. Bernie wouldn't have been any help here. To him the moral dilemma at the heart of the crime would have held no interest, no validity, would have seemed a wilful confusion of straightforward facts. She could imagine his coarse and facile comment on Eliza Leaming's relations with Lunn. But the Superintendent might have understood. She could imagine herself talking to him. She recalled Ronald Callender's words that love was as destructive as hate. Would Dalgliesh assent to that bleak philosophy? She wished that she could ask him. This, she recognized, was her real danger—not the temptation to confess but the longing to confide. Did he know how she felt? Was this too, part of his technique?

There was a knock at the door. A uniformed constable came in and handed a note to Dalgliesh. The room was very quiet while he read it. Cordelia made herself look at his face. It was grave and expressionless and he continued looking at the paper long after he must have assimilated its brief message.

She thought that he was making up his mind to something. After a minute he said:

"This concerns someone you know, Miss Gray. Elizabeth Leaming is dead. She was killed two days ago when the car she was driving

went off the coast road south of Amalfi. This note is confirmation of identity."

Cordelia was swept with relief so immense that she felt physically sick. She clenched her fist and felt the sweat start on her brow. She began to shiver with cold. It never occurred to her that he might be lying. She knew him to be ruthless and clever but she had always taken it for granted that he wouldn't lie to her. She said in a whisper:

"May I go home now?"

"Yes. I don't think there's much point in your staying, do you?"

"She didn't kill Sir Ronald. He took the gun from me. He took the gun——"

Something seemed to have happened to her throat. The words wouldn't come out.

"That's what you've been telling me. I don't think you need trouble to say it again."

"When do I have to come back?"

"I don't think you need come back unless you decide that there's something you want to tell me. In that well-known phrase, you were asked to help the police. You have helped the police. Thank you."

She had won. She was free. She was safe, and with Miss Leaming dead, that safety depended only on herself. She needn't come back again to this horrible place. The relief, so unexpected and so unbelievable, was too great to be borne. Cordelia burst into dramatic and uncontrollable crying. She was aware of Sergeant Mannering's low exclamation of concern and of a folded white handkerchief handed to her by the Superintendent. She buried her face in the clean, laundry-smelling linen and blurted out her pent-up misery and anger. Strangely enough—and the oddness of it struck her even in the middle of her anguish—her misery was centred on Bernie. Lifting a face disfigured with tears and no longer caring what he thought of her, she blurted out a final, irrational protest:

"And after you'd sacked him, you never enquired how he got on. You didn't even come to the funeral!"

He had brought a chair over and had seated himself beside her. He handed her a glass of water. The glass was very cold but comforting and she was surprised to find how thirsty she was. She sipped the cold water and sat there hiccuping gently. The hiccups made her want to laugh hysterically but she controlled herself. After a few minutes he said gently:

"I'm sorry about your friend. I didn't realize that your partner was

the Bernie Pryde who once worked with me. It's rather worse than that, actually. I'd forgotten all about him. If it's any consolation to you, this case might have ended rather differently if I hadn't."

"You sacked him. All he ever wanted was to be a detective and you wouldn't give him a chance."

"The Metropolitan Police hiring and firing regulations aren't quite as simple as that. But it's true that he might still have been a policeman if it hadn't been for me. But he wouldn't have been a detective."

"He wasn't that bad."

"Well, he was, you know. But I'm beginning to wonder if I didn't underrate him."

Cordelia turned to hand him back the glass and met his eyes. They smiled at each other. She wished that Bernie could have heard him.

❖❖❖

Half an hour later Dalgliesh was seated opposite the Assistant Commissioner in the latter's office. The two men disliked each other but only one of them knew this and he was the one to whom it didn't matter. Dalgliesh made his report, concisely, logically, without referring to his notes. This was his invariable habit. The A.C. had always thought it unorthodox and conceited and he did so now. Dalgliesh ended:

"As you can imagine, sir, I'm not proposing to commit all that to paper. There's no real evidence and as Bernie Pryde used to tell us, hunch is a good servant but a poor master. God, how that man could churn out his horrible platitudes! He wasn't unintelligent, not totally without judgment, but everything, including ideas, came apart in his hands. He had a mind like a police notebook. Do you remember the Clandon case, homicide by shooting? It was in 1954 I think."

"Ought I to?"

"No. But it would have been helpful if I had."

"I don't really know what you're talking about, Adam. But if I understand you aright, you suspect that Ronald Callender killed his son. Ronald Callender is dead. You suspect that Chris Lunn tried to murder Cordelia Gray. Lunn is dead. You suggest that Elizabeth Leaming killed Ronald Callender. Elizabeth Leaming is dead."

"Yes, it's all conveniently tidy."

"I suggest we leave it that way. The Commissioner incidentally has had a telephone call from Dr. Hugh Tilling, the psychiatrist. He's

30

183

outraged because his son and daughter have been questioned about Mark Callender's death. I'm prepared to explain his civil duties to Dr. Tilling, he's already well aware of his rights, if you really feel it necessary. But will anything be gained by seeing the two Tillings again?"

"I don't think so."

"Or by bothering the Sureté about that French girl who Miss Markland claims visited him at the cottage?"

"I think we can spare ourselves that embarrassment. There's only one person now alive who knows the truth of these crimes and she's proof against any interrogation we can use. I can comfort myself with the reason. With most suspects we have an invaluable ally lurking at the back of their minds to betray them. But whatever lies she's been telling, she's absolutely without guilt."

"Do you think that she's deluded herself that it's all true?"

"I don't think that young woman deludes herself about anything. I took to her, but I'm glad I shan't be encountering her again. I dislike being made to feel during a perfectly ordinary interrogation that I'm corrupting the young."

"So we can tell the Minister that his chum died by his own hand?"

"You can tell him that we are satisfied that no living finger pressed that trigger. But perhaps not. Even he might be capable of reasoning that one out. Tell him that he can safely accept the verdict of the inquest."

"It would have saved a great deal of public time if he'd accepted it in the first place."

The two men were silent for a moment. Then Dalgliesh said:

"Cordelia Gray was right. I ought to have enquired what happened to Bernie Pryde."

"You couldn't be expected to. That wasn't part of your duties."

"Of course not. But then one's more serious neglects seldom are part of one's duty. And I find it ironic and oddly satisfying that Pryde took his revenge. Whatever mischief that child was up to in Cambridge, she was working under his direction."

"You're becoming more philosophical, Adam."

"Only less obsessive, or perhaps merely older. It's good to be able to feel occasionally that there are some cases which are better left unsolved."

❖❖❖

The Kingly Street building looked the same, smelt the same. It always would. But there was one difference. Outside the office a man was waiting, a middle-aged man in a tight blue suit, pig eyes sharp as flint among the fleshy folds of the face.

"Miss Gray? I'd nearly given you up. My name's Freeling. I saw your plate and just came up by chance, don't you know."

His eyes were avaricious, prurient.

"Well now, you're not quite what I expected, not the usual kind of Private Eye."

"Is there anything I can do for you, Mr. Freeling?"

He gazed furtively round the landing, seeming to find its sordidness reassuring.

"It's my lady friend. I've reason to suspect that she's getting a bit on the side. Well—a man likes to know where he stands. You get me?"

Cordelia fitted the key into the lock.

"I understand, Mr. Freeling. Won't you come in?"

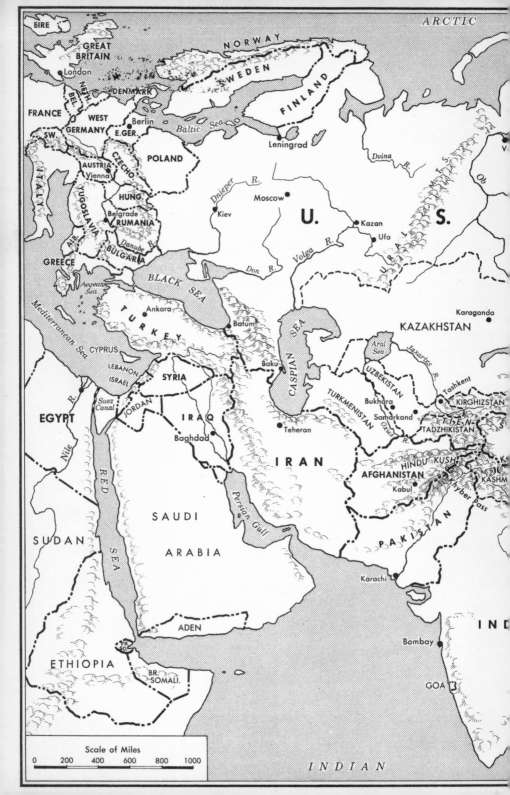

Set in Linotype Times Roman
Format by Marguerite Swanton
Manufactured by The Haddon Craftsmen, Inc.
Published by HARPER & BROTHERS, *New York*